TWINS

Amram Scheinfeld is a member of the Columbia University Seminar on Genetics and Evolution of Man, and a former Research Associate of the Institute of Psychological Research of Columbia's Teachers College. He has lectured widely to both academic and lay audiences. A Fellow of the New York Academy of Sciences and Vice-President of the board of directors of the Community Guidance Service of New York, he is the author of *Women and Men* and *Why You are You*. His first book, *You and Heredity*, published in 1939, enjoyed immediate success, and has been followed by several greatly revised and expanded editions, including *Your Heredity and Environment* (1965), and a condensed book *Heredity and Humans* (1972). Amram Scheinfeld has also contributed to leading scientific publications.

N Hartshorne

1973

AMRAM SCHEINFELD

Twins and Supertwins

*With special editing by Arthur Falek, Ph.D.,
and others herein mentioned*

The first comprehensive account of the
lives of the multiple-born from conception through maturity – their type
differences, health factors, psychological
traits, social relationships, unique experiences, and special problems – as
revealed by scientists, by parents of
twins, and by twins themselves.

Illustrated by the Author

PENGUIN BOOKS

Penguin Books Ltd, Harmondsworth, Middlesex, England
Penguin Books Inc., 7110 Ambassador Road, Baltimore, Maryland 21207, U.S.A.
Penguin Books Australia Ltd, Ringwood, Victoria, Australia

—

First published in the U.S.A. 1967
Published in Great Britain by Chatto & Windus 1968
Published in Pelican Books 1973

The following illustrations by the author were reproduced from his book
Your Heredity and Environment, copyright 1939, 1950, © 1965 by Amram
Scheinfeld: on pages 26–7, 35 (in part), 56, 62, 66, 169, 205, 234.

—

Made and printed in Great Britain by
Cox & Wyman Ltd,
London, Reading and Fakenham
Set in Monotype Times

TO ALL TWINS,
PARENTS OF TWINS,
AND THOSE WHO CARE ABOUT TWINS,
EVERYWHERE

Contents

CONTENTS

List of Illustrations

═══════

(*by the author except as noted*)

List of Tables and Charts

A NOTE BY THE AUTHOR
FOR THE PELICAN EDITION

THE pleasures and problems which go with having twins, or being twins, may vary among families, groups and nations. However, there is little difference in these respects between the British and American peoples, as I found when I made the comparisons on several visits to the British Isles, and talked there to parents of twins, adult twins, and scientists who have studied twins.

Thus, although much of the material presented in this book has come from American sources, the facts and observations should prove equally applicable to British twins and their families. (By the same token, British twin studies which I have drawn upon have proved equally applicable to American twins.) In short, British readers who have twins, are twins, or are otherwise interested in twins (as, of course, almost everyone is!) should find themselves quite at home in the world of the multiple-born which has been explored in this book. Some of the facts and situations discussed may prove familiar, many may be surprising, but all, I hope, will fulfil the principal objective of this book, which is to provide a better understanding of twins on the part of all concerned.

I should also like to take this occasion to express my gratitude to British readers for the attention they have given several of my previous books during past decades. And I am especially pleased that this book is being brought out in a Pelican edition, which should greatly increase its availability to twins-conscious individuals.

New York   AMRAM SCHEINFELD
22 March 1972

Preface

For a lonely young couple in any community, there is an unfailing formula for quickly making friends and influencing people: '*Have twins.*'

The appeal of twin babies is remarkable. No mother can venture forth with a twin baby buggy without evoking an impulse on the part of every passer-by to stop and peer inside, beam admiringly and cluck some cheerful comment. Either infant by itself might not warrant a second glance, but the two together make an irresistible combination.

This interest in twins as special human beings is, and has been, widespread at all times and among all peoples. But not everywhere, alas, are twins looked upon with favour. In various primitive tribes they are feared and rejected, and even in our own culture many old notions, myths and superstitions about twins have plagued and complicated their lives. (Some of the recent psychological precepts about twin-rearing haven't helped, either – as we'll show later.)

What must be recognized is that twins do in certain respects constitute a distinctive group, and that their world may differ in certain ways from the larger world of the single-born among whom they find themselves. Beginning life under more than ordinarily severe conditions, twins may thereafter present special problems to their parents, doctors, teachers, and friends – and, in time, to their mates and other persons. Likewise, they themselves may tend to encounter unique difficulties or disadvantages. But, balancing these adverse circumstances and perhaps outweighing them, there can be for twins special satisfactions and compensations. All these factors going with twinship demand careful attention, clear insight and sensible judgement if twins are to be ensured the fullest opportunity to achieve social adjustment and happiness. Regrettably, however, practical, constructive and non-

15

technical information about twins has been extremely scarce.

Thus it seemed that a book was needed which would not be just *about* twins, but *for* them, their parents, and, indeed, for everyone with a direct personal or professional interest in twins and their welfare: a book dealing with all aspects of twins and twinship – biological, medical, social, and psychological – and going extensively into their everyday experiences and problems. Such a book it has been the author's aim to produce. If he has succeeded, it is in no small measure due to the great amount of aid received from many persons and sources, which, in turn, was bound up with important recent developments.

First, scientists have been showing increasing interest in twins, and much new knowledge about them has become available. Second, large numbers of twin-minded lay people – parents of twins, adult twins, teachers and others close to twins – have readily co-operated in research projects, including those carried out by the author for this book.

It must be recognized, however, that most scientific studies concerned with twins have been conducted chiefly in order to learn, through them, more about human beings generally. Moreover, many of the findings which could have importance for twins and their parents have to a great extent remained sequestered in technical treatises. At the same time, most scientists have given little heed to the practical and personal problems going with or faced by twins, and not encountered with or by singletons.

Fortunately, then, as I began to look outside the scientific fields for essential material, I found that a grass-roots movement had begun to flourish. Mothers of twins, unable to secure the special help and information they needed, were spontaneously following the nursery-story precept, '... "So *I* will, then," said the Little Red Hen.' They got together in clubs, formed one after another throughout the country, with the purpose of learning from each other's experiences and aiding one another in various important ways. At this writing there are about two hundred Mothers of Twins clubs in the U.S.A., affiliated in a national association organized in 1960 with a total membership currently of over 7,000.

It has been through these clubs and their members that a great amount of the original material presented in this book was obtained. Questionnaires dealing with their twins were filled out by more than 500 of the mothers. Much additional information came to me through personal discussions with many of them, as well as with other parents of twins, in connection with lectures which I gave to some of the clubs. Supplementary information was obtained from scores of adult twins in personal interviews, or by way of questionnaires. In all, this book is presenting facts obtained directly from and/or regarding more than 1,100 individual members of twin pairs.

These personal contacts also helped me – and, I hope, will help the readers of this book – to obtain a more intimate understanding of twins and their lives than could have come merely from following ordinary scientific research channels. No less important was my learning, through the innumerable questions asked me, what it is about twins that most people – including twins themselves, parents and others – are anxious to know. For example:

What goes on before twins are born? How are twins of different types produced? How can one be sure which are identical and which are fraternal twins – and why is it important to know? Should or shouldn't twins be dressed alike? put in the same classrooms? kept together in their outside activities and social lives? Are twins as healthy? intelligent? well-adjusted? as likely to succeed in life as singly born children? Isn't there a mystic bond between twins? Are twins an asset or a liability to each other? Should twinship on the whole be played up or played down? These, and hundreds of other questions, stimulated my search for the answers, which are now presented in this book.

One frequent question I've been asked is personal: What accounts for my own interest in twins? I've had to answer – sometimes to the disappointment of the inquirers – that I myself am not a twin, nor am I a parent of twins. In fact, I know of no twins among my near relatives, nor of a twin twig on any close branch of my family tree. Nevertheless, this book is the culmination of a lifelong interest in twins. As far back as I can remember, I wondered about them. There were twins among my early playmates (two of these being the Doctors 'Harry' and 'Elias', who are told about later in the book); and, successively, there were other twins among my schoolmates and friends.

In time my interest in twins, as in human beings as a whole, took a scientific turn. My writings began to deal with twins almost thirty years ago when I referred to them in several articles, and, in 1939, my first book, *You and Heredity*, gave much attention to twins. Subsequent books and articles of mine also dealt increasingly with twins, until the plan developed of doing a book entirely about them.

No work such as this, however, can result from the efforts of a single individual. Scores of doctors, geneticists, psychologists, statisticians, and others active in twin research helped enormously in the gathering and analysing of the scientific material, and in checking and reading the manuscript. The names of only some of them appear in the Acknowledgements, for it would be impossible to list all. Here I would like to express my thanks to Dr Arthur Falek, formerly of the New York State Psychiatric Institute, Columbia University, and now Chief, Division of Human Genetics, Georgia Mental Health Institute, Emory University, who, in the latter stages of the preparation of this book, helped greatly with additional research and final editing. (Dr Falek is often consulted on problems of twins.) Many other of my professional friends contributed information, advice and suggestions during the years in which the work on this book proceeded. Among them were Dr Alan F. Guttmacher, himself a twin and a noted authority on the subject of twins; the late Dr Franz J. Kallmann, long one of the world's leaders in twin research, and Dr Bronson Price, a psychologist widely known for his analyses of twin-study methods. The foregoing (whose affiliations are given in the Acknowledgements following this Preface) all read sections of my manuscript. Others who read parts of the manuscript and made helpful suggestions were Dr M. G. Bulmer, of England, an expert on twinning incidences; Joseph Schachter, who aided in the compilation of statistics on twin births; Dr Halbert L. Dunn, former chief of the National Office of Vital Statistics, and Dr John Storck, an associate; Dr Alexander S. Wiener, expert on blood types, and Dr Jacob A. Arlow, who has given special attention to the psychoanalytical studies of twins. Also extremely helpful were many of my colleagues of the Columbia University Seminar on Genetics and the Evolution of Man.

It need hardly be said how much the book owes to the hundreds of mothers of twins, and to the great many adult twins – all of whom contributed to my studies. Although they cannot be thanked individually, I hereby express my appreciation to them collectively, with particular thanks to many of the Mothers of Twins clubs.

Not least, my affectionate thanks go to members of my own family, who helped in innumerable ways: to my wife, Dorothy; my late sister, Rosalie (the 'faithful clipper'); my other sister, Ruhamah; and my brother Aaron and his wife, Sylvia.

To those mentioned, and to the many others who helped in one way or another, my fervent thanks are given, coupled with the hope that this book will prove worthy of their interest, and will add constructively to a better understanding and appreciation of some of the world's most fascinating people – twins and supertwins.

New York   AMRAM SCHEINFELD
December 1966

Acknowledgements

The manuscript of this book was read and helpful suggestions provided before publication by the following specialists:

Dr Arthur Falek, Chief, Division of Human Genetics, Georgia Mental Health Institute. (The entire manuscript.)

Dr Alan F. Guttmacher, President, Planned Parenthood–World Population, and former Chief of Obstetrics, Mt Sinai Hospital, New York. (All chapters and sections dealing with the conception, prenatal development and birth of twins.)

Dr Franz J. Kallmann, late Chief, Psychiatric Research, New York State Psychiatric Institute, and his associates, Drs John Rainer and Lissy F. Jarvik. (All chapters and sections dealing with genetic, medical and psychological aspects of twins.)

Dr Irving Lorge, late Director, Institute of Psychological Research, Teachers College, Columbia University. (All chapters and sections dealing with the education of twins and their psychological aspects.)

Dr Halbert C. Dunn, former Chief, National Office of Vital Statistics, and his former associates, Joseph B. Schachter and Dr John Storck. (All sections dealing with the statistics of twins births and twinning.)

Dr Alexander Wiener, Senior Serologist, Office of Chief Medical Examiner, New York. (Chapter 4, 'The Twin Types'.)

Dr Frank Falkner, Director, Twin-Study Project, University of Louisville. (Chapter 12, 'Growing Pairs'.)

Dr M. G. Bulmer, University of Oxford, England. (Chapter 5, 'The Chances of Having Twins'.)

Dr Jacob A. Arlow, New York, former President, American Psychoanalytical Association. (Chapter 21, 'The Analyst's Double Couch'.)

Dr Bronson Price, Children's Bureau, National Institutes of Health, Washington, D.C. (Chapter 23, 'The Studies of Twins'.)

Mothers of Twins Clubs. The author extends special thanks to those members of the following Mothers of Twins clubs who filled out questionnaires and supplied information cited in the text: California – Sacramento and San Fernando Valley clubs; Illinois – Chicago, Pekin, and Peoria clubs; Indiana – Indianapolis; Kentucky –

ACKNOWLEDGEMENTS

Louisville; New Jersey – Bergen County and Essex County clubs; New York – Long Island and Westchester clubs; Ohio – Cleveland; Washington – Spokane; Wisconsin – Milwaukee.

CHAPTER 1

How Twins are Conceived

FROM the time human beings first began taking notice of twins there must have been speculation as to how twins were produced, and what accounted for the three varieties: (1), the 'look-alike' twins of the same sex; (2), the 'look-different' twins of the same sex, and (3), the twins of opposite sex.

If the Cave Man didn't know, neither did the wisest men and the greatest scientists, up until the latter part of the past century. Only then were theories advanced that the 'look-alike' twins might come from a single fertilized egg, the 'look-different' twins from two different eggs. Not until the early 1900s was supporting evidence for this forthcoming. In the decades that have followed, as more and more scientific study has been given to twins, one age-old question after another about them has been cleared up.

Let us start with the facts about how a single child is conceived. As almost every reader must know, the conception of a baby takes place when an egg from the mother, carrying a quota of her hereditary factors (the 'genes', which determine the hereditary traits), is fertilized by a sperm from the father, carrying a matching quota of his hereditary factors. Ordinarily, *only one egg at a time* is released – from one *or* the other of the mother's ovaries – about once every twenty-eight days. The egg then drops into the funnelled open end of the Fallopian tube nestling below the ovary from which the egg has come. If, about this time, the woman has had sexual relations, the egg may be met by some of the sperms which have come in from her mate, and one of these sperms may enter the egg, starting the process of fertilization.

But suppose that instead of producing the customary one egg at a given time, the woman produces *two* – and that each egg is fertilized by a different sperm? This is, indeed, how the '*two-egg*' twins are conceived. The twin eggs may come from the same ovary, and be fertilized in the same tube. Or one egg may come from each ovary, and fertilization occur in the two separate tubes. The end result, as the eggs travel down into the womb and become implanted, will be the same. Further, because each egg carries a different combination of hereditary factors, the two eggs will develop into two quite different, or 'fraternal', twins.

The process for the 'one-egg' twins is much more complicated. Here it is required that, at some stage following fertilization, the one egg must divide in such a way that the result is *two separate babies with matching hereditary factors*. We can see how this might be accomplished if we follow the course of an egg after it is fertilized. Inside the egg is now a tiny inner cell, or 'nuclear packet', containing the hereditary factors brought in by the father's sperm, which have joined the factors from the mother that were already there. These factors in chains are called 'chromosomes', and as soon as the two sets from the parents are brought together, the cell containing them churns into action. First, all the chromosomes draw on material in the egg and become double in size. Then each chromosome splits in half, so there now are two for each previous one. And almost at once the cell itself also begins to divide, with a duplicate of every chromosome going into each half. So we now have *two* cells, each with exactly the same chromosomes.

The process of chromosome doubling and dividing goes on and on, followed each time by the cells also dividing and multiplying. The two cells become four, the four eight, the eight sixteen, and so on, until eventually there are the billions of cells, like living building bricks, needed for a complete baby. Of course, babies are not just piles of 'bricks' – even 'living bricks'. Very soon after the cells have multiplied up to a certain point, they begin turning into different specialized forms in different locations, to develop into bones, muscles, skin, blood vessels, nerves, organs, features, and all the rest of the body's needed parts and equipment.

The division of the cell mass that is to produce twin babies must therefore take place *before* development has gone too far – that is, before there is anything like one whole baby which would have to be 'cut down in the middle'. In most cases this division occurs at a very early stage, sometimes when only a few cells (or even just two) have been formed inside the fertilized egg. At this stage it is quite possible that the egg itself may divide to form two separate halves

THE HUMAN CHROMOSOMES

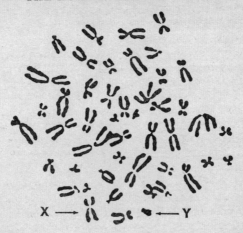

X —→   ←— Y

Shown above are the actual chromosomes of a human male, photographed through a high-powered microscope at the stage in which each chromosome is doubling and about to divide. Arrows point to the 'X' and 'Y' chromosomes, which determine the male sex. (The female set of chromosomes has two 'Xs'.) The Text pages give details regarding the way the chromosomes, and the genes they carry, work to produce the hereditary traits, the sex differences at birth, and the distinctions between identical and fraternal twins. (*Photograph by Dr Orlando J. Miller, Columbia University College of Physicians and Surgeons*)

matching each other in their contents; then, if the two halves break apart completely, they can go on as though there had been two fertilized eggs to begin with. They can move down into the womb separately and become implanted at any distance from each other, *just as if a pair of two-egg, or 'fraternal', twins had been conceived*.

The division between one-egg twins may, however, take place at a considerably later stage (and usually does) after many cells have been formed – although not beyond the point where the development of the foetus has become so 'set' that the cell mass can no longer be safely divided.

HOW TWINS ARE PRODUCED

'Identical' Twins

Are products of a *single sperm* and a *single egg*.

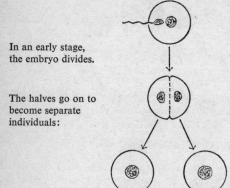

In an early stage,
the embryo divides.

The halves go on to
become separate
individuals:

Having come from the same sperm and the same egg, these two twins carry
the same chromosomes and genes:*

Thus, identical (one-egg) twins are always of the same sex*

... Either two 'look-alike' boys

... or two 'look-alike' girls

* For exceptions, see Text.

'Fraternal' Twins

Are products of *two different* eggs, fertilized by *two different* sperms.

They go on to develop into two different individuals:

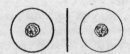

They carry different assortments of chromosomes and genes:

Thus, apart from having been born together, fraternal twins are no more alike than any two children born separately in a family. They may be:

Both of the
SAME SEX   Two boys

                                           ... or two girls

Or a
MIXED set   ... a boy and a girl

At any rate, regardless of when the division occurs that causes twins to develop from a single egg – whether it be at the two-cell stage or at a later many-cell stage – these twins will still be an 'identical' pair. But one should fix in mind that the term 'identical twins' refers *only* to the fact that such twins have *identical hereditary factors*, since all their cells have exact duplicates of the chromosomes that were in the fertilized egg from which they both came. It need not follow that they must be identical in their appearance, their constitutions or their behaviour, however, because the influences of *environment* before or after birth may produce differences between them.

How about the two-egg, or 'fraternal', twins? What, exactly, causes them to be so much more *unalike* than one-egg, or identical, twins? The answer lies in the fact that in addition to any differences in environment, fraternal twins come from two different eggs and sperms and so may be very different in their hereditary make-up. Here we must understand something more about the process of heredity:

As we have noted, every individual at conception receives two sets of hereditary factors carried in the chromosomes, one set from each parent. Each set consists of 23 chromosomes (the two sets making the 46 required to start a human baby on its way), and each chromosome consists of a string of infinitesimally tiny sections, the '*genes*'. These genes are potent little units of life substances acting in thousands of different ways to produce all of a person's hereditary traits.

As we also have noted, the original two sets of chromosomes received at conception, and all the genes of which they consist, are duplicated, reduplicated, and multiplied again and again until there is an endless number of exact replicas. One function of these chromosomes and genes is to direct the workings of every cell in the individual's body, from before birth and throughout life. Another function, when the person matures, is that of *reproduction:* In the woman, the eggs she produces contain replicas of her chromosomes with their genes; in the man, the sperms he produces contain replicas of his chromosomes and genes. *Not all* the chromosomes of either parent go into every egg or sperm, however; for, if this were so, each fertilized egg of any two parents would be the same, and it would make no difference whether twins were from one egg or two eggs. As it is, only *half* of any parent's chromosomes – 23 of the 46, as noted before – go into any particular egg or sperm. And which 23 they are is entirely a matter of chance.

Before babies are conceived, the parents' chromosomes are shuffled and dealt out into each sperm or egg – somewhat as with playing cards – with one deal apt to be quite different from the next. Likewise, in different eggs and different sperms brought together from any two parents, millions of different combinations of their chromosomes and genes are possible. Thus, no two children in a family, conceived from different fertilized eggs, can ever be expected to be the same in all their hereditary factors.

Here, then, we have the important distinction between identical and fraternal twins. How the parents' chromosomes and genes have been dealt out in a particular egg can make no difference to twins derived from the same egg, for they will have exact duplicates of each other's hereditary factors. But, in the case of the fraternal twins coming from two different eggs and sperms, they can be as unlike as any two children in a family who have been conceived and born at different times. Hence the term 'fraternal', from the Latin word *frater*, meaning 'like brothers'. (*Supertwins* – triplets, quadruplets and quintuplets – will be discussed in detail in Chapter 19.)

What about *brother–sister* twin pairs? What causes one twin – or any single child – to be a male, another a female? Again we turn to one of the processes of heredity – that of sex determination. As many readers will already know, a baby's sex is determined *at conception* by which types of 'sex chromosomes' it receives. These sex chromosomes are of two kinds: One, large, is called the 'X'. The other, small (only a third the size of the X), is called the 'Y' (which is the male-determining chromosome). The sexes differ genetically in that females carry only pairs of X chromosomes; in males, each sex chromosome pair consists of an X and a Y. Accordingly, when women produce eggs, since they have only X chromosomes, each egg can get only an X. Males, carrying both X and Y chromosomes in equal numbers, can produce either 'X-bearing' or 'Y-bearing' sperms. Thus the whole process of sex determination comes down to which type of sperm from the father reaches and fertilizes a given egg.

In the case of single babies, if an X-bearing sperm has fertilized an egg, the result is an 'XX' individual – a girl.

If a Y-bearing sperm has fertilized an egg, the result is an 'XY' individual – a boy.

So with one-egg twins, or identicals, there are *two* possibilities:

(1) If an X-bearing sperm fertilizes an egg, and this egg divides to produce twins, the result will be *identical girl twins*.

(2) If a Y-bearing sperm fertilizes an egg, and this divides to produce twins, the result will be *identical boy twins*.

In the case of two-egg, or fraternal, twins, there are *three* possibilities:

(1) If each of the two eggs is fertilized by an X-bearing sperm, the result will be *fraternal girl twins*.

(2) If each of the two eggs is fertilized by a Y-bearing sperm, the result will be *fraternal boy twins*.

(3) If one egg is fertilized by an X sperm, the other by a Y sperm, the twins will be a *girl and boy pair*.

Before ending our account of how twins are conceived, we might take note of certain unusual situations in the twinning processes. First, in rare instances a mother may carry two babies conceived at different times – one of them days or even weeks after another. In most of these cases the mother has a two-compartment womb (in medical terms, 'bicornuate'). Again, on rare occasions, fraternal twins may have had different fathers. This can happen if, after a woman has produced two eggs, she has relations successively within a matter of hours with two different men, and each egg is fertilized by a different man. In one celebrated case in Chicago in 1938, after a woman who ran a boarding-house gave birth to twins, two boarders laid claim to being the father, but blood tests indicated that each man had sired one of the twins. (Readers should be cautioned, however, that 'two-father' twins are so extremely infrequent that the mere fact of two twins looking very unlike – or one apparently not resembling the husband – is no cause for suspicion. How marked differences in fraternal twins can appear will be brought out in Chapter 4.)

Finally, there is the theoretical possibility – still not proved –

HOW SEX OF TWINS IS DETERMINED

---

1. Every egg of a woman carries an 'X' sex chromosome:

But a man's sperms carry either an 'X': or a 'Y':
(half the sperms with one, half with the other).

---

*2. If an egg is fertilized by an 'X' sperm, the result is an 'XX' baby
– a girl*

*If an egg is fertilized by a 'Y' sperm, the result is an 'XY' baby
– a boy*

---

3. In identical twins, *a mother's single 'X' egg, if*

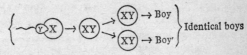

– fertilized by an 'X' sperm, and egg divides:

– fertilized by a 'Y' sperm, and egg divides:

---

4. In fraternal twins, *mother's two 'X' eggs, if*

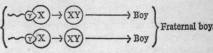

– both eggs are fertilized by an 'X' sperm:

– both eggs are fertilized by a 'Y' sperm:

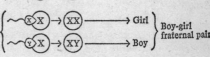

– one egg fertilized by an 'X' sperm:
– other egg fertilized by a 'Y' sperm:

31

that twins may be half identical, half fraternal. The theory behind this is that under unusual circumstances a single egg, dividing internally *before* conception, may be fertilized by two different sperms, resulting in twins who are identical with respect to the hereditary factors from the mother, but different (or fraternal) in the factors from their father.

Looking over the facts presented, it becomes clear that the word *twins* refers only to children who are paired in some way before or at birth, but whose relationship may take various forms.* To say that 'twins are babies conceived by a mother at the same time' applies invariably only to identical pairs; for, as we've seen, fraternal twins sometimes may be conceived many hours – or even days, and possibly weeks – apart. Still less can we always refer to twins as 'babies born together'; for, even with identicals, one birth may follow considerably after another. In fact, the only twins who are indisputably twins in the fullest sense of the word – conceived at exactly the same time, nurtured in the same womb, and born at exactly the same time – are *Siamese* twins.

Obviously, then, none of the terms used today for classifying twins is completely satisfactory. Scientists have leaned towards the 'one-egg' and 'two-egg' classification, though usually using the technical equivalents, 'monovular', or 'uniovular', and 'binovular'; or 'monozygotic' and 'dizygotic' (*mono-*, 'one', and *di-*, 'two', with *-zygotic* referring to the zygote, or fertilized egg). But the general public hasn't taken kindly to the 'egg' designation for twins. (As one young lady said to me, 'Calling us "one-egg" twins makes us feel like an omelet.') The terms 'identical' and 'fraternal' twins have thus become more popular, although both have their drawbacks. The public must be continually reminded that 'identical' refers only to the hereditary factors; and as for 'fraternal', it is all right for brother twins, but not – strictly speak-

*The word *twin* derives from the stem *twi-*, which appears in the ancient Frisian German words *twina* and *twine*, meaning 'two together'; in the Old Norse as *twinnr* and *twennr*, for 'two' or 'two pairs of'; and in Anglo-Saxon *getwinn*, which is related to such words as *twaining*, or *two-ing*, implying 'divided in two'. The German word for twins, *zwillinge*, derives from *zwei* or 'two'. The French word for twin is *jumeau*, masculine; *jumelle*, feminine; plural, *jumeaux*, *jumelles*. The Italian equivalents are *gemello* and *gemella*; plural, *gemelli*. The Spanish is *gemelo(s)* or *mellizo(s)*.

ing – for sister twins, who might more properly be referred to as 'sororal'. And what about the twins whom the experts can refer to only as 'opposite-sex fraternals'? We'll just have to make do here with such terms as 'opposite-sex', or 'male–female' or 'boy–girl' or 'brother–sister' twins.

It could be argued: 'What's in a name? Twins are twins.' But that isn't so. Even Shakespeare, who wrote the 'What's in a name' lines, must have known perfectly well (particularly as he himself was reported to have been the father of a boy–girl twin pair) that it does make a big difference how any twins are labelled, and what meaning this label conveys. As we will find in succeeding chapters, precise knowledge as to the type of a given pair of twins, and of how this type is distinguished from other twin types, may have a direct bearing on many aspects of their lives – their rearing, health, thinking and behaviour, and their relationships to each other, to their families, and to people in general.

CHAPTER 2

The Two-Lane Road to Birth

BETWEEN the conception of twins and their birth there lies a stretch of months filled with many perils and unique adventures. Even a single child may not find the road to birth an easy one. Where there are two little beings crowded into a place ordinarily designed and provisioned for one, we can expect many additional complications and difficulties. The adventures and experiences may vary, however, according to whether the twins are fraternal or identical, and how they begin their journey.

First, let us see what happens with fraternal twins. Each starts off in exactly the same way as would any singly conceived child. As each fertilized egg moves down the Fallopian tube towards the womb, the cells inside have been multiplying, while on the outside little tendrils have been sprouting, so that the egg looks like a tiny burr. On about the seventh day after conception, each egg as a rule has reached the womb and become implanted there. This process involves growing a placenta into the lining of the womb, through which nourishment and oxygen can be drawn from the mother. Further, attached to the placenta, each egg – now called a 'foetus' – forms about itself a thick outer bag, the 'chorion', and inside of this a plastic-like sac, the 'amnion'. This amnion fills with the fluid in which the foetus grows, connected by its umbilical cord to the placenta (see Illustration p. 35).

All the foregoing facts regarding the placenta, bags, and sacs have special meaning for twins, both with respect to their prenatal development and in providing clues to their relationship when they are born. But there are many misconceptions as to how much can be learned from the presence of one placenta, or of two placentas. As an example, *fraternal twins do not always have two separate placentas*. Usually they do, being implanted some distance apart. But occasionally they become implanted close together, and their placentas may fuse and have every appearance of being one.

PRENATAL LIFE OF TWINS:

I. IMPLANTATION

Fraternal (two-egg) twins:

(A) The two eggs usually reach womb separately, and may take root far apart

(B) But sometimes the two eggs become implanted close together, and placentas may fuse

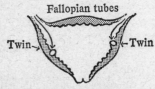

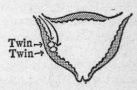

Identical (one-egg) twins:

(A) Egg division usually occurs *after* implantation, and the twins develop closely together, with same placenta

(B) But sometimes egg divides *before* implantation, and the halves may take root well apart (like fraternals)

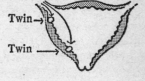

II. DEVELOPMENT

Most fraternals

Most identicals

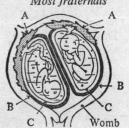

A. Separate placentas
B. Separate outer bags (chorions)
C. Separate inner sacs (amnions)

(But some identicals may also develop this way. See Identicals; (B), above.)

A. One common placenta
B. One common outer bag
C. Separate inner sacs

(Some fraternals may have fused placentas, but outer bags will be separated.)

35

However, the outer bags (chorions) and inner sacs (amnions) in which each fraternal twin grows are invariably separate and distinct.

With identical twins the situation may be much more complicated. As was explained in the preceding chapter, the division of a fertilized egg to form identical twins can take place very early or at a more advanced stage; and *when* and *how* the division occurs may have considerable importance for the twins. If the egg divides almost at once, it is possible for the two halves to separate completely, and then move on and grow apart as if they were two different eggs. While this would not affect their being identical twins – that is, their hereditary traits – their development in the womb would be no different from that of fraternal twins. They could become implanted at some distance from one another, and each identical twin could form its own placenta and outer bag. *No one could tell at this stage, or until after these twins were born, whether they were indeed identicals, or were fraternal.* (How errors are often made in diagnosing types of twins will be told in detail in Chapter 4.)

In the majority of cases, however – in about three out of four pairs – identical twins are not separated in the womb. The two foetuses continue to develop closely together inside their one outer bag (chorion) and with one placenta, to which each twin is attached by its own umbilical cord. Also, almost always each twin is contained in its own fluid-filled amniotic sac. But in rare instances these separate inner sacs are missing, and identical twins are suspended in the same sac and fluid. This can be an extremely dangerous situation, inasmuch as their cords may become entangled, or one twin may crowd and injure the other. A large percentage of these one-sac identicals fail to survive.

Various other hazards can confront twins along the road to birth, whether they are one-egg or two-egg twins. At any time after conception one or both of the twin foetuses may fail to take root properly in the womb or, at a later stage, may be unable to keep alive. Undoubtedly many more twins are conceived than are born, and many a baby born single may originally have started out with a twin. Where twins do survive together, they often show at birth the effects of their competition in the womb for nourishment, or of

36

'jockeying' for position, or perhaps of one twin's having drained blood from the other. The result may well be that one twin emerges much larger or healthier than the other, or that one may be fully normal, while the other is defective.

Whether twins are fraternal or identical can affect the nature of any inequalities between them at birth. In the case of fraternal twins, differences may be due not only to greater environmental disadvantages for one compared with the other before birth, but also to differences in hereditary factors. These differences may destine one fraternal twin to be born smaller or less healthy, or deviant in some other respect, from his or her twin. The clearest example of how hereditary differences can show themselves in fraternal twins at birth, whether or not their prenatal environments were different, is offered, of course, by the boy–girl twins. (There will be much more about them in Chapter 19.)

When identical twins differ considerably at birth, one usually must seek the reasons solely in their prenatal experiences. In various respects these experiences can be unique for identicals, and the hazards greater than for fraternals. At the very beginning, if a fertilized egg geared to produce only one baby is split in half, this in itself is a disruptive process. Among other things, the same amount of food stored within the egg to start one baby on its way must now be divided between two, with these rations having to last until the egg (or two halves of the egg, if separated) becomes imbedded in the uterus and can begin drawing nourishment from the mother. When the twin foetuses are enclosed in the same outer bag, and attached to the same placenta, there are the conditions of crowding we have mentioned, made especially hazardous if the twins do not even have separate inner amniotic sacs.

One of the odd accidents that can occur only with identical twins is their failure in some cases to separate completely during early development, so that they are born as conjoined, or 'Siamese', twins. Those that achieved birth and survived were extremely rare in the past, which accounts for the fact that two who did survive – Chang and Eng, born in Siam in 1811 – became world-famous as the 'Siamese twins', and gave their name to the condition. (We will tell more about these two in a later chapter.) Siamese twins may be joined in any way and in any degree, depending on the stage at which the separation of the halves of the egg – or the foetus – from which they came occurred.

Still another odd accident of one-egg twinning is that in which one twin 'absorbs' the other at a very early stage, and carries the twin thereafter as a growth inside his body. Such cases have occasionally come to light when surgeons, after removing a tumour from a patient, have found therein a mummified foetus, or parts of a foetus, of what should have been a twin of the individual.

But such unusual cases represent only a very small minority of twin experiences. Granted, then, that the great majority of twins follow quite normal courses from conception onward, we come to this question: How – and how soon – can it be known that twins are coming? The first suspicions may arise if the mother shows signs of carrying an unusually heavy baby-load for her stage of pregnancy, and also if she suffers more than normally from various pregnancy complications. Where twins were suspected in the past, confirmation depended mainly on outer touch diagnosis ('palpation') – feeling the mother's abdomen for evidence of the presence of twins. This method of predicting twins, while still used, has often proved unreliable.

The development of new techniques has made it possible to reveal accurately the presence of twins during the fifth month of pregnancy, and sometimes earlier. One method is by X-rays, which may involve some risks. For, if the X-raying is done too early in pregnancy, and if the dosage is not properly controlled, the twin foetuses may sometimes be harmed; further, there might possibly be some hereditary changes in the underdeveloped eggs of the mother's ovaries. Dr Alan Guttmacher believes, however, that fears on this point have been greatly exaggerated. Offering reassurance to twin mothers who had been X-rayed, or to expectant ones who will be, he told me:

If X-rays were or are made in the latter part of pregnancy – in the sixth or seventh months (the thirtieth week or thereafter) – and with the minimal amount of exposure required, any small risk involved is far outweighed by the resulting benefits. The foreknowledge provided by X-rays that twins are being carried can help enormously in preparing the mother properly for twinbirth, and the clues given the doctor as to the positions of the twins can help greatly to insure their safe delivery.

At Mt Sinai Hospital such X-raying is considered an essential routine practice which has proved invaluable, and with no evidence of harmful results.

The possibility that prenatal twin diagnosis may be made without X-raying, at a much earlier stage and with no risk whatsoever, is held forth by several other methods now being developed. Among them is the *heartbeat recording* method. This involves applying electrodes to the pregnant mother's abdomen and registering the dual foetal heartbeats when twins are present – detectable sometimes as early as the sixteenth week of gestation. Other methods in prospect for detecting the presence of twins before birth are *ultrasonograms*, pictures taken with ultrasound; a *telemetering device*, reported as being able to detect heartbeats of unborn babies as early as the fourteenth or fifteenth week of foetal life, and *thermography*, a technique of revealing placental positions by photographic imaging of the skin-surface temperature over the womb.

Knowing how unpredictable single babies may be about picking the time for their arrival, one must prepare for still more uncertainty in the case of twins. Often they are in a hurry to be born,

When Twins get Born

Proportion of twins born at different stages of gestation (estimated by weeks)*

Weeks of Gestation (*Approximate*)	Percentage Born at this Stage	
	Twins	*Singletons*
Under 28 weeks	4·0%	0·5%
28–31 weeks	5·2%	0·8%
32–35 weeks	10·8%	1·9%
36 weeks	12·7%	8·4%
37–39 weeks	14·9%	8·8%
40 weeks	51·4%	76·4%
41 weeks and over	1·1%	3·2%

*'Gestation age' often represents a guess, and figures given here, according to government reports, 'can be taken as being only suggestive of what the actual situation might be'. (*Data from U.S. National Center for Health Statistics, Series 21, No. 4, July 1965, Table D.*)

which is not surprising, considering the fact that their crowded quarters become increasingly more uncomfortable as time goes on. Again, while each twin may weigh less than a single baby at the same stage of gestation, two twins together represent a much heavier load for the mother: For example, two 4-pound twins in the thirtieth week outweigh an average full-term single baby in its thirty-sixth week. So, with both the twins and the mother under extra pressure, one can usually expect twins to arrive ahead of the single-baby schedule – on the average by about three weeks. In other words, where the length of gestation – from the onset of the last menses to birth – averages 280 days for single babies; for twins it is about 259 days, or 22 days less. How important this is for the survival, health and development of twins will be told in the next chapter.

CHAPTER 3

Double Entry

'THERE'S another one coming!'

How often has this exclamation been heard from persons attending a childbirth!

In the past, the great majority of twins came as a complete surprise. Even among the recent crop of twins in the past decade, from one-third to one-half came with no suspicion on the part of the doctor or the mother that they had been carried. Such surprises are becoming fewer as a result of the new techniques for detecting the presence of twins. Yet, whether heralded or not, the advent of twins still is, and always will be, an occasion for excitement; for the entry of twins into the world is fraught with far more thrills, difficulties, and dangers than attend a single birth.

We have already told why and how the prenatal journey of twins may be much more complicated and perilous than that of the foetus travelling alone. In crossing the threshold into the outside world there are some new hazards, the nature and extent of which depend on a number of factors: How well developed and healthy the twins are; the ease or hardship of the delivery, and what measures are available in case emergencies arise (this latter being a major reason why twin deliveries, wherever possible, should be in a hospital). Not of least importance is the mother's own condition, which may be much influenced by her age and previous childbearing experience. The mature mothers who have had several children previously are apt to have less difficulty in bringing forth twins, and the risk to the twins is usually less than when the mothers are young and the twins are their firstborn.

But in most cases twin labours are not too severe. The fact that twins tend to be smaller than singleborn children may help to ease their birth. Also, nature often helps by conditioning the womb and birth canal *earlier for twin delivery*. So, although there are two babies to be delivered, the labour period for both

41

combined is ordinarily only a little longer than for a single birth.

An unusual aspect of many twin births is the manner in which one or both babies emerge into the world. In *single* births, almost 96 per cent of the babies emerge headfirst ('vertex', or 'cephalic', delivery) – the easiest and safest way. Only $3\frac{1}{2}$ per cent of single babies try to come out with their little buttocks first (known as 'breech' delivery), and only rarely do single babies lie crosswise in the womb, and seek to emerge shoulder first, or with a leg or arm ahead. Again, in the ordinary course of events, as birth approaches the baby revolves in its sac so that it is head down and in the best position for the exit. But with twins a large proportion do not have time, or are too crowded, to make this adjustment, and so one can find them awaiting birth in every which way.

How twins present themselves when arriving is revealed through a study of 1,212 births, made by Drs Alan F. Guttmacher and Schuyler G. Kohl in New York. The findings indicate that out of every 100 sets of twins 47 pairs will present themselves with both headfirst; 37 pairs with one headfirst and the other breech (buttocks) first; 8 or 9 pairs will be both breech first; 5 pairs will have one headfirst and the other lying crosswise; and 2 pairs will have one twin breech and the other crosswise. In only one out of 200 cases will both twins be lying crosswise. From these facts one can see that the doctor is required to manipulate twins into a proper position for delivery much more often than is necessary for single babies. (See the illustration on page 44).

The interval between the birth of the first twin and the second is usually short. Some studies have reported that three-fourths of all twins are delivered within less than an hour. But in some instances one twin has followed the other only after several days, or even weeks. One of the most amazing cases was that of an Ohio mother who, in 1955, after having a boy baby, gave birth to a twin girl 48 days later. (The second twin was said to have been developed outside the womb, in the mother's abdominal cavity – presumably in a Fallopian tube.)

Once twins are born, the first thing to be noted is their sex. Slightly more than half of all twins at birth are boys – the average birth ratio of twins in the United States being about 101 or 102 boy to 100 girl pairs. (Among singly born babies the ratio at birth is more than 105 boys to 100 girls, with the ratio for Whites being almost 106 boys to 100 girls, and for Negroes, between 102 and 103 boys to 100 girls.) Roughly speaking, slightly fewer than one in three pairs of twins born are of unlike sex.* Among the twin pairs of like sex, one in two pairs are both boys, with the other pair being both girls. With the same-sex twins, the question as to whether they are identical or fraternal often cannot be determined by examining the placentas (as explained in Chapter 2), or by other evidence at birth, and may have to wait for the results of various tests.

Of most immediate concern when twins are born may be their weight. For, going by what is shown at the 'weighing in' which comes after the twins have been tagged as 'No. 1' and 'No. 2' (or, in some hospitals, 'A' and 'B'), a twin will be either treated as an ordinary baby or listed as 'premature' and given the preferential treatment of a 'preemie'. Here it is necessary to clear up some of the confusion regarding use of the term 'premature', in contrast to 'full-term', for classifying babies at birth (whether twins or single-born). The technical designation 'premature' does not actually refer to a baby's gestation period – that is, to birth before the normal full period – but only to the baby's *weight* as a rough indication of its stage of development. If a baby at birth weighs no more than $5\frac{1}{2}$ pounds (2,500 grammes or under), it is considered as not having gone through full prenatal development and is classed 'premature'. If the baby weighs over $5\frac{1}{2}$ pounds, (2,501 grammes or more), it is considered to be 'term' – that is, a 'full-term' baby.

This method of determining prematurity has many flaws, as we will presently show. Why, then, is it used? Quite simply, because it is seldom possible to fix the exact time of conception of either twins or a singleborn child, or to estimate precisely how long a given baby has been carried. So the doctor makes a guess on the basis of the baby's weight. True, if a baby is three or four pounds under the average weight at birth (which is $7\frac{1}{2}$ pounds for the singleborn), it has in all probability not completed the full course of prenatal

*Among Negro twins more than one pair in three is a male–female pair, which is in line with the fact that Negro mothers produce proportionately more fraternal twins, although their production of identical twins is about the same as in Whites.

TWIN POSITIONS AS BIRTH APPROACHES

Manner of 'presentation', with approximate percentages of each

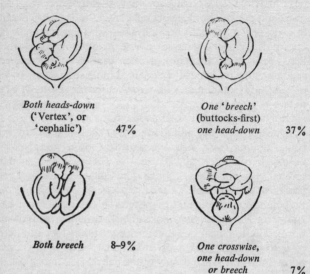

Both heads-down
('Vertex', or
'cephalic')   47%

One 'breech'
(buttocks-first)
one head-down   37%

Both breech   8–9%

One crosswise,
one head-down
or breech   7%

Drawings adapted from Dr Alan Guttmacher's *Pregnancy and Childbirth*.

development. But uncertainties often exist in the border area close to either side of the 5½-pound (or 2,500 gramme) mark. And it is within this area that most weights of twins will be found.

Thus, going by weight alone, more than half of all twins (about 54 per cent in the United States as a whole – 52 per cent among Whites, 62 per cent among Negroes), and up to 65 per cent in some groups studied, reach no more than 5½ pounds at birth and are classed as premature – almost eight times as many as among the singleborn.* Moreover, about one in twenty twins weighs not over

* Negro babies – including the singleborn – weigh less at birth on the average than do White babies, and thus in general have a higher percentage classed as premature if judged only by weight. While this racial difference

2 pounds 3 ounces, whereas only one in 200 singletons is that small.

One of the biggest flaws in applying just the weight standard for prematurity or degree of prematurity to both twins and singleborn alike is this: At the same stage of gestation and development twins are usually smaller than a singly-carried baby; and even when classed as full-term, twins average about 1¼ pounds less than full-term singletons. Further, being 'underweight' at birth does not have the same degree of adverse meaning for twins, since a 5-pound twin is likely to be sturdier than a 5-pound singleborn infant.

The clearest proof that birth weight may not be an accurate measure of the length of gestation lies in the fact that although both twins of a pair have been conceived at the same time, they may differ considerably in weight at birth – it being, indeed, the exception when both twins weigh exactly the same. Thus, in many cases, one twin weighs over 5½ pounds and is technically a 'term' baby, while the other weighs under 5½ pounds and is listed as a 'preemie'. This is especially likely to happen with boy–girl pairs, in which the girl twins average about three ounces less at birth than their boy partners. In fact, taking all twins together, about one-fifth more girls than boys are classified as premature – which is wrong not only because the gestation period for girl twins is probably no shorter than for boy twins (and certainly not when a girl is paired with a boy) but even more because, as will be brought out in Chapter 18, girls at the same period of gestation and at birth are considerably ahead of boys in development.

We are giving so much attention to prematurity in twins because it is by far the biggest reason for their high casualty and death rate before, during, and after birth, and for many of their childhood problems. Since so many more twins than single babies come into the world inadequately developed to cope with the first trying stages of life, it is not surprising that their death rate initially is about five times that of the singleborn. The biggest part of this mortality, of course, is among the 'preemie' twins; and it also follows that the greater the degree of prematurity, the greater the

---

may be due in some degree to inferior prenatal conditions for Negro babies, there is reason to believe that hereditary factors also may contribute to making them lighter in weight at birth than White babies, yet not necessarily any less well developed or sturdy, ounce for ounce.

TWINS AND SUPERTWINS

risk of death. Thus, for twins achieving birth in the United States, the average chance of surviving 24 hours or longer is only 13 per cent for those weighing less than 2 pounds 3 ounces. But above this weight the survival rate rises – to 50 per cent for twins weighing up to 3 pounds 4 ounces; 86 per cent for twins weighing from 3 pounds 5 ounces to 4 pounds 6 ounces; and 98 per cent for twins weighing 4 pounds 7 ounces or more. Among 'term' twins – those weighing 5½ pounds or over – the survival rate in the first days following birth is almost the same as for singletons; and at ages one week to four weeks only a tiny fraction of the 'term' twins – less than two in a thousand – fail to pull through. In all, about 87 per cent of the twins born in hospitals are discharged alive.

Comparing identical and fraternal twins, a somewhat larger proportion of the fraternals pull through safely, mainly for the reason, noted previously (in Chapter 2), that identicals may be confronted with more prenatal dangers. Again, among twins of either type, when only one of a pair survives, it is somewhat more likely to be the first-born, because the second-born more often is exposed to greater dangers during delivery (having a greater chance, for example, of requiring manipulative or mechanical assistance during birth). The difference is most pronounced among the lighter weight 'preemies' – twins weighing under 2,000 grammes (4 pounds 6 ounces), where fatalities for the second-born may be as much as one-third higher than for the first-born.

So far we have been speaking of twin deaths in general. But, regardless of whether they are premature or full-term babies, twins' hazards and death rates vary considerably according to their type (fraternal or identical), their sex, their race, the age and condition of their mother, and other factors. Here are some of the influences which bear on the chances of survival for twins:

Sex. The girls among twins, whether of girl–girl or boy–girl pairs, generally have a better chance of surviving from birth onward than have boy twins. This also is true of girls and boys among the singleborn, but the difference is more marked in twins. Thus, among premature twins, where the most casualties occur, the death rate for boys is about 37 per cent higher than for girls (205 per thousand versus 150 per thousand), according to United States reports. Another interesting fact is that the twins of opposite-

46

sex pairs have a better chance of surviving than do those of the same sex. (Double casualties at birth are almost three times as frequent among same-sex twins as among opposite-sex twins. One reason for this is that half of the like-sexed twins are identicals, who, on the average, have higher mortality rates than do fraternal twins.)

Race. The death rate among Negro twins before birth is much greater than among Whites in the United States – about 50 per cent higher – and in the first month after birth, 25 per cent higher. There is nothing to suggest that Negro twins are inherently weaker, inasmuch as a higher death rate also applies to singleton Negro babies. The reasons may be found largely in the generally worse prenatal and postnatal conditions among Negroes. With improvement in these conditions, differences between Negroes and Whites in mortality rates for both twin and singleton babies have steadily declined.

Mother's age and condition. In all groups, twins born to very young mothers run a greater risk of not surviving than do those born to mothers at later ages (except for ages over forty). Further, when twins come with the mother's first pregnancy the initial risks for them are considerably higher than if she previously had borne three or more children. These facts are in striking contrast with the situation for singleton babies; for, in their case, the ones born to younger and first-time mothers are in the more favoured position. This doesn't hold for twins because any prenatal advantages offered them by a younger and healthier mother are outweighed by the special advantage of the older mother: her womb will be roomier, more flexible, and better able to carry twins; and, with the added fact that her childbearing apparatus and reflexes have been better conditioned by her previous maternities, she will be able to give birth to twins with greater ease and safety than can the young first-time mother.

Up to this point we've been stressing survival among twins for the reason that, unfortunately, it plays such a much bigger part in the first stages of their lives than it does in the case of the single-born. But now, to brighten up our story, we can clear up the notion that the twins who do survive – and they *are* the biggest proportion – need be inherently more defective than singleborn children. We must always bear in mind that it is largely because so many twins develop under difficult conditions and are pushed out into the world too soon that they suffer high initial casualty rates. But their dangerous period is concentrated mainly at birth and in the critical first few days thereafter. While a crisis may continue another few weeks for the very premature or defective twins, *the great majority of twins – almost nine out of ten pairs – once they have passed their first month safely, have just about the same chance of survival as have singly born infants.*

In fact, if one considers only premature babies, *both* singleborn and twins, the twin 'preemies' – weight for weight – tend to be healthier, sturdier, and with a better chance of survival. The reason is simply that prematurity, or underweight, among twins – true of half of them – is a natural consequence of the fact that two babies ordinarily cannot be as well nourished or carried as long as can a single baby. But among single babies prematurity is the exception – occurring in only 3 per cent of them – and so is much more likely to be the result of something amiss in the mother or some defect in the baby, or some prenatal upset or accident.

Among full-term babies, however, twins, because of their extra prenatal and birth hazards, do have a somewhat higher death rate in infancy and early childhood than do the singleborn, but after a year or two this difference virtually disappears. Also to be stressed is the well-attested fact that the toll of deaths or defects among twins, whether premature or full-term, could be greatly reduced if various preventive steps were taken. Earlier detection of expected twins through the use of such methods as heartbeat recordings would lead to improved prenatal care and better preparation for their safe entry into the world. Prolonging twin gestation as much as possible would reduce the risks coming with premature birth. Further, improvements in facilities and methods for delivering twins and safeguarding the 'preemies' among them would save additional numbers.

Altogether, there is nothing in their twinship itself which pre-destines twins to have a life history, either in health or in other respects, inferior to that of the singleborn. In fact, once twins have safely run their initial hazardous gauntlet – so much more rigorous an experience than the average single baby undergoes –

they have given extraordinary proof that 'they can take it'. In many ways, indeed, they are the elite of babies. Their future can hold bright prospects, and, if nothing else, more excitement and interest than awaits most singleborn children.

CHAPTER 4

The Twin Types

—————

'WHAT kind of twins are they (or, are you) – identical or fraternal?' This is almost always the first question asked about twins of the same sex, at birth and throughout life. It is an important question – more important than most people realize. Nor can the answer be given quickly or easily in the case of many twins. In fact, because of mistakes in diagnosis made at the time of birth, there are thousands of twins now regarded as identical who are actually fraternal, or twins classed as fraternal who are really identical. How is one to know?

Opposite-sex twins, of course, can only be fraternal. (Extremely rare exceptions, due to chromosome abnormalities, are discussed later.) It is with the boy–boy pairs, or girl–girl pairs, that errors are so often made, especially if it is assumed that one placenta proves twins are identical and that two placentas prove they are fraternal. Earlier in our book we told why this doesn't hold true for a sizable proportion of twins: (1) It is possible for identical twins, if their separation comes at an early state, to develop apart from each other with two different placentas, two outer bags (chorions), and two inner sacs (amnions) – exactly as do most fraternal twins; and (2) fraternal twins may sometimes develop close together, with one fused placenta. What *can* be told definitely by examining the afterbirth of a twin pair (see the illustration opposite), is that if there is one placenta and clear evidence of *only one outer bag*, it is virtually certain the twins are identical. In sum, anywhere from 25 to 30 per cent of the twins with separate placentas may be identicals, and at least 20 per cent of the twins who have a single placenta may be fraternals.

If the afterbirth often won't tell the story, how, then, are parents to find out definitely if their boy–boy or girl–girl twins are identical or fraternal? The proof sometimes comes quite easily as the twins begin to grow. If they differ in any visible hereditary trait – such as

AFTERBIRTH EVIDENCE OF TWINS

(Shown diagramatically, parts cut and exposed)

A. MOST IDENTICAL TWINS

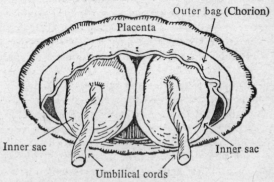

Placenta · Outer bag (Chorion)

Inner sac · Inner sac

Umbilical cords

Proof can be found that twins were identical *only if* (as above):
1. There was a single placenta (not fused),
2. *And* a single outer bag (chorion), usually containing two inner sacs. (Sometimes the twins share only one inner sac.)

B. FRATERNAL TWINS OR IDENTICAL TWINS

(*most*)   OR   (*some*)

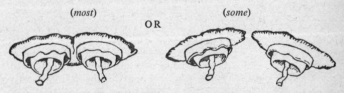

One placenta (made up of two fused together) with two bags, two sacs

Two separate placentas, each with bag and sac

eye colour, hair colour or hair form (one blue-eyed, the other brown-eyed; one blonde, the other brunette; one curly-haired, one straight-haired) – they are almost certainly fraternal. If they are so much alike in every detail of their looks that most people – and sometimes even family members – confuse one with the other, in all probability the twins are identical. Confirming this, a group of Swedish specialists on twins sent out a questionnaire in 1961 to 600 like-sex twins, asking among other things, 'Are you as alike as two peas in a pod?' and 'Were you mixed up by parents, sisters or teachers?' Among those who answered *yes* (and who also reported having the same eye colour and hair colour), blood-group tests later confirmed that all except a few were identical twins. Further, of those who answered *no* to the questions, more than nine out of ten were proved to be fraternal twins.*

But looks cannot always provide an absolute standard for establishing twin types. As we have seen, identical twins may have marked differences in environment before birth, and so be born with differences in makeup and appearance. One may be average in size, the other stunted; one may be normal, the other deformed; and, while their colouring and various bodily details remain the same, their features often may have been modified sufficiently by environmental influences to make their parents think they must be fraternal. On the other hand, some fraternal twins may have a high degree of resemblance if they have an unusual proportion of matching hereditary factors – that is, while fraternals (or any two singletons in a family) on the average have about 50 per cent of their genes in common, some may have many fewer, and look very unalike, and some may have many more, and look sufficiently alike to be mistaken for identical twins (at least in their early years).† This may be so especially if the twins' parents are similar

---

* Results much like the foregoing were obtained in a subsequent study in the United States in 1966 by investigators for the National Academy of Sciences Twin Registry. This registry has files on 16,000 White male twins who served in the armed forces. When 300 of these twin pairs were queried as to whether they were identical or fraternal, 93 per cent gave correct answers, as proved by scientific test findings (unknown to them) of their blood groups, fingerprints, and feature correlations. Of the 84 pairs of identicals, only two wrongly thought they were fraternal – most likely because of the assumption that identicals must always be completely alike in such traits as height and weight.

† Although some fraternal pairs may have many more hereditary factors in common than other pairs, it is virtually impossible for any two fraternals to be 100 per cent alike in their entire hereditary makeup, as identicals are. The chance that two fraternal twins would be genetically identical is *less than one in 64 trillion*. The reason is simple: Each parent is capable of producing any of 8,388,600 different combinations of his or her chromosomes in every sperm or egg (based on the fact that each parent has 23 pairs of chromo-

in colouring and in various features, and have many of the same genes (as when they are first cousins). In fact, if human beings were as pure-bred – or even approached being as pure-bred – as pedigreed dogs, cats and cattle, with their parents thus having a big proportion of matching hereditary factors, it would be almost impossible to distinguish by looks alone between fraternal and identical twins.

On the whole, though, one can expect most identical twins to be unmistakable 'look-alikes', and most fraternal twins to look no more alike than any two separately born children of a family. The uncertainties usually relate to the in-between group – identical twins who do not look identical, and fraternal twins who start out looking very similar. It is for this uncertain group, comprising up to 10 per cent of all same-sex twins, that special tests are necessary to clear up the doubts.

Most important of the twin-typing tests, in the great majority of cases, are the 'blood tests'. These are based on the fact that every person carries many kinds of chemical substances in his blood. Each of these substances comes in several or many varieties, the particular type in any individual being determined by heredity. Some of these blood substances are in the 'A–B–O' groups. Others include the well-known 'Rh' types – the 'Rh-positive' and 'Rh-negative' substances, with many varieties and combinations; the 'M' and 'N' substances; and various additional blood substances, called 'S', 'P', 'Kell', 'Duffy', 'Lewis', and so on.

Since each special type of blood substance is inherited, *all of the blood substances must be exactly the same in identical twins. If there is any difference in any one of the substances, the twins must be fraternal.* This need not mean that when the blood substances are alike in twins this conclusively proves them to be identical, because, as with looks, it is possible for even two non-twin children in a family to be alike in a great many hereditary traits. The chances

---

somes, and only one of each pair, at random, is passed on to a child, making 2^{23} possible combinations). The chance that exactly the same chromosome combinations would be received by two *non*-identical twin children in a family, whether fraternal twins or successive singletons, is $(1/2^{23})^2$, or, as said before, less than one chance in 64 trillion (and if other genetic factors are added, it would be virtually nil).

PROOF OF TWIN TYPE

IDENTICAL (one-egg) twins are always alike in each one of the hereditary traits shown below. If twins of a pair *differ* in any of these traits, they are FRATERNAL (two-egg).

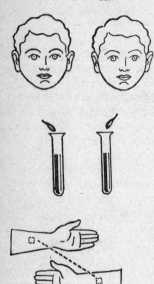

LOOKS

Hair form
Hair colour

Skin colour

Eye colour
Eye shape

General features

BLOOD GROUPS

Every hereditary
blood substance
(A, B, O; Rh; M, N, etc.)

SKIN GRAFTS

A patch of skin
from one twin
always takes root
in the other if
they are identicals.

that various blood substances in non-twin siblings would also be identical is largely dependent on how alike the parents are in their own blood types. For example, if both parents have blood types 'AA', 'MM', and 'Rh-negative', all the children will have these blood types, regardless of whether they are identical twins, fraternal twins, or singletons. Altogether, there may be 5 per cent of the same-sex twins whose type (fraternal or identical) cannot easily be established by the present blood tests alone.

Other twin-typing tests which can be made whenever blood tests leave doubt include the following:

Body chemicals. In addition to the blood substances, many other chemical substances are developed in individuals according to the genes they have inherited. Examples are the 'haptoglobins' and 'gammaglobulins', saliva secretions, etc. Identical twins always will be alike in these inherited substances, and any marked differences will show that they are fraternal. (Dogs, by their 'sniffing test', have their own unusual way of distinguishing between members of an identical or fraternal twin pair. Checking on how body chemicals of individuals assert themselves, Dr H. Kalmus found that hunting or police dogs could quite easily distinguish between the scents of fraternal twins [also non-twin members of a family], but could be confused at first by the similar body odours of identical twins. However, after special training and familiarization with the scents of both members of an identical twin pair, the dogs were then able to distinguish even the slight differences between them.)

Fingerprints, palm prints and footprints. Heredity produces in identical twins very similar patterns in the prints of their fingers, palms of hands, and soles of feet; while in fraternal twins these patterns are apt to be quite different. But to clear up a common fallacy, the fingerprints of identical twins are never *exactly* the same. So, too, patterns of the hand palms, and of the soles of the feet, while never exactly alike in identical twins, are nonetheless much more alike than those of fraternal twins. Thus, while not providing conclusive proof of twin types, finger, palm and foot prints can prove very useful when taken together with other evidence.

Ear shapes. Ear formations of individuals are so distinctive from birth onward, and those of identical twins so much alike, that 'ear prints' may presently take their place alongside fingerprints in helping to distinguish between identical and fraternal twins.

'Taste' tests. These tests for twin-typing derive from the fact that individuals inherit the tendency to be able to either taste or not taste certain chemicals. The test most commonly employed is for *phenyl-thio-carbamide* ('PTC' for short), which to some individuals tastes bitter, but to others seems tasteless. Identical twins almost always are alike in these taste reactions (any difference probably being environmentally conditioned), whereas fraternal twins may or may not have the same reactions.

'MIRROR-IMAGING' IN IDENTICAL TWINS

Various physical traits – inherited or otherwise – may sometimes appear on opposite sides of the twins.

1. Hair whorl *at top centre of head: Counter-clockwise in one, clockwise in the other.*
2. Larger eye *on right of one, on left of the other.*
3. Mouth *tilted up, and crooked* tooth, *on right side of one, on left side of the other. (Mirror-imaging may also occur in other features.)*
4. Birthmark *on right shoulder of one, left shoulder of other.*
5. Handedness: *One right-handed, one left-handed (but this occurs in only a minority of identical twins).*

'*Mirror-imaging*' *and opposite-handedness.* These traits, involving reversed patterns in twins, were formerly considered more important in establishing twin types than they are now. Some mark, detail of the body, or aspect of functioning (such as handedness), may appear on the right side of one twin, and on the left of the other; and these reversals may be much more common among identical twins than among fraternals. In some cases the trait may result when the division forming identical twins takes place after the right and left sides of the cell mass have begun to be laid out. Thus, as our illustration shows, quite often among identical twins one will find the same quirk in some feature of bodily detail appearing on opposite sides – that is, reversed, as with an image in a mirror (hence the term 'mirror-imaging'). Internally, in rare cases, one may also find some organ in one of the twins, such as the heart or stomach, in a reverse position from the normal and from the other twin.

As for *opposite-handedness* – one twin right-handed, the other a 'lefty' – there is growing evidence for abandoning the idea that this is a special twin trait. The most conclusive study on the point has been made by Dr Torsten Husen (University of Stockholm), who checked on all male twins called up for military service in Sweden over a recent five-year period. He found, first, that the proportion of twins recorded as left-handed (6·2 per cent), was only slightly greater than the proportion among singleton draftees (4·8 per cent), and that even this slight difference could have been due to the fact that the twins had been questioned more carefully. Second, the frequency of left-handedness among identical twins was virtually the same as among fraternals. And, third, the proportion of identicals with the same handedness – both right or both left – was almost exactly the same as that of fraternals.

In any case, although mirror-imaging or reverse-handedness may be thought of as an interesting contrasting trait when it appears in a twin pair, it can provide little evidence for determining twin types. At best, it may be helpful only in conjunction with other facts, and is only a drop in the bucket compared with the blood-test possibilities.

Skin grafts. If all other tests are inadequate, the 'skin-graft test' provides an almost certain way of proving whether twins are or are not identical. Since identical twins are completely alike in the hereditary makeup of all the tissues of their bodies and in all hereditary blood and chemical substances, it is possible to take skin or flesh from one and graft it onto or into the other twin, with complete assurance that the graft will 'take' – just as if it were from one part to another part of the same body. But when this is attempted with fraternal twins, or with any other two members of a family, or with two unrelated individuals, the grafted skin will slough off before long.

A dramatic example of how both the blood and skin-graft tests were applied for twin-typing was provided in the Swiss village of Fribourg some years ago. One night in 1941, two mothers in the village hospital gave birth: one to twin boys, the other to a single boy. A harried nurse tagged the infants, and presently the mother of the presumed twins took them home. Before long it was clear that the two boys – whom we'll call 'Victor' and 'Pierre' – differed in many ways, so it was accepted that they were fraternal twins. But a mystery developed when the boys reached the age of six and were sent to school. There was another boy in the school, 'Eric', who looked almost exactly like Victor, and repeatedly, when the three boys were together, it was this outsider boy, and not Pierre, whom people took to be Victor's twin.

It isn't hard to guess the rest. When suspicion arose that there had been a baby mix-up, Swiss experts were called in (Drs A. Franceschetti, F. Bamatter and D. Klein) to examine the boys. Blood tests soon showed that the supposed outsider, Eric, was indeed the true twin, and skin-graft tests proved that he and his twin brother were an identical pair. The required transfers were then made between the two households, and after some difficulties of readjustment the reunited twins were raised happily together, although retaining cordial contact with the 'ex-twin'. (At last report the twins were embarked on professional careers, while the ex-twin had become a postman.)

The possibility of a similar mix-up occurring now is extremely remote in view of the greatly improved methods used in hospitals for 'tagging' babies at birth. Further, if there should be the slightest doubt about any pair, it could quickly be resolved by twin-typing tests such as those described above.

CHAPTER 5

The Chances of Having Twins

'Am I going to have twins? You know, they run in my family!'
This is a familiar question put to doctors by pregnant women. And
often an expectant mother who has already borne twins will ask,
'Is there a chance lightning will strike twice – that I'll have twins
again?'

Whether the possibility of having twins – or a repeat twin birth –
is regarded with pleasure, concern or alarm, it can never be
ignored. On the average, twins may be expected among American
and European mothers in about one in every hundred pregnancies,
but with marked variations above or below this average, depending
on certain factors which we'll deal with presently. So the answer to
'What are *my* chances of having twins?' (or 'twins again?') may
be quite different for one mother as compared with another.

To begin with, what may well be most unusual about human
twin births is that they normally are the marked exception. For in
all but a small proportion of living creatures it is the rule that
offspring come in multiple sets, or litters. However, when human
mothers do produce twins (not to mention triplets or quadruplets),
this by no means makes them more like all lower animals, as some
may think, because twinning is even rarer in some of the lower
animals, such as horses and elephants, than it is in human beings.

In general, the average number of offspring produced in a given
pregnancy is hereditarily determined for each animal species.
Where progeny are developed within the mother and brought forth
alive, a major factor is how many the mother can carry. One might
expect, then, that the larger animals would have more offspring at a
time than the smaller ones. But the reverse is true in most instances.
The largest litters are usually found in the smallest creatures –
mice, guinea pigs, rabbits, cats, dogs and so on (up to ten or more
young at a time) – whereas the largest animals, ranging from
humans through gorillas, horses, cattle, giraffes, elephants, and

whales, usually have the fewest offspring – seldom more than one at a time.

In some way nature (or the process of evolution) has adjusted matters so that the number of offspring usually fits in with the special combination of circumstances and requirements of each species. Animals which quickly run the gamut of a short prenatal life, very early maturity and reproduction, with a high risk of death and a short life span, produce many offspring. In the natural state this applies to most of the litter animals. Contrariwise, those animals whose young take longest to develop prenatally, and to grow up and mature, and which also have a relatively good chance of survival and a fairly extended life span, produce fewer offspring. Human beings are in this latter category, perhaps more than any other animals.

The number of breasts available for feeding the young might also seem to be some indication of nature's plan for the offspring normally expected. Animals which bear large litters have the required number of breasts and nipples. Thus, since the normal human female has two breasts, she might be considered as prepared to bear and nurse twins quite regularly. By what process is she kept from doing this?

If we think first of fraternal, or multiple-egg, twins, it is not because of an egg shortage that human mothers do not ordinarily have more than one baby at a time. The ovaries of an average women may contain several hundred thousand rudimentary eggs, which means that she could theoretically produce twins, triplets, and quadruplets in profusion. The reason she does not do so is primarily because only about 400 of her store of eggs usually ripen during her reproductive life, and ordinarily only one egg comes out of the ovarian storehouse each month. However, sometimes two, three or more eggs may develop and emerge, and, if fertilized, can result in fraternal twins, triplets or quadruplets.

But individual women vary greatly in their chances of producing more than one egg at a given time, and enabling these to develop through to birth. The mother's age and previous childbearing experience have most to do with this (and also affect the chances of twin survival, as noted in Chapter 3). Many studies have shown that the peak period of twin production (referring mainly to fraternals) is in mothers from age 35 to age 40. As shown in our accompanying Chart ('A Mother's Twinning Chances'), a mother within that age group is about three times as likely to produce twins as is a mother under twenty; and if the older mother is having her fifth or over childbirth, she is more than five times as likely to produce fraternal twins as is the mother under twenty having her first childbirth. From age 20 on, the chances of having twins increase until the peak period of mid-30; then, from age 40 on, the chances of bearing twins drop again (probably because the chances of carrying twins through to birth are much reduced by unfavourable prenatal conditions in older mothers). It also has been found that whatever a mother's age, the more children she has borne previously, the greater the chance that she will produce twins in the next pregnancy.

These facts provide the clue to what formerly would have been considered a fantastic statement: That the religion, income, social level, and education of the given parents can affect the chances of their having twins.* For a moment's thought will show that all these factors may influence the number of children a mother will have (with twinning chances going up as family sizes increase) and the extent to which she will bear children into the later and most 'twin-prone' ages. On this basis one can expect more twins, on the average, among the less privileged, lower-income, less educated groups, where conscious family limitation is not so extensively practised as in the more favoured groups. One may also expect more twins among those whose religion may incline them to have large families. (In Ireland, for instance, the combination of late age at marriage – about twenty-five or twenty-six for women, on the average – with religious aversion to artificial birth control has led to extensive childbearing into the older 'twin-prone' ages, with a resulting high twinning rate of about one pair in every 67 births.) With continued social change and increasing limitation of childbearing – especially among older women – a decline in twinning incidences has been taking place in the United States and many other countries.

*This point was initially brought out by the author in a paper given at the Second International Congress of Human Genetics, in Rome, in 1961. (See Bibliography.)

A MOTHER'S TWINNING CHANCES*

... And how they are influenced by her age and previous childbirths

An expectant or prospective mother should note where the vertical line for her age group is cut by the dotted line for previous childbirths, then look across to the number at the right. The chances the twins will be identical are shown in the shaded lower part of the graph.

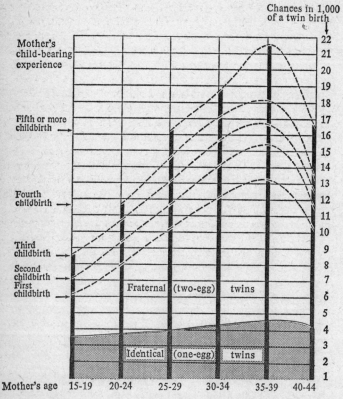

*Figures given are for White mothers. Among American Negro mothers twin-bearing chances are about one-third higher, and among Mongolian mothers (Japanese, Chinese) about one-third lower than those of Whites. The racial differences are mainly with respect to fraternal twins. (See Text.) Chart adapted from 'Bio-social effects on twinning incidences,' by Amram Scheinfeld and Joseph Schachter, *Proc. 2nd Intl Congr. Hum. Genetics*, Vol. 1, 1963.

But the variations in mothers' chances of producing twins, one should remember, apply preponderantly to fraternals. As is strikingly shown in our chart, the bearing of identicals is very little influenced by the mother's age or previous childbirths: The nineteen-year-old mother, with a first pregnancy, has only a 25 per cent less chance of bearing *identical* twins than has a thirty-eight-year-old mother with a sixth pregnancy. Moreover, among different races and ethnic groups the incidence of identical twins is almost uniform, usually from 3 to 4 per thousand births. But in the case of fraternal twinning there can be enormous differences, with the rate being many times higher in some racial groups than in others. Altogether the marked differences that exist among human groups the world over in twinning rates are due primarily to the relative numbers of fraternal twins which are produced.

On a racial basis, the highest rate of twinning is among Negroes; the next highest among Caucasians (Whites), and the lowest among Mongolians, such as Japanese, Chinese and American Indians. The world-record twinners are African Negroes, with a rate in many tribal groups of about one twin pair in 40 pregnancies and reported as reaching the astounding average of one twin pair in 22 pregnancies among the Yorubas of Nigeria. (Negroes in the United States, who are of considerably mixed ancestry – African and White, with some Indian – have a twinning rate now averaging about one pair in 73 births.) At the opposite extreme, the Japanese average only one pair in about 160 births, and even lower rates have been reported for other Mongoloid groups.

Within groups of the White race there also are marked differences in twinning frequencies, but these may be ascribed largely to the social factors previously discussed which influence the twinning chances of mothers. Thus in a given recent period the twinning rate among Whites ranged from a low in Spain of about one pair in 110 births – close to the present rate for Whites in the United States – to a high in Finland of one in 65 births. (Going back to earlier years, there was the extraordinary rate of one twin pair in 53 births on the isolated Finnish island of Aland during the two centuries from 1750 to 1959. Dr Aldur Eriksson, who reported this figure in 1964, suggested as possible reasons that (*a*) much inbreeding on the island could have intensified the chances that any hereditary factors for twinning would come together, and (b) there had been much childbearing into the older, twin-prone ages.)

Whatever the reasons for the differences in twinning rates among human beings, there is little question that these differences relate mainly to the proportionate numbers of fraternal twins that are produced.* Thus, in the United States, Negro mothers may produce from 15 to 20 per cent more fraternal twins than do an equal number of White mothers, although there is little racial difference in identical-twin production. As a result, of every 100 twins among American Negroes the ratio is currently about 71 fraternal pairs to every 29 identical pairs, whereas among Whites the ratio is about 65 fraternal to 35 identical pairs. Going further, among the Yoruba African Negroes, with record fraternal twinning, the ratio is about eight fraternal pairs to one identical pair; and, at the other extreme, among the low-twinning Japanese, it is the identicals who outnumber the fraternal pairs by a ratio of almost two to one.

Within each racial or ethnic group, however, it also appears that mothers of some families or stocks are much more likely to have twins than are other mothers. Among the reasons for so concluding are the many instances where a single mother has repeatedly borne twins. Here are just a few examples: In 1961, a Jacksonville, Florida, mother, Mrs M. L. Pearson, at age thirty-seven, bore a

*To estimate the proportion of identicals among twins born in a given population, a simple method is the formula devised by a German scientist, W. Weinberg, back in 1908. Taking the known number of opposite-sex pairs among the twins, one doubles this to get the total of all fraternals, and the remainder of the twins will then be the identicals. The formula derives from the fact that among fraternal twins at birth, the odds – as in matching coins for heads and tails, are that one in four times there will be paired boys, one in four times paired girls, and two in four times a paired boy and girl – in other words, equal proportions of fraternal twins of the same sex and of opposite sex. Thus, knowing the number of opposite-sex twins, and hence of all fraternals among the twins born, one can readily determine the percentage of identicals. For example, to get the proportion of identical and fraternal White twins born in the United States in 1958 (as reported above) we took the known percentage of 31·65 for boy–girl pairs, doubled this to 63·3 per cent to include the like-sex fraternal pairs, and then subtracted this 63·3 per cent from 100 per cent, which gave us the estimated 36·7 per cent of identical twins.

record *seventh* set of twins. Previously, in 1944, Mrs Rosa Trembly, of St George, Canada (near Quebec), bore her sixth set of all-surviving twins in eight years of marriage. In 1959 a Rochester, New York, mother, Mrs Ernest L. Kittleberger, aged thirty-eight, also had her sixth set of twins (of whom three pairs survived, three died); while a Buffalo mother, Mrs Joseph Volk, had her fourth consecutive set of twins. In Menominee Falls, Wisconsin, the John Burgs have five sets of twins, plus seven singletons. A radio 'Queen of the Day', Mrs Lillian Cassidy, reported in 1954 that she had three sets of twins and one set of triplets among sixteen children in all. And what may be a record for rapid-fire twinning was established by Mrs Gene Murphy, of Cedar Rapids, Iowa, who (with no singletons) in 1958 gave birth to her third consecutive set of twins in 27 months – the second pair having come 15 months after the first, the third set 12 months later.

These examples, even if big exceptions, would still offer support to the findings that once a mother has borne twins, her chances of having twins again in a subsequent pregnancy are increased much beyond the average twinning rate. The odds of a repeat twin birth for her have been estimated as from three to ten times as great as the initial twinning chance of a mother who has not had twins. Governing the odds may be various factors already discussed, such as the mother's race, age, and previous childbearing. Also, the chance of a twin repeat is generally much higher if the first pair were fraternals than if they were identicals. Even the sister of a woman who has borne twins has about twice the average chance of producing twins in a given pregnancy. Furthermore, mothers who themselves are twins also have a greater than average chance of producing twin babies (although fathers who are twins are hardly more likely to sire twins than are men in general).

The facts, therefore, strongly suggest that there are inherited degrees of the twinning tendency. That 'twinning' genes do exist among lower animals is quite clear. Among cattle, for instance, different breeds show wide variations in the incidence of twins. Most dairy cattle produce twins about once in every 50 births, but in the Swedish Friesian breed the rate is about once in 33 births, and in the Simmental spotted Swiss cattle, the incidence is almost one twin pair in 20 births. Among beef cattle, twins are much rarer,

HEREDITY IN TWINNING

How the 'twinning tendency' may work

In producing FRATERNAL twins:

1 *Mother's ovaries* may be extra active and often produce two or more eggs a month instead of one.

2 *Father's sperms* may also be extra active and fertile, increasing chances that if two eggs are waiting both will be fertilized.

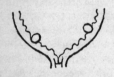

3 *Mother's womb* may provide an especially good environment in which twins can develop safely.

In producing IDENTICAL twins:

A special inherited tendency for eggs to divide may result from ...

4 Something in the *eggs* produced by the mother, causing them to divide easily in the early stages.

5 Something in the environment of the mother's *womb*, acting on the egg to cause division.

6 *'Twinning genes'* in the father's sperms, combining with 'twinning genes' from the mother to impel division.

coming only about once in every 200 to 250 births. Sheep and goats also show marked breed differences in twinning frequency. In some breeds of sheep, twins occur more often than do single-born lambs, but in other breeds fewer than one in five pregnancies results in twins. Also worth noting is the fact that among domestic animals the twins are preponderantly fraternal. In cattle the ratio is about twenty fraternal pairs to one identical pair. Among horses, too, with about $1\frac{1}{2}$ per cent of pregnancies resulting in twins, the paired colts are almost never identical. And, coming closest to humans in the animal kingdom, the *marmosets* – a species of tiny primate distantly related to the primate forms of man's remote forebears – produce twins as a general rule, and these almost always are fraternal pairs.

Most authorities assume, then, that among human beings there also are inherited twinning tendencies. Some experts have estimated that perhaps one in every four or five women has a special predisposition to produce twins. But just how this tendency may be inherited, and how it works, is yet to be established. For one thing, it is not enough to say that twins have 'run' in such and such a family, because it is important to know whether the twins – or how many of the sets – were fraternal or identical. And evidence on this score is often hazy or incorrect.

Since the two types of twins come about through different processes, any influence in their production – either hereditary or environmental – must be different for each type. In the case of fraternal, or two-egg, twins, the determining influences might be largely those which could enable a mother to produce more than one egg at a time. In the case of identical twins, the influences might be those which would cause a singly-produced and ferti-lized egg to divide and result in two separate babies. The added requirement that a mother should be capable of carrying and nurturing twins through to birth would be almost the same whether they were fraternal or identical.

Again, with respect to fraternal twins (but not identicals), we must recall that their production is enormously influenced by the age of the mothers (those between thirty-five and forty having four times the chance of bearing such twins as have mothers under twenty). This would justify the assumption that even if there is some hereditary tendency to produce fraternal twins, the main factor in whether they are actually conceived and born is an environmental one – that is, there is something inside the mother which is governed by different stages of her productive life. Such an environmental explanation holds best for mothers of the same race. But how can we account for the big racial differences in fraternal twinning – four times as frequent among Whites as among Japanese, and with the frequency among Negroes still higher? Here we must conclude that there are inherited racial as well as individual differences in the capacity for producing such twins.

As for identical twins, since their incidence differs only slightly among mothers of all groups and ages, there are these possibilities: (1) that identical twinning results purely from some environmental accident or happening which causes a particular egg to split in two, and thus form two babies; (2) that the split occurs because of something in the hereditary makeup of certain fertilized eggs; or (3) that a given egg splits and forms twins both because of an inherited impulse to do so, and because of some condition in the mother at the moment which gives it the extra push toward this result. Actual evidence so far exists only for the second possibility, and this only with respect to a lower animal, the nine-banded armadillo. In this species, the mothers produce one egg at a time, but each egg has the quality of habitually dividing, and then redividing, to result in identical quadruplets at each birth. However, either or both of the other two possibilities may in time also be found to be factors in the twinning of other species.

Whatever the facts may be about human twinning inheritance, authorities agree that its workings probably are complex, and that any 'twinning' genes would come from both sides of a family. That is to say, in the case of fraternal twins a woman's predisposition to produce two eggs at a time might result from the combined action of certain genes she received from both her father and her mother. But, given a wife who has this fraternal twinning tendency, it is not unlikely that the husband may also play a part in helping twins to be conceived. This could be possible, some experts believe, if the husband's sperms are more than ordinarily 'aggressive' and 'durable', so there would be an extra chance that if the wife did produce two eggs at a time, both would be fertilized.

We may speculate further that tendencies towards identical-twin production could also have some hereditary basis and, if so, that, as with fraternals, such tendencies could come through both male and female sides. The simplest possibility, then, would be that if a woman received 'identical-twinning' genes from both her parents, the eggs she produced would be more ordinarily prone to split and form two babies. A second possibility is that such genes might be carried in both the husband's sperms and the wife's eggs, and that when they combined in a given fertilized egg – presto! – identical twins would result.

But another important point should not be overlooked: In any human group, or for an individual mother within any group, the ability to conceive twins of either type is one thing; the ability to carry them safely through to birth and to have them survive is another. In the past the death toll among twins was enormous, for even single babies had a mortality rate many times higher than that of babies today – even higher than today's twins – and medical provisions and facilities to cope with the extra hazards of twin babies – particularly the 'preemies' – were minimal. Nor do we have to go only into the past, for everywhere today there are great differences in the survival chances of twins born in the more favoured as compared with the less favoured groups. (Examples of this were given in Chapter 3.) Nevertheless, in all groups the mortality rate among twins is being steadily cut down through better prenatal care, improved obstetrical techniques and added facilities for seeing more twins safely through their critical period.

So this brings us to an interesting question: If the chances that twins will survive are continually improving, should we not be seeing more and more twins among children growing up? The answer, strangely enough, is No! For, under existing conditions, the increase in twin survival has been outweighed by a counter-force – the trend towards a decreasing incidence of twin conceptions and births (mainly of fraternals) due to the growing proportion of children born to younger and less 'twin-prone' mothers, and the smaller proportion born to older mothers in the 'high-twinning' brackets.*

* Twinning incidences among White populations of other countries have not been too different generally from those in the United States for com-

The foregoing trend has been taking place under normal and natural circumstances, but now medical science has provided means of artificially changing the twinning picture and – if desired – reversing the downward trend in twinning incidence. This has come with the discovery of hormone treatments, which can enormously increase the chances of a woman's producing not only twins but supertwins if and when desired. Details about this will be given later. Let us first look more closely at the twinning situation as it has been to date.

In the United States (among Whites), we find that from a rate in the late 1920s of about 12 twin pairs per 10,000 births, the incidence in the 1960s had dropped to between 9 and 10 pairs. Stated in another way, where the earlier average had been about one twin pair in 85 births, the ratio in the mid-1960s was only about one in 110 births. (The triplet incidence also had dropped sharply.) Similar marked drops in the reported twinning rate occurred in many countries – Norway, Sweden, Denmark, Belgium, the Netherlands and Germany, among others.

We should note, however, that this drop in twinning incidences relates largely to fraternal twins, for, as was previously shown, these twins are the ones whose production is most strongly influenced by a mother's age and previous childbearing – the very factors which have been undergoing great change. Production of

parable periods. The identical twinning incidence almost everywhere has hovered close to 3·5 pairs per 1,000 births, plus or minus a fraction. Fraternal twinning incidences (governed by various maternal factors, as noted) have differed considerably, however, with rates during the 1950s ranging from a low of about 6 fraternal pairs per 1,000 births in Spain to a high of 10 pairs per 1,000 in Denmark. Combining identical and fraternal twin births, the total twinning incidences in Europe during approximate matching years in the 1950s were about as follows (from low rates to high rates): Spain, 1 twin pair in 110 births; France, Belgium, Austria, 1 in 92; West Germany, Switzerland, Sweden, Netherlands, 1 in every 87 to 85. In Norway the rate was 1 twin pair in 83 births; Italy, 1 in 81; England, 1 in 80; Denmark, 1 in 71. In Australia the rate (1947–9) was 1 twin pair in 87 births; in Israel (1952–7) 1 in 90 births. All the foregoing figures, one should bear in mind, are for previous years. The current twinning incidences in any given country may be somewhat different, and probably lower if the situation with respect to younger maternal ages and decreased childbearing is similar to that in the United States.

identical twins, on the other hand (as we have noted) would be only slightly affected by these factors. Accordingly, another aspect of the changing twin-incidences has been an increase in the proportion of identical to fraternal pairs among the twins being born. Where, two generations ago, identical twins in the United States constituted about 25 per cent of all twin pairs at birth, by the mid-1960s they were making up about 34 per cent, or about one identical to every two fraternal pairs. Yet this trend, too, may be affected by the new twinning-induction treatments; for the effects of these treatments are confined almost entirely, it seems, to the induction of *fraternal*-twin conception and birth.

What are these treatments, and how do they work? First administered to induce ovulation and conception in previously sterile women, the treatments involve the use of certain hormones of the pituitary gland ('FSH' and 'LH') which regulate the development and release of eggs – normally one a month – from a woman's ovaries. The surprising finding was that a large proportion of the women so treated not only conceived and bore children but also, for good measure, produced twins or supertwins. In short, the artificially administered pituitary hormones triggered the release, as often as not, of more than one egg at a time.

Specifically, Dr Carl Gemzell, a Swedish doctor who pioneered with this treatment (another pioneer was an Italian doctor, Pietro Donini), reported in 1964 that multiple births had occurred in nearly half of a large group of previously barren mothers in whom pregnancy had been induced by hormone administration. Two of these women conceived quadruplets, one set surviving healthfully; and in 1965 two sets of quintuplets were born through the treatment – one set in New Zealand, with all five surviving, and another set in Sweden, only one of which survived. (Even a set of sextuplets was conceived, though all miscarried.) Meanwhile, the fertility treatments were also being given in New York at the Columbia-Presbyterian Medical Center, and again many of the women so treated had multiple births, including two sets of quadruplets (one set in 1964, one in 1965).

Thus the possibility – long predicted by geneticists – that twins or supertwins may be produced to order *if and when desired* is approaching reality. At the same time, the risk of unwanted multiple births because of the treatments is being eliminated by controlling the hormone dosage.

An important point to stress again is that the hormone treatments to date have produced, and can be expected to produce, only *fraternal* twins or supertwins, coming from different eggs, inasmuch as the process involves the induction of multiple ovulation. Scientists anticipate the development of means for also inducing identical twinning, however, perhaps by treating prospective mothers in such a way as to cause fertilized eggs to divide at an early stage (and perhaps to redivide, if identical quadruplets are desired).

How far and to what extent these twinning-induction methods will be utilized may depend upon how strong is the desire for twins. The attitudes of parents and prospective parents on this point may be much influenced by the facts which will be brought out in ensuing chapters of this book.

CHAPTER 6

But Mothers Don't Have Four Hands

―――――

SOME years ago a Midwestern housewife got an hysterical phone call from a young woman cousin who not long before had become the mother of twins – her first children.

'The babies are driving me crazy!' sobbed the nineteen-year-old parent. Details poured out wildly: How she'd been desperately trying to cope with two different feeding schedules (one twin was premature, the other not) ... the endless nappies, bathing, laundering, with no outside help ... the inability to get both twins to sleep at the same time ... the continuous chorus of nerve-jangling crying. And worst of all, everything she'd dreamed of as a bride had been shattered. The previously spotless, jewel-like home had become an untidy mess; the appetizing, beautifully served dinners had given way to pickup snacks out of tins and frozen-food packages; her young husband and she, with nerves frazzled, were quarrelling constantly, and their love life was nil. Everything had been disrupted because of the twins.

'I can't stand it any more ... I'm going to kill myself!' shrieked the young mother.

The older woman knew just what to do. She quieted the girl, told her to sit tight, and immediately called up a friend who was a member of the Mothers of Twins club of her community. Telephone wires hummed. In no time an experienced woman who had brought up two sets of twins sped to the distracted mother's home (much in the manner of an Alcoholics Anonymous envoy responding to a plea for aid). And, before long, immediate problems were being straightened out and a happier life for the new twin mother, her babies, and her husband had begun.

Unwittingly, however, this young woman had experienced and expressed what most parents of twins have gone through in some degree. 'Everybody tells you how cute your twins are, but nobody can even dream what goes into the production,' one of them said. For, after all the fuss made over the new twosome at the hospital, there comes the down-to-earth reality of taking them home and nurturing them towards a healthy, well-adjusted existence. Parents who have had only singly born babies can hardly realize what special problems may be presented by twins. To think that twins require merely a doubling up of the effort needed for rearing a single child is a great understatement. In almost every detail of feeding, bathing, clothing, equipment, sleeping, toilet training, discipline, and adjustment to themselves and to other children – as well as in their effect on the parents' lives – twins present problems that are not found with singletons.

What we will do here, then, is to summarize facts and practical information about the care of twins derived from various sources – much of it from mothers of twins directly, and some from booklets, books, or other publications listed in the Appendix. (If at times the 'Life With Twins' drama seems like a tragedy, remember that there are many delightful interludes and that, after the worst is over, very few parents of twins consider themselves as anything but fortunate.)

The 'crisis' – the really rugged period in the raising of twins – is generally concentrated in the first few months, when most of the horrendous experiences of the young mother occur. As twins grow – and, if they were 'preemies', as they begin to catch up to normal – they become steadily easier to handle. Nevertheless, most mothers who've reared twins say that during the first year they require anything from one-and-a-half to three times the work and strain involved in raising a single-born infant. Thereafter, as the twins settle into their routine and the family and household adjust to them, many mothers feel that twins are not only no more trouble than two children raised separately but may be even easier to care for than two singletons who are close together in age. This is because, first, much time is often saved in doing the same thing for the two at once, and, second, because twins after a while can amuse each other and do not demand so much individual attention.

How much of a problem any pair of twins presents varies greatly with individual circumstances. Much depends on the nature of the twins themselves; on the mother's experience and skill with babies; on the money available for extra help; on the husband's capacity to pitch in and do things; and, not least, on what other children there are in the family and whether they contribute to or detract from the care of the twins. Almost invariably – and certainly during the twin's first year – the whole family must co-operate in their rearing, and many ordinary aspects of family life will have to be more or less neglected.

In the first year, also, it usually makes little difference whether the twins are identical or fraternal, and of the same sex or of opposite sex. What counts most is whether they are premature or full-term, sickly or healthy, difficult or easy as infants; and, particularly, whether they are much alike in needs and responses, or very different and thus require two types of handling. These are among the many specific aspects of the care and feeding of twins which we will now discuss.

THE MOTHER. Nature may have been very wise in regulating twin births so that the chances of having them would be least for the youngest and newest mothers, and would increase according to the mother's age and previous childbearing. For, as a rule, the more mature and experienced the mother, the more easily she can rear twins. But this can be greatly influenced by such factors as the mother's health, how much time she must give to other children, and how prepared she was, psychologically and emotionally, for the advent of the twins.

SCHEDULES FOR TWINS. In almost every aspect of their care, the mother of twins soon finds that she has to make adjustments and arrangements different from those that apply to the single baby. Where demand feeding is all right for singletons, it won't work for twins: One can go frantic trying to feed each twin when he or she wishes (and not always being sure which one has been fed, or when and how much). Unless there is some special reason why one twin has to be fed more often or differently from the other, twins themselves are apt to be happier if they are adjusted to the same feeding schedule.

Again, there's the matter of *bathing*. For a single baby many mothers consider the daily bath a must. But for twins it can over-tax the mother's time and strength. Doctors may advise, therefore, that it is usually enough to bathe twins every other day unless there are skin afflictions, and that, except in hot weather, even twice a week may be enough.

The *sleep habits* of twins may mean sleepless nights for the parents if one twin is continually awakening and triggering off the other with his or her crying. Not until twins are trained to sleep and awaken at the same time can there be peace in the family. In *toilet training* of twins, on the other hand, mothers find it wisest not to try to enforce harmony, for often one twin is prepared to learn earlier than the other (particularly with a girl–boy pair, where the girl is usually ahead).

EQUIPMENT. Appliances and time-saving gadgets of many kinds may be much more essential when there are twins than when there is only a single baby to cope with. Laundering for twins is a formidable task, even if there is a nappy service. Still to do are endless nightgowns, undershirts, sweaters, bibs, blankets, socks, and so on and on. When asked what they needed most, the great majority of mothers of twins said, 'A washer and dryer – and if only one can be bought, a dryer.' Incidentally, the most useful 'household appliance' in caring for twins, many mothers observed, is a *resourceful and willing husband*. In fact, in almost every case when twins arrive, all preconceived notions about the woman's job and the man's job in taking care of the home and children have to be brushed aside.

EXPENSE. 'Wow!' is the best descriptive term when speaking of what twins cost initially. There is first the fact that two each of innumerable items are required simultaneously; whereas, when children come singly, one item can often do for all in succession. Cribs, play pens, and high chairs are examples. While some things bought for twins can be used for later babies, what can be done with a double baby carriage or a double stroller? Or two play pens, which are needed to keep twins from hurting each other? Here is where the Mothers of Twins clubs, with their sales of used twin equipment, have effected great savings for members.

Similarly, *clothing* for twins presents special problems. Hand-me-downs from other children can be of little help where two of everything are needed; and if twins are dressed alike – as most mothers prefer when they are babies – there is even more expense and effort in buying duplicates of every item and seeing that matching outfits are always available. (Only with boy–girl twins, when they begin to be dressed differently, is the problem eased.) But one can sometimes profit by the policy of certain stores and mail-order companies of supplying double layettes at no extra cost if an advance order for a single outfit was placed before the babies were born.

All in all, for a considerable period twins usually entail much more expense than do any average two single babies. True, when the births are easy and the twins are full-term and healthy, parents may get a break from the fact that some doctors make it a 'two for the price of one' delivery. But in the more than half of the cases in which the twins are premature, particularly if their birth has been attended by difficulties and incubator care is required, the stork's C.O.D. charges may be staggering.

Nor is this all. Further boosting the initial expense of having twins is usually the need for extra household help, unless willing relatives are constantly available. The mother who can manage things alone when she has only a single baby seldom can do so when confronted with two. ('Get outside help even if you have to borrow or beg to pay for it!' is the most urgent advice given by mothers of twins to newcomers in their ranks.)

No wonder, then, that the cautious husband who prepares for any financial emergency may want to take out 'twin' insurance. Such insurance, first instituted by Lloyds of London in 1946, is much like a bet: The company weighs the chances that a given couple will have twins (obviously before there can be knowledge that twins are on the way), and decides on the odds. The premium may be as low as $2\frac{1}{2}$ per cent of the policy's pay off or as high as 20 per cent – depending on the calculated risk of the mother's having twins: her age, previous childbearing, and the family history of twinning. According to information given me by R. C. Norwood, a New York insurance man whose firm writes such policies, about 1,500 to 2,000 of these are issued annually in the U.S.A. The average 'twin' insurance policy is for $1,000, but many go much higher – the record being one on which a father of twins 'won his bet' for $40,000.

However, the need and demand for 'twin' insurance has been decreasing as more parents are being covered by medical and hospitalization cost reimbursement plans.* In any case, the extra expenses that come with twins may cause serious concern only in the first year or so. Thereafter twins may be little or no more expense than any two other children in a family.

ADVANTAGES AND DISADVANTAGES OF TWINS. Most of the practical difficulties in raising twins seem less and less onerous as time goes on, and the more favourable aspects assert themselves. This is clearly shown in the answers mothers gave when they were asked to list the advantages and disadvantages of having twins. We've already reported the principal gripes, but here's how one mother summed them up in verse form:

The Joy(?) of Twins

Drudgery that's double or more
Laundering till your hands are sore;
Tangle of lines with soggy things drying,
Day and night chorus of yelling and crying,
Endless chores and no end of expenses,
Worries that drive you out of your senses.
Everyone bothering you with questions,
Everyone giving you crazy suggestions,
Husband complaining you're no kind of wife,
Everything mixed up in your life.
If I knew whom to blame for twins, I'd sue 'em.
– *Those who want twins are welcome to 'em!*

But for every mother who echoed these sentiments (and this mother admitted she was only kidding), there were many more who held that the joys of having twins far outweighed the drawbacks. Among the advantages most frequently cited (together with quotes from mothers' own statements), were these:

Getting two babies with one pregnancy. 'You don't have to go through another eight or nine months to have a second child.' . . .

*In Great Britain somewhat different conditions pertain, due to her National Health Insurance and welfare services – Ed.

'Twins are the easiest way of getting a family fast.' . . . 'If you'd planned on having just two more babies, why, there they are!'

Pride at being among the parents singled out to have twins. 'Twins are a very special blessing bestowed on a couple who can meet the challenge.' . . . 'The fuss they create when you're out with them makes you very proud – as if you've really accomplished something.' . . . 'Twins make all the rest of the family special.' . . . 'The glory helped carry me through the difficult period.'

The good effect on the parents. 'Twins help bring the husband and wife closer together.' . . . 'My husband thought I was wonderful for having twins, and I respected him more when I saw how smart and considerate he was in helping to care for them.' . . . 'Parents with only single children are cheated – they miss a lot not having twins.'

The fun of having twins. 'Twins are twice the work but three times the fun.' . . . 'Life is never boring when you have twins.' . . . 'Twins are so exciting to watch as they grow up.'

Twins as the mother's character-builder. Here we'll just quote a Westchester County, N.Y., mother of *two* sets of twins: 'Having a large family practically overnight helps one to see values more clearly. I've been forced to organize my time more effectively, retaining only the friends and interests that are really vital to me. I've learned how to say No to myself, my children and others. So, although my twins have drained me physically for a while, on the whole they've helped me to grow, and now, five and one-half years later, I'm more energetic and do more than I ever have.'

It is not surprising, then, that so many mothers of twins refer to themselves as 'doubly blessed' (these words being used as the name for some of their clubs), or proudly sign their letters, 'Twincerely yours.' The exuberance and exhilaration over having twins usually comes, however, only after the parents have weathered the physical storm – perhaps about the end of the first year – and may not last too long. Once the twins are safely and healthily launched into babyhood, parents may be confronted with some new problems of a psychological and social nature which are uniquely related to twins or brought on by their presence in a family. In fact, these problems, as we will see next, may often have begun sprouting as soon as the twins arrived.

CHAPTER 7

The Reception Committee

'WE'D lost our only child, a lovely little girl of five, a few months before. When the twins arrived, it was like a gift from heaven – a little girl to replace the one we lost, and a boy as a bonus baby.'

'So far our twins have meant only trouble. We already had five children – the youngest six – and we thought that was enough. Then the twins suddenly came and upset everything.'

'Having twins was an exquisite, awesome experience.'

'I wasn't excited one way or another about my twins. People make altogether too much fuss over them.'

'With three girls in a row, you can imagine how we'd wanted a boy for the next one. When the twins turned out to be two more girls, wow! – my husband would hardly speak to me for days.'

'Twins are a miserable trick of nature on a woman.'

'The twins were wonderful for my ego.'

What you have just read are excerpts from statements by mothers of twins. As can be seen, they reflect the marked differences in the way twins are received by parents. Knowing, then, how much importance is attached today to a child's earliest emotional experience, it should be evident that the precise manner in which the stage is set for the arrival of a pair of twins may have much to do with all the events that follow for them – and, indeed, for other members of the family as well.

First, there are the mother's reactions to bearing twins. These may be tied up with her whole feeling about motherhood. Reading between the lines of some of the quotations given above, one can distinguish the woman who glories in childbearing, and the one who resents it. To the former, twins are a special joy. To the latter, they are almost an insult. In many cases where twins are strongly

THE TWIN MOTHER'S 'LOAD'

A woman's general attitude towards motherhood can have much to do with how burdensome twins may seem to be.

resented one may find marital or psychological problems which would have led to reluctance to bear even a single baby.

Among the happy mothers of twins, psychoanalysts have noted that for some the twins are a fulfilment of secret wishes going back to childhood. British analyst Dorothy Burlingham, in her book *Twins*, refers to this common daydream of having another self – a person so close and similar to oneself as to be much like a twin. 'It is a conscious fantasy,' she writes, 'built up by some children who haven't been emotionally satisfied.' It involves 'the child's search for a partner who will give him all the attention, love and companionship he desires and who will provide an escape from loneliness'. For many women in later life becoming the mother of twins may, therefore, be a substitute fulfilment of the early fantasy.

From another direction, the mother's reception of twins may be affected by whether they are sturdy and full-sized babies or puny 'preemies'. In the case even of the singleborn, studies by Dr Barbara M. Korsch, Cornell Medical College pediatrician, and by Drs David M. Kaplan and Edward A. Mason, of the Harvard

School of Public Health, have shown that many mothers are seriously upset when their babies are premature. The emergency atmosphere in the hospital before, during, and after delivery . . . the sight of the hushed figures in white gowns and masks, the scientific paraphernalia, the incubator, the 'unnatural' methods by which the baby is fed and kept alive . . . the sympathetic and guarded words of visitors . . . the delay in the christening and sending out of cards . . . the fear that the baby won't survive – all this stirs up the mother's anxieties and makes her wonder how she, an ordinary woman, will be able to cope with caring for the fragile mite she's borne when she takes it home.

But, though these negative effects may be heightened when instead of one 'preemie' the mother has two, there may also be a favourable balancing influence: For, while the investigators found that the mother of a single 'preemie' often has a feeling of guilt or inadequacy because of the premature birth, the mother of twins is aware that prematurity is normal with twin births, and she may be further compensated by pride in her achievement. Nonetheless, the effects of the first strains may continue to be felt long after the twins are safely home, and the mother's lingering subconscious fear that they are more fragile and more precious than ordinary babies – or, sometimes, her resentment that they caused her undue suffering – may continue to affect her attitude towards them.

But, whether twins are premature or full-term, it is not hard to see that the mother's initial reaction to them may have much to do with how she thereafter judges the task of rearing them. The mother who did not want twins in the first place, or who was fearful when they arrived, is likely to find the task more burdensome and trying than the one who was delighted when the twins came. But in many cases, perhaps most, both negative and positive feelings may be combined. This was noted by psychologist Emma Plant, of Western Reserve University, when she interviewed a large group of mothers of twins in Cleveland. Often there was a conflict in the same mother between pride and resentment: The sense of exaltation that 'I was *privileged* to be the mother of twins', clashing with the feeling, 'Why did *I* have to be picked to have them?' Fortunately, in most mothers the pride usually overwhelms the resentment.

Now to the father, the next important member of the twins' 'reception committee'. His mental preparedness for twins and the devotion and willingness he is prepared to show in helping to take care of them may contribute almost as much to their successful rearing and emotional development as does the mother's effort and influence. (When the husband has fallen down in this respect, many a mother of twins indicates that he is almost as much of a problem to her as are the twins themselves.)

What counts most may well be the relationship of the two parents towards each other. To a greater degree than is true with the arrival of singly born babies, *well-adjusted parents provide the best start towards well-adjusted twins*. (In fact, many psychological problems associated with twins are likely to melt away under the warmth of parental love and understanding.) But one must recognize that even with ordinarily compatible parents, twins will impose an unusual strain, and call forth the utmost in love, maturity and unselfishness in the home. Also, because of the scarcity of outside help, the rearing of twins for most couples may have to be a co-operative enterprise and may play havoc with preconceived notions of what constitutes the 'woman's role' and the 'man's role' in caring for children. To the man who has strong feelings on the subject the compulsion to do jobs he had thought of (or scorned) as 'women's work' – nappy-changing and feeding babies, washing clothes, shopping for food, cooking meals, housecleaning – may be seriously upsetting.

Various other aspects of having twins may strain the husband–wife relationship. If the father is a shy man he may be disturbed by all the kidding he gets when twins arrive, ranging from hints about his potency to, in reverse, sly references to 'who helped you?' (We may recall here that among many primitive peoples twins are believed to result from the wife's having had sexual relations with two men.) If the husband and wife have not been getting along well the arrival of twins, and the accompanying new problems, may greatly increase their tension. The wife who did not want twins may resentfully blame her husband for her new predicament; the husband who had been growing cool towards his wife may somehow regard her bearing twins as a trick to shackle him. The sex of the twins may also have great importance. When either or both parents have ardently wanted a child of one sex, and twins of the opposite sex arrive (as in one of the situations quoted at the beginning of this chapter), this may serve as an excuse for new recriminations.

An especially aggravating element to many husbands is the interference with their sex life. Even when a wife is devoted to her husband, the mere physical strain of bearing twins and caring for them may often exhaust her for a while, to the point where she has little capacity for sexual response. This situation need not persist for long; under ordinary circumstances the mother who has borne twins may be able to fully resume her normal sex life almost as soon as after bearing a single child. (If there was no abnormality or injury to the woman's sex organs, this may be almost immediately, according to Dr Alan Guttmacher.) There is, however, a psychological angle: To the woman who did not like sex previously, or who did not love her husband, the arrival of twins may be an excuse to avoid sexual relations as much as possible. Frigidity on the wife's part is not infrequently reported as an aftermath of twin-bearing. But almost invariably it can be ascribed to a sexual problem that had existed before.

In happy contrast to these situations are the many cases – and they may well be in the large majority – in which couples are brought closer together by their twins. Wives repeatedly tell how husbands who had been indifferent towards single babies became dynamos of responsiveness and helpfulness when twins arrived. In part this may be because a single baby's bond to the mother is often so close that the father is left out, whereas with twins there is less exclusive attachment to the mother and more need and opportunity for the father to share in their emotional upbringing. In that sense twins may be said to have two 'mothers' – the 'maternal' one and the 'paternal' one. If the twins are different in personality and behaviour, each parent is often drawn to and identifies with one of them in particular. This is most likely to happen if there is a boy–girl pair, in which case the father may identify with the boy, the mother with the girl.

We come now to other members of the twin 'reception committee': the *siblings* – that is, any children in the family who precede the twins. These children may not only have an important effect on the twins and, in turn, be affected by them but they may also influence the parents' attitude towards the twins. Much has been said and written about sibling rivalry or jealousy, and there are few parents who are not aware of this or who have not seen it in action among their children. When the family includes twins and singletons, special complexities of sibling rivalry are apt to develop. (In this chapter we will focus on the effect of twins on the other children in the family. How the siblings affect the twins will be told in the next and later chapters.)

If there are only single children in a family the rivalry effects are mainly in terms of the younger and older ones. In the past, parents worried mostly about the older child, and his fear of being displaced by the new baby. Recently Dr Alfred E. Fischer, New York paediatrician, found that the younger child is more often the one who shows unhappiness, frustration and abnormal behaviour (starting between the ages of one and three), because of trying to compete with the older child. But with twins, both the children who precede them and those who come after are frequently disturbed.

In the case of an older child or children, 'new-baby jealousy' hits with full force when, instead of just one interloper, there are two arriving in a whirl of excitement and admiration. Also, the fact that twins demand so much of the parents' time – often to the neglect of the other children – is enough reason for antagonism and disturbances to develop. To quote from the Ohio Twin Mothers booklet, *Twin Care*:

To your other children, your complete absorption in these new babies and your apparent rejection of them, is much the same as it would be to you, the mother, were your husband to reject you and bring into the home a younger, more attractive wife.

Although the single child may show no outward sign of antagonism to the twins, this need not mean that the feeling isn't there. It may be expressed in several ways. Be wary if the single child shows overmuch devotion to the twins and extreme solicitousness about their welfare. While sometimes sincere, this concern may mask a deep inner resentment which can be worse in its effects than if the antagonism were expressed openly. In the preschool-age sibling of twins the inner turmoil may reveal itself in a reversion to infantile habits, such as bed-wetting, whining, baby talk (to command attention), and quarrelling with playmates. In the school-age sibling one may note poor classwork, indifference to studies, and reports of unruliness.

Whether the effect of twins on their siblings is only of brief duration or long lasting may depend largely on the type of twins they are, what the relationship between them may be, and the ages of the children. During the first year or two, when the twins are babies, it makes little difference whether they are identical or fraternal (often not even the parents know). But, as the twins grow, if they are identicals who continue to attract attention and who are extremely close to each other, the effect on siblings will be much greater than if they are fraternal twins developing more inconspicuously and more as individuals. The sex of twins may also be a factor: Identical girl twins may disturb a younger or older sister more than they would a brother. Similarly, identical boy twins may evoke more sibling rivalry and jealousy from a single brother than from a sister. In all cases, the closer in age that the twins and the singleton are, the more acute the effects will tend to be.

Some revealing insights into twin-and-sibling situations are given in the following statements from mothers of twins:

Our oldest daughter, nine, has been so unhappy because of her four-year-old twin sisters we've had to seek help for her at a child guidance clinic.

The twins have been welcomed by their brother, who is six, but their little sister, only two, is so jealous she wants to get into the crib with the twins and be fed with them from the same spoon. Sometimes she uses her doll to pretend that she, too, has a twin.

Our little boy, one and one-half when the twins came, was all confused and kept asking when the babies were going to be taken back where they came from.

The twins are aged three, and our two older boys, five and one-half and four and one-half, always try to act like twins, too. When one goes to the store, the other must go along.

Coming after the twins who are five years older, our little fellow of three acts wistfully as if he isn't quite complete – that he must have had a twin and lost him.

How do mothers handle these twin-and-singleton problems? Most, on looking back, feel that the best 'ounce of prevention' lies in the way the other children have been prepared for whatever the stork might bring. When children feel secure in their parents' affections, they are seldom too concerned about the arrival of a new single baby. But, since twins present many special problems, extra 'preconditioning' efforts must be made. This is easiest when parents have some advance knowledge that twins are coming (as has become possible with the new prenatal 'twin-detection' techniques). In any event, once it is certain that twins are on the way, the parents should impress the other children with how they will share in the excitement and distinction of having twins in the family, and also how they will share in the responsibility of caring for them. At the same time, nothing must be said or done to make the single children feel that they will be any less important than the twins.

Some parents who have one singleton a little older than the twins let him or her 'adopt' them; alternatively, if there are two singletons, each is 'given' one of the twins to 'adopt', or care for. One mother who did this says, 'Although the twins now are ten, each older child [a girl and a boy] still refers to one of them as "his" or "her" baby.' Still another mother writes, 'At first the twin's three-year-old little brother was very nervous, talked incessantly, and laughed and cried almost hysterically. But we made him feel the twins belonged to him, too; he now introduces them to company as "his" babies, with much pride.' And here's another 'prescription for jealousy' that worked: 'Our little girl was resentful of her twin baby brothers, but when we put them in separate strollers and let her, at age three, push one of them, she was immensely pleased at having people admire the "little girl who was helping mummy".'

An Ohio twin mother tells (in the booklet *Twin Care*) of one little boy who took the briefing about his new twin sisters very much to heart. He went around the neighbourhood explaining, 'Poor Mama . . . She's got those lousy new babies on her hands, and so we've all gotta pitch in and help her, and maybe some day they'll grow up into girls or something.' The mother added, 'He was very important and happy about the whole thing.'

Another injunction to be observed after twins arrive is that as much as possible must be done to keep the regular established routine of the other children from being interrupted. 'Try to set aside some special time in the day, no matter how brief, for each of them,' say mothers who've been through this. Here are some other suggestions:

Bedtime for the single ones must be as pleasant an occasion as possible, for the telling of stories, hearing prayers, going over the day's events, playing some little game, getting hugs and kisses from mother and father, etc. ... During the day, one might relax a few of the previous restrictions on the single child, to make him or her feel more grown up. ... To offset the unusual attention given the twins, one should try to make the lives of the single children a little fuller and livelier by giving them extra treats, taking them places (that's the father's job, mainly), having relatives and friends invite them out, making their birthday parties extra special, and so on ... Any toys given to the twins by either parents or other persons should be more than matched in gifts to the single children ... And never, *never*, let the other children think you're showing the twins favouritism – for example, not spanking them when they're naughty, as you might the others.

To offset any envy or jealousy of the twins because of the attention they attract by being dressed alike, some parents resort to providing matching mother-and-daughter, or father-and-son outfits for the single children and the parent of the same sex. (Such clothing can be bought in many stores, or parents can contrive to make or buy something similar.) A single girl who is just a little older than her twin sisters may be most conscious of dress, and if, on occasion, she can be dressed like her mother it will give her a feeling of 'twinship' with the parent and lessen her jealousy of the twins. So, too, when the twins are boys, getting the singleton brother some clothes to match his father's can increase his sense of belonging and self-importance. (Other suggestions for easing the twin-and-sibling dress situation will be given in a later chapter.)

The foregoing hints will be most helpful in dealing with siblings who are not too much older than the twins. If there is a considerable gap in ages – six or seven years, or more – the single child will be progressively less affected by the twins. Particularly, as he or she approaches adolescence, there will be a growing tendency to treat the twins tolerantly, or condescendingly (or, best of all, *kindly*) as just little brothers or sisters.

What of children who come after the twins? Here it is the twins who must be conditioned so that life for the new arrival will be happier. If the twins have been the sole centre of attention, they should be made ready to yield some of the spotlight to the younger child. Often, when the new baby appears, parents induce the twins to 'adopt' him or her, and make them feel the baby belongs to them, too, and requires their aid. As the younger child grows and becomes more conscious of the twins, it is increasingly important that he should not feel himself overshadowed and put in the position of an outsider. One of the greatest dangers, mothers report, is that twins may form a 'closed partnership' and gang up against the single child or children.

Again, this is the dark side of the picture. In most families in which there are twins (if we can judge by the many we've been in touch with), the sibling situation is seldom very serious or long lasting. The effects are even less when the twins are fraternal and different in physical makeup and personality than when they are much-alike identicals; and least of all if the twins are a boy–girl pair, who seldom stay together as they grow, and thus create no more difficulties among the other children in the family than do the singly born brother and sister. Further, the twin-and-sibling situation in a given family generally follows this rule: Just as emotionally well-adjusted parents can quite easily adapt to most problems presented by twins, so well-adjusted children will be little bothered by having twins in their midst.

The more secure and happy the singly born children – and the less spoiled and self-centred – the more likely they are to feel that twin brothers or sisters, whether older or younger, are an asset to the family and a source of added importance and value to themselves. This may also hold true for most parents. Later attitudes, of course, depend largely on the twins themselves, and on their relationships to each other and to the rest of the family as they grow older.

CHAPTER 8

Problems

A PSYCHIATRIST tells about a young mother who came to him with two happily gurgling, very pretty one-year-old girl babies. 'They're twins,' she sighed, and stopped. When she added nothing more, the psychiatrist asked, 'So what is the problem?' The young mother looked surprised. 'Why, I don't know,' she exclaimed. 'Aren't *you* supposed to tell me?'

So much has been written and said about serious psychological problems involving twins that many parents assume such problems are inevitable. Undoubtedly, there are various unusual situations or difficulties presented by twins and their relationships, and modern psychology has done much good in directing attention to them, and suggesting how to handle them. But there also has been a negative result: The new psychological spotlight thrown on twins may have aroused more worries and fears than there need be, and in some ways may have created an atmosphere not too unlike that in primitive tribes which surround twins with superstitions and taboos. Replacing these, we now have a host of modern beliefs which plague twins' parents: That twins, unless carefully conditioned otherwise, will tend to become emotionally maladjusted, develop a morbid closeness to and dependence on each other, forfeit their sense of individuality and be retarded in their mental and social development; also, that they may be beset by either open or subconscious mutual antagonism, resentment, jealousy, rivalry, and even hatred.

How important the worries on this score have become may be seen in a questionnaire prepared by a committee of a Mothers of Twins club for members to fill out. Among the questions asked were the following: 'Tell whether the personality of each twin is "Dominant" or "Submissive" . . . Did the twins have more, or less, tensional outlets than is considered average for young children? . . . Which nervous habit was manifested: – Stuttering?

– Whining? – Headbanging? – Tantrums? ... If the twins were antisocial, what steps did you take to counteract this?' And so on with other questions which touched on fighting between twins, possible language handicaps, dislike of their twinship, etc.

As we proceed to explore these situations, and to see how far they really do threaten any given pair of twins, let's keep in mind that almost all the psychological problems listed as going with twins are not uncommon among single children of a family. The question is whether or not these problems are more frequent and acute in twins, and if they take unusual forms because of the twinship.

At the very start of their lives twins – no matter of which type – do come up against a unique circumstance: Each enters a world in which a competing baby of exactly the same age is always present, always making equal demands, and always, as a rule, being given equal treatment. Each twin sees and feels that he is not the only pebble on the beach, unlike the singleton baby, who is a little tyrant in a world revolving around him. At first thought this matter of twins sharing attention would seem to be all to the good in teaching unselfishness and co-operation. Yet many psychologists take the opposite view: That it is part of a child's normal development to start off being intensely self-centred and oblivious to anyone's needs but his own, and that it hurts his ego development if he doesn't enjoy for a while the sense of being the sole object of his mother's attention.

But twins, by the foregoing theory, tend to have their 'selfishness drives' frustrated from the very beginning. They have no time to adjust individually to the presence of another equally demanding child. From their first moment they are projected into an atmosphere of competition for love and attention. Here, then, might be the seeds of any special resentment, antagonism or jealousy later observed.

There is no doubt, however, that each twin needs as full a quota of parental love and care as would be given to a single child. Moreover, each twin must feel that he or she is at no time neglected in favour of the other. This feeling of neglect sometimes does develop if one of the twins is much smaller and weaker than the other, and requires much more attention. But the favouritism towards one twin that may be most serious in its psychological impact on the other is that which arises from a conscious or unconscious preference on the part of one parent or both. This most often occurs when the twins are fraternal and quite different in appearance or behaviour, and especially when they are a boy–girl pair, and may thus evoke different responses from the two parents. Even with identical twins there frequently are minor differences between them which may lead to some degree of preference by parents. While the distinctions parents make between twins are seldom as marked as those they make between children born separately, the effect of any parental discrimination, however subtle, is likely to be felt more by twins because of their intimate relationship.

As twins pass through infancy and into the more self-conscious and perceptive stages of babyhood and childhood, any conflicts developing between them may be expected to become intensified. Yet the degree to which this actually occurs depends considerably on how much their parents and others tend to promote competition in general, and to place a premium on it. In a family where there is constant talk of 'getting ahead', 'beating the next guy', or excelling in one thing or another, one can expect twins to be more concerned with their relative worth and performance than they would be in a family where competition is not highly stressed. Often the cure for extreme rivalry between twins will be found in having the parents soft-pedal the emphasis on always 'being the best'.

Of equal importance, parents and others in or outside the family must not be constantly looking for differences in twins which can be interpreted in terms of one's superiority over the other in this or that respect. There may be a tendency to do this with twins more than with other children, or at least to make comparisons on a much finer scale. This follows logically from the fact that since twins are of exactly the same age and are always in close proximity, the minor differences between them will show up more clearly than between any two singletons. But, in part, it is also because many parents today, being so intent on distinguishing between their twins, are more apt to magnify the minor differences. For instance, would a mother of little singletons be moved to say, as did a mother of *eighteen-month-old* twins in describing them to me, that 'Johnny is an extrovert, Jimmy an introvert'? (Even a trained psychologist would hardly venture so definite a diagnosis of tots at this age.)

Should there be a significant difference between twins at any given time in some trait or performance, there is always the possibility that their relative positions may change later (especially if they are identical). The 'seesaw' situation, in which one twin is 'up' in some respect at one time – in size, health, vigour, mental performance, aggression, looks, or some other trait – and at another time is 'down' while the other twin is 'up' in that respect, is very frequently observed. This is hardly surprising, since every individual in relation to himself tends to fluctuate considerably in various traits from one period to the next, and thus twins can also be expected to do so in relation to each other. On the other hand, there may be the 'snowball' effect, wherein what starts out as a small difference between twins may grow bigger as time goes on. This can happen by chance if one twin takes the aggressive lead, and the other twin resigns himself to being submissive; or if one twin shows a slight superiority in some kind of performance – a sport, or a subject in school, or music – and works to become better at it; while the other twin, reluctant to compete, gives up trying to develop himself in the same activity.

When differences persist and become marked between twins (or singletons as well), and are apparently related to inborn factors, the parents must seek to bring their children to an awareness that inequalities in makeup, capacities, and performance are bound to exist among people. What can be stressed at the same time is that no one can be best at everything (nor need this be essential for happiness), and that each child has his own individual excellences. In the case of twins it is especially important that parents should take note of these individual qualities, and should give each twin the encouragement and opportunity to develop his or her own capacities to the utmost.

Another common form of comparison that warrants comment is that of referring to twins as the 'older' and 'younger'. It is a practice that might well be discouraged. To place stress on the fact that one child was born a matter of minutes before another can have psychological repercussions, both for the parents and the twins, going far beyond its importance. In times past, or in countries today where the right of primogeniture – the claim of the first-born to the father's title or estate – was or is observed, the question of which twin came first would have enormous significance. (We might recall the Biblical episode of Jacob and Esau.) Among royal families in Europe there has long been the practice of having a high official present at every birth to a queen or princess of a possible heir, so that should twins be born the right to the succession would not be in dispute. Primitive royalty also has its headaches over the twin problem. Anthropologist Edwin M. Loeb found that among the Kuanyama of Southwest Africa, when twins were fathered by a king, one of the babies would be killed by the midwives.

In more ordinary ranks of society today the question of the birth order of twins may also have practical importance. Legally, in certain cases, there is the matter of wills which make special provisions for a first-born and which may therefore discriminate against one twin of a pair. Further, there are the instances – perhaps one in several hundred twin births – in which one twin is born just before midnight on a given day, and the other just after midnight, so that their births are recorded as occurring a day apart. The different legal birthdays of these twins could then have significance in any situation where precise age is a qualification, and the specified date falls on either of the twins' birthdays. For instance, the older twin could be at a disadvantage in the army draft; or in applying for insurance where the premium is based on age at the last birthday (up to a certain period); or in getting or holding a job with an exact age limit. The younger twin's disadvantages could come if his birthday (but not his twin's), was just a day short of that required to make him eligible for voting, or for holding some public office, or (in the early years) for admission to public schools.* Perhaps in most of the one-day-apart twin birthday situations, red tape and technicalities are or can be dispensed with. If not, some attention might be given to legal means of setting straight such twin inequalities.

At any rate, there is little doubt that undue stress on the birth order of twins can only create problems, particularly of a psychological nature. If friction is already developing between twins, their

*In the U.S.A. 'public' schools are state schools – Ed.

being made aware that one was born before the other may be seized on to heighten their conflicts. Frequently, the 'older' twin may have the feeling he is superior, the 'younger' one that he is inferior, and rivalry between them may then be intensified – the one striving to maintain his position, the other to reverse his. At the same time, the twin known as the 'oldest' may feel ashamed, bitter and resentful if he or she lags behind the 'younger' one in any important respect – growth, strength, ability, or attractiveness. In short, one might well recommend that parents 'lose' the record of which twin came first, and if they are asked about it later, say they can't remember or don't know. One mother told me she explained it to her twins this way: 'Both of you were ready to be born at exactly the same time. It was just a question of whom the doctor helped to come out first, and it all happened so fast we weren't really sure which one did.'

Another special problem may arise in disciplining twins. Not infrequently they are harder to handle than are two single children. This may, in part, be due to the fuss made over them. Like stage children, twins, too, can be spoiled and become show-offs if they are the constant centre of attention. Again, the twins born as premature babies (more than half of the total) often create so much anxiety at the beginning that parents thereafter continue to indulge and overprotect them. This in itself may lay the basis for various behaviour difficulties, and, when twins do misbehave, it may be more disturbing to parents than are the acts of single children; for, if twins do something bad together, the double impact may make their act seem worse than the same thing done by singletons separately. As one Cleveland mother wrote: 'It's unpleasant to hear a young child repeat dirty words. But when you hear them from two children at the same time, it's horrible – like a nasty chorus.'

How to punish twins when they misbehave puts many mothers in a quandary. Suppose that one of a twin pair, sight unseen, has been very naughty – messed up a room, broken something valuable, or hurt a pet – and the mother doesn't know which twin is responsible, or neither twin confesses? Said a mother of the Westchester, N.Y., club: 'Unless I myself saw one do the evil deed, I punish both, for children are notorious liars at this age. I use a long paddle which we call "Applied Psychology".' But another club member disagrees: 'I punish as a team when the crime is a joint one, and individually when a lone one. But if it's a whodunit and I can't solve the mystery, I don't punish either. Better the guilty should escape than the innocent suffer.'

Perhaps this is one of the problems which parents of twins tend to magnify. When I queried several child-psychologist friends about the twin-spanking matter, they pointed out that it is little different from the discipline problems which constantly occur in families where there are two young children of close to the same age, and the parent doesn't know who is guilty of an act. Usually one doesn't have to be a Sherlock Holmes to identify the miscreant before too long. Often certain patterns of misbehaviour tend to characterize each child, and this may be so with twins as well, even the identicals. If the parent remains at a loss, psychologist Lili Peller believes the mere fact that the mother has shown her disapproval of the act will in itself constitute punishment, and that this will be felt most severely by the guilty twin.

Generalizations about problems of twins often have little meaning with respect to a particular pair, and may lead to mistaken advice or cause needless worry if one does not consider what type they are – identical boys or girls, fraternal boys or girls, or a boy–girl pair. The psychological problems may be different in nature or degree for each type. *Some twins* – the identicals – *are born with twinship in their genes*, which continues throughout their lives; *some twins* – the fraternals who are not too dissimilar – '*achieve*' *twinship* by being drawn together through mutual experiences, affections and needs; and *some twins*, who are as unlike as can be – the very dissimilar fraternals, and particularly the boy–girl twins – *have twinship 'thrust upon them'* by their parents and others, although there may be no reason why, if they wish and as soon as they are able, they should not go on in life as separately as any two single children.

Specifically, in the case of the identicals, many aspects of their unusual psychological situation may indeed be said to be born in them or with them. If they look so alike they can hardly be told apart, it is inevitable that they will have many experiences and encounter many situations different from those not only of two single siblings but of fraternal twins who look unalike. Fully as important, the identical hereditary makeup of one-egg twins which produces marked similarities in their appearance also causes their bodily and mental mechanisms to be geared in much the same way. Thus the whole pattern of behaviour, thinking, and social relationships of identical twins – and any resulting psychological problems – would tend to be different from those arising with fraternal twins. In fact, just as most of the stories and beliefs regarding twins centre upon the identicals, so do most of the major psychological problems that are associated with twins.

But among identical twins themselves there are differences in the situations confronting individual pairs. Where the twins are very much alike in makeup, development, and capacities, their problems may relate mostly to too great attachment to and dependence on each other. On the other hand, where identical twins are much less alike, different and even more acute problems may arise. Since everyone expects identical twins to be *identical* in virtually all respects, any marked difference between them which puts one at a disadvantage compared with the other – as with a girl pair when one is less attractive, or with a boy pair when one is not as strong or as outstanding in athletics as the other – will hit much harder and create more problems than would any difference between twins identified as fraternal.

Turning to the fraternals, any uniqueness associated with them arises from the coincidence of their having been conceived and born to the same mother at the same time; for, whether they are both of one sex or of opposite sex, they have in their hereditary makeup nothing more in common, or more unusual, than have any two singletons in a family. If there are special problems going with fraternal twins that do not ordinarily develop with two single siblings, it can only be because these twins are reared in unusual proximity from birth and *trained* as twins. In other words, only to the extent that twinship is imposed and impressed on fraternal twins are they likely to be affected by it psychologically; and this is especially so in the case of fraternals who do not look alike – and, even more, those of opposite sex – who would not be taken for twins unless people were told they were.

A different situation is presented by fraternal twins who look enough alike to be mistaken for identicals. In their case, they are expected to be also alike in behaviour and mental performance. Yet, as geneticists know, the fact that fraternal twins may have 'look' genes which make them very similar in appearance need not at all mean that their 'behaviour' and 'mental' genes are any more alike than those of any two average single siblings in a family. So, if they are under continual pressure to try to be the same in their development, behaviour, schoolwork, and social achievements, these 'look-alike' fraternals may often have difficulties greater than those of identical twins.

The boy–girl twins are least likely to be affected by the problems ordinarily associated with twins. The 'sameness' angle, of course, has no meaning for them; their difference in sex will be constantly in the foreground. Because of this great basic difference, however, these twins may be beset by many special psychological situations which do not arise with twins of the same sex, either identical or fraternal, or with any single brother and sister in a family. In a later chapter devoted to the boy–girl twins we will tell how they may be affected by the fact that the girl usually develops more rapidly than the boy, not only psychologically but socially; by pressure on the boy to take the masculine role, the girl the feminine role, and possible conflicts with respect to this; and how, as life goes on, various sex differences, biological and social, may bear on their adjustment as individuals and to each other.

What has been brought out so far suggests that the difference in types of twins also has much to do with the relative difficulties of rearing them. Parents often ask: 'Which are harder to bring up, fraternal or identical twins?' The answer is that there are troubles and advantages going with each type. Initially, in early infancy, if fraternal twins are very different in their makeup and needs, they may be harder to take care of than are identical twins who, being more alike, would tend to synchronize more in their feeding and sleeping schedules and other habits. Fraternals, too, may clash more in temperament; they may show greater differences in rate of development, both physically and mentally; and they may be more unalike in health and in their reactions to diseases. These differences may create certain kinds of problems more often in fraternal twins. But the greater 'sameness' of identical twins can lead to problems of a different nature in rearing them, as we shall see in our next chapter.

So far we seem to have dwelt largely on the negative, or unfavourable, aspects of twinship. This, in a sense, is a reflection of the fact, noted earlier, that modern psychology has devoted so much attention to these aspects. Understandably, the twins most apt to be studied by the psychologists, psychoanalysts and psychiatrists are the ones who have difficulties. But it is no more fair to judge all twins by those than to judge all singletons by the ones who require treatment for emotional disturbances. Indeed, while we will have much more to say on the matter in later chapters, we now stress two points: First, there actually is no evidence at this writing that twins are more likely to be problem children than are singletons; and, second, most of the parents – judging by the hundreds we've heard from directly – believe their twins are, and will be, happier than, or at least as happy as, the single children in their families.

This is said with full awareness of all the special problems and difficulties that do confront twins, some of which we already have discussed and others of which we will now proceed to explore in detail.

CHAPTER 9
Individuality

OF all problems involving twins, the one on which most attention has been focused may be summed up in the word *individuality*.

According to modern psychological thinking the major threat to twins is that they may grow up with minds and emotions so linked with each other – like 'psychic Siamese twins' – as to be unable to achieve the independence considered essential for well-adjusted and socially mature individuals. This may explain why one Mothers of Twins club's booklet has as its dedication: 'To you who seek independence and individuality for your twins.' In the booklet issued by another club, the 'rules for visitors' caution that on meeting twins for the first time, 'Greet them individually and don't dwell on their twinship . . . or make any special comments.' Sometimes this may be asking too much. It reminds me of the story of the mother who warned a caller, 'When you see my little boy, pretend there's nothing unusual about him.' 'Is there?' asked the visitor. 'Well . . .' the parent sighed. 'He has two heads.'

Twins are by no means freaks, and yet, when one sees two children who are apparently exact duplicates of each other, it is hardly possible not to take note that they are linked in a special way. Nor do most parents want this to be ignored, as is obvious when twins are painstakingly dressed alike. So why so much concern about the individuality of twins?

In our preceding chapter we spoke of the psychological theory that it is normal for every infant to start off intensely self-centred, and that it interferes with his ego formation if he finds another infant competing for his mother's attentions. Going further, the theory holds that before a child can know he is a distinct individual, or 'somebody', he must see and feel himself as separate from any other person. Ordinarily, with a single child, the process requires becoming detached psychologically from his mother. Before birth, of course, he was attached physically to her by the umbilical cord.

After he is born, the child may continue to feel his body as part of his mother's when she nurtures him, and especially when she breast-feeds him. It may take a while, then, before he senses that she and he are separate individuals.

As the singleton child develops, he comes to realize that not only is he distinct from his mother but also from the other individuals in the little world about him. He sees himself more and more clearly in relation to other persons – affecting them, and being affected by them, as an individual. The boy may identify, as a male, with his father and brothers; the girl, as a female, with her mother and sisters. With each step in attempting to imitate other persons different from himself, the child also develops his own pattern of behaviour, and thus, more and more, his individuality.

Now what happens with twins? Each twin is required not only to go through the process of becoming aware that he is separate from his mother but also that he is separate and distinct from his twin. That isn't so easy. This other baby who is always with him, who is fed and held with him, whom he feels close up against himself – is this person not part of him? To illustrate, psychologist Marjorie Leonard (herself the mother of twins) tells of watching two three-month-old twins sleeping peacefully side by side in a twin-baby carriage, the thumb of one in the mouth of the other. A Larchmont, N.Y., mother observed the same habit in her twin babies, and it wouldn't be surprising if it happens with many other twins.

The 'mirror-imaging' aspect of twins – in which physical traits may appear on reverse sides in the two of them – also has a psychological parallel. For a while twins may think of each other as a single baby does when he sees his own reflection in a mirror. It may take additional time for the twin to grasp the full distinction between a mirror reflection and the actual flesh-and-blood presence of his twin. For example, Dr Helen Thompson, observing a pair of two-year-old girl twins, 'T' and 'C', saw T looking in a large standing mirror for the first time. T thought that she was seeing C through a glass pane, and reached behind the mirror to touch her twin. At that moment C came into the room, and as T looked from C to the reflection of the 'other' baby in the mirror, she was badly confused.

As twins grow up a new mirror angle develops. Psychologist Leonard reports seeing two eight-year-old girl identicals dressing up for a party in exactly the same costumes. Their room had no large mirror, but ingeniously one twin said to her sister, 'Stand over there a minute – I want to see what I look like.' A similar situation was described by the mother of six-year-old girl identicals. When one of these twins asked how her hair or dress looked, the other would say, 'Look at me. I look the same as you.'

When other people also see one twin merely as a reflection of the other and get mixed up as to which is which, it is hardly surprising if twins themselves become confused about their identities, or think of themselves as interchangeable halves of a unit. British twin expert Dorothy Burlingham cites the case of two young twins who would take turns crying whenever the mother prepared to leave them for a while. One day the mother asked the twin who was being quiet why she, too, wasn't making a fuss. 'Sister's crying,' came the answer, 'I don't need to.'

Efforts of twins to become individuals may be unwittingly impeded by parents. For instance, a harried mother may find that it is easier to treat her twins as a unit. 'I must go now and feed the twins,' reflects a simpler situation than 'I have to take care of Johnny and Jimmy,' with a thought to the special needs and character of each. In a previous chapter we noted that the 'permissive' approach of letting each child dictate how and when it is to be fed and cared for may not be too difficult when there is only one baby, but becomes almost impossible when there are two at a time. This is especially so if the mother has no extra help, and must care for other young children. She may then accept with relief the thought that her twins do not require too much individual attention, and that they can be left alone to develop in happy and peaceful adjustment to each other. We find this attitude reflected in statements from mothers such as these:

'My seven-month-old girl twins amuse each other all day. They leave me plenty of time for my housework.' . . . 'Twins always have a playmate – a carbon copy of themselves – so one need never worry about their feeling lonesome.' . . . 'Our twins have happier dispositions than our other two young children. They are less demanding and more self-sufficient.'

But it is precisely such a close relationship that the experts worry about. For, they say, one result of this twin closeness is a curtailing of the benefits which ordinarily come to a child through association with persons different from himself in age, personality, capacities, and experiences. Twins, however, if left too much together, may be impelled to imitate and learn from each other; and since they are at the same stage of development, and with no differences in background or training (or, if they are identical, in personality tendencies), anything new that one can learn from the other is limited. Another familiar drawback is that some twins may develop their own private 'twin language', not only of made-up words but also of signs and expressions which only they can understand. As an example, a Larchmont, N.Y., mother tells this story: 'My girl twins began talking when they were about sixteen months old, but at first it was a language which we couldn't understand. I remember one day watching them at play, and one of them stood up tentatively, jabbered something, and the other twin then rushed across the room like a crab and brought back a toy to her sister.'

Whether twins employ this private language for any length of time (and those that do are probably in a minority) or communicate closely in other ways, the effect must be to weld them more strongly into a unit. So, where single children are forced to reach out and make friendships, twins, by their very lack of loneliness (which in some ways is certainly an advantage), risk becoming ingrown and, to a more or less extent, remote from and for a time inaccessible to others of their age.

Possible psychological dangers in too great a physical closeness between twins also have been given attention. One parent wrote to me, 'I'd like my girl twins to be independent, so how can I get them to sleep apart? They're five years old now and have separate beds, but in the morning we always find them in the same bed. Even when we've tried putting them to sleep in different rooms – well, in the morning, there they are snuggled together in one bed.' In more or less degree this kind of physical attachment between twins is reported by many mothers, and is considered as hindering the development of their individuality.

The greatest danger which some see in too much physical closeness between twins is that it may lead to sexual complications. Dr Dorothy Burlingham cites the case of a pair of twin boys with a fondness for wrestling, punching, mauling and rolling over each other like puppies, this practice going on into adolescence. A certain rhythmic way in which they went at this roused the strong suspicion that it had a sexual quality. Obviously, when twins are of the same sex there is a chance that mutual sexual stimulation might conceivably lead to some homosexual manifestations. Twins of opposite sex, of course, may present other sexual problems. (Further discussions on this subject will be found in Chapters 21 and 22.)

Yet, while many parents worry about their twins becoming too attached, others are concerned that they aren't sufficiently so. 'How can I stop my twins from fighting with each other?' 'What can I do about the constant jealousy and bickering between my twins?' These are questions frequently asked by mothers. Whether the twin conflict is beneath the surface or pops out forcibly, the most favourable way to interpret it is as being a struggle by the twins to achieve the individuality and independence from each other which is considered desirable for them. An amusing episode, pertinent here, is reported by a Mount Kisco, N.Y., mother of identical twin boys of eleven who are just about as identical-looking as can be imagined. One day, during a quarrel, one of the twins turned angrily to his spit-and-image brother and exclaimed, 'I just can't stand your face!' Dr Burlingham notes, however, that when twins sometimes say to each other (or think), 'I wish you were dead!' the feeling of guilt which follows may serve to make them cling still more closely together.

Again, the seesaw effect in twin behaviour, previously mentioned, may also show up in their mutual relationships. To quote psychologist Leonard, 'At one moment twins will be very close to each other, and will gang up against another child or a parent, and in the next instant they will be going at each other hammer and nail.' But this is no different from the behaviour of many singletons in families; in fact, as with other aspects of twin relationships, the special concern about twins fighting may arise from the tendency of parents to scrutinize them more closely and to magnify into a problem the behaviour which in singletons is ignored. Children in any family are generally expected to be competitive, to quarrel on occasion, and to differ in their desires and attitudes. When there are similar conflicts and sharp contrasts in twins, it somehow doesn't seem proper.

So here we find many parents in a quandary. If they feel that it is important to develop individuality and independence in their twins, it would certainly appear that rivalry and disharmony would be steps towards that goal. Yet one of the most common questions from worried parents is, 'How can I prevent Tommy from being so dominant and Terry so easygoing?' or 'What can I do to make Jessie catch up with her twin, Joan?' Quite clearly, the worry here is about the *lack of sameness* in the twins. Moreover, if parents and others constantly take note of the differences between twins, this should bring their individualities into sharper focus and diminish the tendency to regard them as a unit. Yet, again, one finds another parental pull in a completely opposite direction. For one of the very things that parents are cautioned against, or spontaneously resent, is to have one twin constantly measured against the other.

'What I hate is people always making comparisons between my twins, expecting them to be exactly alike in everything,' a mother will protest. 'They don't realize how it hurts the twins if they hear someone say that one is prettier or smarter, or a better athlete, than the other.' But if twins are to be thought of as *distinct* individuals, comparisons are inevitable. It can lessen or prevent hurts, how-ever, if one always tries to couple a compliment for one twin with praise for the other for some trait or accomplishment in which that twin excels. It is rarely that one can't find something equally nice to say to or of each twin.

Another complication is that while many psychologists and educators seem intent on suppressing the twinship of twins, many parents, and twins themselves, have a strong desire to emphasize the relationship. The mother who has gone through a great deal to bear the twins and rear them may not take kindly to the notion that she should hide their twinship under a bushel. She may want all the regard and distinction that is coming to her for her achievement. This will be especially true when the twins are identicals. Says Dr Burlingham, 'If a mother hears remarks about a dissimilarity of her identical twins, she will often behave as if a disparaging remark had been made about them, and react by pointing out their like-ness.'

When the twins are fraternals, one also finds that parents who had achieved importance for a while because of them begin to feel let down if the two grow up to be so unalike that no one takes them for twins any more. (Twins, too, who have grown to like the fuss made over them, may feel resentful when people ask, 'Are you really twins? You don't look it!') Aggressively, some mothers will go on trying to dress such twins alike when it ill becomes them (sometimes even when the twins are a boy–girl pair), and do all they can to make them be like twins. If the twins resent this there may be complications. Psychoanalyst Douglass W. Orr told of a fraternal twin undergoing treatment whose problems arose mainly from attempts by his parents to suppress the differences between him and his twin brother, and to fit them into preconceived notions of how twins should behave towards each other. This had in truth kept him from developing his sense of identity. (On this point a mother wrote me, 'I hope somewhere in your book will appear the suggestion that parents not use their twins to make themselves feel important and different, not make a hobby of their twins, not set themselves apart from the world by endlessly focusing on this acci-dent of birth ... Maybe I would feel different if my two were identical twins, but actually they are very unalike fraternals – just two small boys who happened to arrive in our house on the same day.')

At the other extreme, one can also go too far in trying to overplay individuality and kill twinship. I was struck by a reply from one mother, who said emphatically, 'In our house we *never* refer to our boys as twins – only as brothers. They and we have accepted their twinship as merely "an accident of life".' A few lines on she spoke worriedly of the repeated fighting, squabbling and tattling of her twins, and that they were much happier when separated. Was it merely a coincidence that the parental aversion to twinship was accompanied by hostility between the twins themselves?

How, then, is the parent to handle the 'individuality' problem? Considering all angles, the first thing one might say is, 'Take it easy.' In most cases the situation will work itself out – most always quite easily if the twins are dissimilar fraternals. Apart from this, parents of twins, as well as of singletons, should be aware that the great stress on individuality is of comparatively recent date, and is given most importance in the United States. Elsewhere in the world the stress is generally more on 'conformity'. In fact, even among Americans the emphasis on individuality is likely to be more a matter of theory than of practice. Consider the strong pull of teenagers to be as much like their peers as possible in clothes, behaviour, and interests; of adults to live like the Joneses; of men not to wear anything too different from other men, and of the kick they get out of dressing up in uniforms or matching outfits in parades. For many persons the greatest fear (and the cause of the greatest difficulties) may be of being thought *too* individual.

Thus, if the drive of many persons is to be distinctive, and yet to belong, twins – notably the identicals – seem to have a psychological advantage in that they can achieve both ends at the same time. To the extent that twinship is maintained, the sense of belonging – of knowing that one matters to someone else, of not having to live exclusively within oneself – is always there. The drawback in being reared as a unit may have some compensation in the training it gives in the habit of coexistence and cooperation. For twins this advantage frequently becomes apparent at a very early age. As many mothers complain, twins often use their combined strength to move a heavy object or to knock over a table (usually the one with the most expensive lamp on it). 'Jail-breaking' also is a common stunt of twin babies. A White Plains, N.Y., mother tells how her little boy twins, when just over a year old, would manage to escape from their play pen: 'One would climb up on the other one and would be able to get over. Then he would drag a chair up so that his brother could get a foothold and pull himself up and over, too.' And one of the cutest escape stories came from a Bedford Hills, N.Y., mother of boy–girl twins, who were only thirteen months old at the time: 'I have seen just lately that the boy twin takes the rungs out of the play pen, and the girl twin crawls out. The boy doesn't attempt to leave the pen, and the girl doesn't attempt to help take the rings out.' (Precocious chivalry indeed!)

As twins learn what they can accomplish through cooperation, they may in time turn this to many useful purposes. Their helping to dress each other is repeatedly mentioned: 'They snappered each other's pyjamas from an early age.' ... 'If a button is stuck or a shirt caught over one's head, the other helps.' ... 'My twins became impatient waiting their turn to be dressed or undressed, and began doing it for themselves, together, long before my single children did alone.' One also hears how twins give each other rides on wagons, work together in operating toy train systems, build things, solve problems, and work or have fun cooperatively in many ways seldom possible for a singleton. And often it's woe to any child who picks on a twin, for he may find himself having to fight two. As we will see in later chapters, this pattern of cooperation between twins may go on for many years or for life.

Again, if closeness between twins may retard their development in some respects, it can be a stimulus in other ways. Many times we have heard how one twin began to walk, talk, feed himself, or become toilet-trained, and the other quickly followed suit. To quote one mother: 'Linda crawled first, Lorrie watched all afternoon, and by evening she also was crawling.' So the competition between twins, which sometimes seems regrettable, may none the less mutually stir them to activity in a greater degree than would be true of a single child with no one of the same age to measure himself by.

It is true that some of the initial psychological problems which bear on ego development, apply to all twins: For example, the insult to one's self-importance of having to start life with an ever-present competing baby; the effect of not being able to monopolize the mother's love and attention, and the confusion to one's identity resulting from being treated with the other twin as a unit. But the importance of these problems for given twin pairs, either from the start or as they grow, may depend on whether they are identicals or fraternals of the same sex, or twins of the opposite sex. For all except the identicals, and only some of the similar fraternals of the same sex, the problem of individuality takes care of itself as time goes on and the developmental paths of the twins diverge more and more. Certainly, the average boy–girl twins have little to keep them together as a unit for very long. With these (and perhaps most fraternal twins of the same sex as well), the need appears to be less for training them to be individuals, than for permitting them to freely follow their natural tendencies, and not trying to force them into a twinship pattern.

Whether or not all twins, regardless of type, are left with a permanent psychological impress of their twinship feelings in infancy is a moot question. But there is little doubt that, as time goes on, the conscious effects of twinship are felt mainly by the identicals, and it is these for whom the problem of cultivating individuality may have the most importance throughout childhood and adolescence. Yet, even among the identicals, it is rare when some definite trend towards individuality does not soon become apparent – sometimes at birth or shortly after. Beginning with the fact that it is the exception for newborn identicals (as with other twins) to be exactly the same in size and physical development, it also is in time the exception for them to be exactly the same in their behaviour and temperament, in their response to training, in the time when they begin to walk and talk, and in other developmental phases. Moreover, there almost always are some differences in appearance and mannerisms which enable parents and immediate family members to distinguish quite easily between identicals, and to make them aware of this distinction. With the added effects of the combined differences in the twins' inner makeup and outer experiences, there is therefore little likelihood that even the most 'identical' identicals will not normally develop some definite sense of selfness and individuality.

The question, then, is *how much* individuality should be developed in twins. The good effects of twinship should not be overlooked or minimized. Concern may arise mainly in cases where the unity of the twins, with their dependence on each other, seems to be taking abnormal or harmful directions and impeding their proper mental and social development. It is mostly these disturbed twins who have come to the attention of the psychiatrists and psychologists and who have stirred up most of the worries about twins in general.

What must also be clear is that the extent to which any twins may become maladjusted will be strongly influenced by many factors not necessarily related to twinship itself. Twins Billy and Bertie, with one type of physical and mental makeup, might react badly if forced to compete with each other. Another set of twins,

Johnny and Jimmy, different in makeup, might enjoy and thrive on competition. Again, in a pleasant home environment, with understanding, loving parents and happy siblings, twins might become well-adjusted; whereas in an unhappy home, with inept, neurotic parents and difficult siblings, the twins could well turn into problem children.

In other words, what happens with twins may often be only an extension or enhanced outgrowth of what would happen if each twin had been a single child with the same mental makeup and in the same home. If a child as an individual would tend to become maladjusted, he might sometimes become more so if coupled with a twin. But, in other cases, it could well be that twinship would give two children added strength, security and importance, and make them happier and better adjusted than if each had been a singleton. As psychologist Leonard puts it technically, 'Loss of individual identity may in large measure be compensated by the supportive aspect of the twin relationship. . . . The *identité à deux* substitutes for the identity as individuals.'

Thus, one cannot set forth hard and inflexible rules for the psychological training of twins, or glibly assert what will happen if all of them are or are not conditioned one way or another. As we go on now to discuss special aspects of twin psychology, it will be left to the reader to decide how the points brought out may concern a particular pair of twins.

CHAPTER 10

'Separateness' or 'Togetherness'

THE question of just how far to play up or play down the twinship of twins confronts their parents from the moment the two are born.

Shall the twins be given 'twin-type' names – as has been a common practice since the days of the legendary Romulus and Remus – or as untwinlike names as possible? Shall the twins be dressed the same or differently? Given the same or different toys? Put in the same classroom in school or separated? Encouraged to keep together or draw apart in their activities, friendships, social relationships?

As we saw in the preceding chapter, a growing trend is towards individualizing twins. Separateness, therefore, is encouraged; togetherness discouraged. For example, in a widely syndicated advice-to-parents newspaper column, two child-rearing experts recently told a worried mother of four-year-old twin boys, 'It is much better to bring out the individual differences in the twins than to accentuate their sameness. We would advise you to dress them differently, try to develop different skills in each, and separate them in nursery school and later in school.' In another leading newspaper column for parents, a mother was quoted as writing: 'So many strangers ooh and ah and comment on "the twins" every day that I try never to use the horrid phrases identifying them as twins. If I'm speaking about one twin to the other I'll say, "Your brother," but certainly not "your twin".' The columnist approvingly added, 'The growing resistance to treating twins as twins is soundly based.'

But the fact is that this deliberate and generalized playing down of twinship *is not* 'soundly based'. It derives chiefly from assumptions, superficial observations, and some very limited analyses of disturbed twins. Only one professional study with scientific validity has been made to date on the question of whether twinship – and keeping twins together – does or does not adversely affect the psychological and social adjustment of twins. And this study (by Dr Howard Mittman, awaiting publication and details of which will be given in the next chapter) *strongly questions the existing dogmas about separating twins.*

In any case – whatever the adverse theories – we noted in the preceding chapter that there is a deep-rooted conflicting pull on the part of many parents to emphasize the twinship of their twins. Checking on 340 pairs of twins whose names were reported to me, I found that more than four pairs in ten had twin-type names – that is, with the same initials or with similar sounds, or with linked meanings. Examples: 'Steven and Stanley', 'Ronald and Donald', 'Nancy Jean and Nora Jane', 'Mitzi and Betsy', 'Lorene Anne and Anne Lorene', 'Theodore and Dorothea', 'Jack and Jill', and so on. By sexes, girl pairs were more often given twin-type names than were boy pairs or boy–girl pairs. Of the girl pairs, more than half had twin-type names; of the boy–boy or boy–girl pairs, only a third. As to identical twins compared with fraternal twins of the same sex, there was no significant difference in the proportions given twin-type names. This is not surprising, inasmuch as in most cases it was not established at the time of christening whether the twins were identical or fraternal; and, if known, no special reason was foreseen for favouring twin-type names for the one kind rather than the other.

Among mothers whose twins had been given dissimilar names (which was the case with almost three out of five pairs), only a minority said this was done with the deliberate intent of playing down the twin relationship. Often the parents hadn't cared one way or the other, and had merely given the twins names from those they'd already had in mind when only one baby was expected. ('We'd picked "David" if the baby was a boy, and "Dena" if a girl, and, luckily, we could use both names!' one mother reported.) Also there were mothers who said they might have picked twin names if it hadn't been necessary to please two grandparents or two other close relatives by naming a twin for each.

Generally there may be good reasons for not giving twins similar names. One important element in a child's achieving self-identity is in his being able as soon as possible to know his name and to think of himself as the unique possessor of that name in the family.

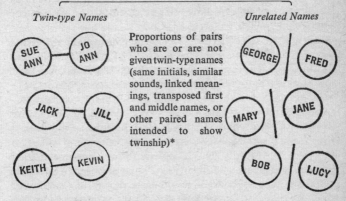

Twin-type Names

Unrelated Names

Proportions of pairs who are or are not given twin-type names (same initials, similar sounds, linked meanings, transposed first and middle names, or other paired names intended to show twinship)*

Type of Twinship	Per Cent with Twin-type Names	Per Cent with Unrelated Names
Male Twin Pairs: (Ident. & Fraternal)	33%	67%
Female Twin Pairs: (Ident. & Fraternal)	56%	44%
Male–Female Twin pairs	33%	67%
All Twin Pairs Together (Average):	43%	57%

*Based on names of 340 pairs of twins, as reported by parents to the author.

When the child has a twin with a closely similar name the process is slowed up. Checking this point, Dr Irène Lézine, a French psychologist, found that when twins and singletons at the age of twenty-four months were asked, 'What's your name?' the proportion of twins who did not know was 50 per cent higher than of non-twins. Between themselves, also, young twins are quite often confused about their names, as when one twin comes when the other's name is called. Likewise, twins may be slow in learning each other's names, or a twin named John may start by speaking of his partner as 'Other Johnny'.

Twins may be further held back in name identification if parents, siblings, and friends get into the habit of referring to them as 'the twins' instead of calling each by name. A Chicago mother complains: 'When children pass our house they always say, "That's where the twins live," not where Eva and Mary live, and they speak of me only as "the mother of the twins".' Another parent says her special peeve is that 'Friends and relatives tease my twins by purposely calling them by the wrong names. The twins get mad, then the people laugh, and then the twins get confused and one will say she's the other.' Of course, identical twins themselves often enjoy confusing other persons as to which is which, and the more alike their names are, the harder it will be for others to learn to distinguish between them. Moreover, as they grow up, too great similarity in twins' name may lead to mixups in records of schools, colleges, hospitals, the Army, and employers, or in newspaper stories, reports of accidents or deaths, and so on. For various reasons, then, some authorities might counsel giving twins dissimilar names.

But it is also unwise and unfair to give twins names that are dissimilar in appeal, pronounceability, implication or familiarity, so that one is at a disadvantage compared with the other. Imagine the plight of a twin named 'Cholmondeley' when his partner is 'Charles'; or of an 'Iphigenia' whose twin is 'Inez'. Any hint of favouritism must also be avoided in twins' names. To name one boy twin '—, Junior', after his father or one girl twin after her mother can put each in a special position. It may also be discriminating unfairly to name twins after two grandparents or two relatives who are of unequal importance (perhaps one a celebrated person, the other a nonentity), or when the one relative may be in a position to do much more for his namesake than the other.

'What's in a name?' With twins one might answer, 'A lot!'

DRESS

Closely following the naming question comes the one of how to *dress* twins. Here practical as well as psychological factors must be considered. From the standpoint of work and expense, there is every reason for dressing twins differently. Providing duplicate outfits for various occasions usually costs more. Among other things, it precludes the use of hand-me-downs from previous single children; it prevents taking advantage of sales where there are only one-of-a-kind items in the size; and it may mean discarding both costumes if any one of the matching items becomes unusable, or is outgrown by one of the twins.

Apart from the expense, twin outfits mean much extra work for the mother. If one twin messes up anything, both twins have to be changed; and if the twins are girls and all their items are matched for colour – hats, dresses, stockings, shoes, and so on – one spotted dress may require a complete change in the whole outfit of both. Laundering imposes the additional burden of always doing two of everything washable, in order to keep both outfits equally fresh. Further, the very fact that matching outfits are designed to call special attention to the twins also means that everything they wear will be much more closely scrutinized for good taste and neatness than are the clothes of singletons. So, shopping for attractive twin outfits will mean extra time and trouble, especially if funds, as well as available store selections, are limited.

Now remember that the twins' mother already is groaning under the many added and complex chores of caring for and feeding her twins. Why, then, should she tax herself still further with dressing them alike? Well! – one doesn't know the mothers of twins if one thinks that mere practical considerations will easily deter them from displaying their twins to the best advantage and inviting all the admiration due them. Among the hundreds of twins' mothers we queried (most of them fully familiar with the 'twin-individual-izing' theories) about four out of five of those whose twins were of the same sex (83 per cent with girl twins, 73 per cent with boy twins) said they were dressing or had dressed their pairs alike during babyhood, and were planning to keep on dressing them alike (or had done so) until the children themselves decided other-wise. Boy–girl twins, also, were reported in many cases as being dressed alike during infancy, and in matching boy–girl outfits during childhood – sometimes even on into adolescence.

But there were also occasional dissenters. Here are some typical statements showing how individual mothers felt about the twin-dressing problem. A mother of fraternal girl twins: 'The public expects to see your twins dressed alike, and when they are not, people think there's something wrong with you.' A mother of three-year-old identical boys: 'I said I never would dress twins the same, but I honestly like to have people say, "Look at the twins!"' A mother of identical twin girls, four and one-half years old: 'We dressed them alike until two and a half. It's no point in having cute twin girls without making a big deal of it.' A mother of fraternal boys, aged four: 'I've been dressing them the same way, and will until they complain. It's great fun, and I'm not going to forgo it for some phoney guilt complex.' A mother of fraternal girls, aged eleven: 'I think there's too much stress on dressing twins differently "so they'll be individuals" – they'll be individuals anyway.' And many mothers of dissimilar fraternals say something like this: 'Dressing them alike is the only way to show they're twins.'

Occasionally there is a commercial aspect in dressing twins alike, as when there is a chance of getting fees for their acting as models, or on TV, or in the movies. This is a tangible asset in Hollywood, where the Mothers of Twins club of the vicinity reported that there is considerable paid work available for twins. In New York and other large cities also, model and theatrical agencies keep a roster of young twins to be called upon to pose for advertisers, or sometimes to make TV and stage appearances.

Only in a minority of cases is there strong opposition to matching outfits for twins. A most unusual and amusing situation was the one in which a mother wanted to stop dressing her identical boys alike, and the father (who ordinarily is all for different attire) was the one who resisted. As the mother tells it: 'After the boy twins were eight I said, "You're each an individual, and you should dress differently." But their Pop insisted that they keep on dressing alike, which they did until they were twelve, when I finally won out by arguing, "Are they going to marry the same girl, too?"'

Sometimes the twins insist on having matching outfits. Says one mother of six-year-old boy identicals, 'If I dress them differently, they undress and swap around until they look the same.' Even a boy–girl pair might like to dress alike, as this mother of twins aged ten reports: 'They enjoy their twinship, and like to call attention to it by wearing matching socks, shirts, or whatever other articles a boy and girl can.' From another mother, of fraternal girls aged

TWIN DRESS: SAME OR DIFFERENT?

 How mothers dress, and/or plan to keep dressing twins of the same sex, until twins decide for themselves, as told in questionnaire replies*

Type of Twins:	Dressed same way	Dressed differently	Undecided
Identicals:			
Boys	78%	22%	—
Girls	88%	7%	5%
Fraternals:			
(of same sex)			
Boys	68%	27%	5%
Girls	78%	20%	2%
All male twins			
(Ident. & Frat.):	73%	25%	2%
All female twins			
(Ident. & Frat.):	83%	13%	4%
All twins together:			
(of same sex)			
	79%	18%	3%

*Based on replies from more than 300 mothers of like-sex twins.

five, comes this: 'Dressing twins alike is the simplest solution to keeping down jealousy. If you buy two new dresses that are different, one or the other will think hers is least attractive.'

Contrary views, which favour dressing girl twins differently, are also advanced. One mother of nine-year-old girl identicals says, 'The twins found that always trying to dress alike – down to hats, shoes, hairdos, and so on – brought too many disputes, because they always had to make up "our minds" what to wear, instead of just each one her own mind. So they usually dress differently, and only on special occasions alike.'

Not only must parents consider their twins' attitude about being

117

dressed alike, but, if there are other children in the family who are close to the twins in age, their feelings, too, may be an important factor. A mother of five-year-old identical girls told me, 'The twins draw so much attention that even when I buy their older sister, eight, much more expensive and prettier clothes, she still feels she's cheated. I guess the only solution is to dress the twins differently.' Contrariwise, another mother thinks she has solved the 'sibling-clothes' problem by dressing all her girls – the two singletons (only a few years older) and the twins – in matching outfits. This isn't too hard for her, because she sews their dresses herself.

The least problems in dressing go with boy twins. For one thing boys soon feel that any obvious kind of dressing up is sissyish. Apart from this, mothers know how hard it is to get two normally hyperactive little males to dress neatly at any time. 'I'd love my twin boys to dress themselves alike,' complained one mother, 'but the only way in which they do so can be described in two words: "Both sloppy".'

Fortunately, the twin-dressing problem usually diminishes – to a considerable extent for most identicals; to the largest extent for fraternals, and entirely for boy–girl twins – as they get into the primary-school years. The fraternals who are very different in appearance and build, as well as in personality and interests, soon find little reason to dress the same way, and most look-alike twins also get into the habit of wearing different clothes except on special occasions. It is true that many girl twins find it fun, and to their social advantage, to be singled out as twins by their matching clothes, if by nothing else, and this may go on until they marry and move apart. Much less frequently do male twins continue to dress alike into and through their adult years. (We will tell you about some of these in Chapter 20.) But, for either male or female twins the too persistent and too pronounced practice of dressing alike may eventually become a symptom of weakness and insecurity; what was once cuteness may become silliness or affectation in the adult years. It is with this in mind, perhaps, that parents who start out dressing their twins alike should watch for clues as to how long and to what extent the practice should be continued.

TOYS

Should twins be given the same or different toys? The 'individualists' may favour different toys from the start, but experienced mothers report that this doesn't work out. When twins are very young, mothers report that the only way to avoid squabbles and accusations of favouritism is to give each twin the same plaything. Luckily, most persons who bring gifts to twins do get them similar presents. Toy individualization for twins can to some extent be carried out by choosing different colours, or dolls with slight variations in dress and appearance. If twins are dissimilar fraternals, with eye, hair-colour and hair-form differences, these may be matched in their dolls. After the first few years, however, twins of all types begin to show individual preferences – this can be expected earliest with fraternals, especially boy–girl twins – and the problem of gifts usually resolves itself.

As twins grow, various playthings bought for them jointly can condition them towards a happy coexistence. 'Sharing-toys', as some twins' mothers call them, may include toy automobiles, tricycles, wagons, sledges, swings, and so on, which the twins can take turns riding and helping the other to ride. Games which two or more must play – which their outside friends can join in – are especially good. So are books which can be read to the twins, or which, when the time comes, they can read in turn.

One of the biggest *don'ts* for young twins: Don't give them live pets, such as dogs or cats, or even have these around, if their care will mean an added responsibility to the already overtaxed mother. Only if there are older children in the family who can take complete charge of the animals is it wise to attempt rearing or maintaining pets together with twins.

SEPARATE FRIENDS

Unless twins are unusually close-knit (and if so, this might well be discouraged), it is more than likely that before long each will either attract or be attracted by some special friends of his or her own. This is apt to happen sooner with fraternal twins, but identical twins also face this experience; for, oddly enough, young children are often sensitive to minor personality differences between twins which completely elude adults. Sometimes, too, a chance event may bring one twin and another child together for just long enough to engender a special relationship to which the other twin isn't a party. Alas, then, when some sensitive mothers (forgetting their wish to individualize their twins) tend to see this as a tragedy. One young mother wrote me, 'I almost died when a new little boy on the block favoured one twin and made friends with him, but ignored the other.' These situations usually work themselves out, however, when the neglected twin acquires his or her own pal, or the favoured twin shifts allegiance.

These observations suggest that a compromise is often needed between the desire to maintain the closeness of the twins by having them choose or attract the same friends, and the desire for them to be individuals, which can only be achieved by their having different friends at the possible expense of some friction and grief. One may also note that there is a parental 'overprotective' feeling about twins in the matter of their friends which the same parents are not likely to show with respect to singletons. But all this is generally resolved in time by the twins having some 'sharing-friends' and also some friends who are special for each.

Going along with the problem of friends is a common belief that young twins must always be taken out or invited to visit only together. This is challenged by many parents today. They have found that in preparation for the time when twins may have to be separated by illnesses, operations or school, or for other reasons, it is good to accustom them as soon as possible to being taken to places one at a time. Says a mother of six-year-old fraternal girls, 'I found that many friends were so afraid the twins would be too much to have together that they never invited them, but when I let them know it would be all right to have just one, why, the girls got many more invitations. I always planned something else equally interesting for the one who wasn't asked, and saw to it that she was invited by someone the next time.'

Birthday parties may present another problem. Should twins have a joint birthday party or separate parties? Some individualists prescribe parties on different days. But many mothers feel the 'two-birthday business' is carrying things too far, and involves too much added trouble and expense. The boy–girl twins are in a special position. When these twins are young, a joint birthday party at first solves the problem of having guests of the opposite sex, which always is a headache in the case of same-sex twins; but in the teen ages, as girls begin to choose boys older than themselves, and boys choose younger girls, joint birthday parties for boy–girl twins become more difficult to manage and to make successful. With twins as well, therefore, whenever problems of birthday celebrations become too great, some parents suggest that the joint party be made a family affair, and that at later dates, special parties be given for the twins separately.

TWINS' ROOMS

'For a long time our fraternal twin boys shared a bedroom. One night they had a fight. The "weaker" one moved to another part of the house. Now there is constant visiting back and forth that is wearing on the carpet and the nerves.' This is one of many observations from mothers of twins about whether the two should share one room or have separate rooms – and how soon. It can only be answered by considering the circumstances in each case: the age of the twins, the degree of compatibility or friction between them; whether they are of the same sex or a boy–girl pair; whether or not a room for each is available; and, not least, their own wishes in the matter. During babyhood, keeping twins in the same room is dictated both by expediency and by the fact that they are generally happier together. As the twins grow up they usually make their preference quite clear by word or action. Again and again parents tell of having tried to separate their twins – sometimes by putting them to sleep (or thinking they've done so!) – in different rooms, only to find in the morning that the twins are in the same bed. Yet there also are twins who begin wanting separate rooms at an early age.

Boy–girl twins are often put in separate rooms in the pre-school years, the problem being especially easy to solve if the family has another girl and another boy not too far from the twins in age, so that each twin can double up with a same-sex sibling. A similar procedure can be followed when twins are of the same sex, and there are two additional siblings of their sex. Generally it is found easier for twins to share the same room unless and until the time arrives that their interests and impulses become as different as those of any two single children in a family who want, and are given, separate rooms, if available. Further, training for a boy or girl twin in sharing the same room with someone else, and learning how to adjust to and be considerate of another person's comfort, needs and wishes, can prove highly valuable in many ways: at camp, at prep school, at college, in the Army, or wherever one must have bunkmates or a roommate; and, ultimately, in marriage, where the ability to live together with someone else in the same room may contribute greatly to the happiness of both.

CHAPTER 11

School Daze

LOOKING at the five-year-old twins romping happily down the street with their mother, one would never suspect that they may be moving towards a big crisis in their lives. They are on their way to school – to kindergarten – for the first time, and their mother is wondering with a troubled mind, 'Should they – can they – will they – be put in the same classroom?' And if not, how will they adjust to separation after always having been so close together? We could well call these perplexities regarding twins the 'school daze'.

As we have noted in previous chapters, the idea of separating twins in school is in line with the whole theory of individualizing them. But let us first point out that the belief in its being for the *good* of twins to separate them in school is a comparatively new one. As recently as 1948 a famed authority on twins, the late Professor Horatio H. Newman, was seeking to correct the then widespread impression that it would be *harmful* to ever separate twins in school. Writing in the *New York Times Sunday Magazine*, he said, 'It is a common notion that it is injurious to twins – especially identical twins – to separate them: for example, to send each to a different school or college.' He pointed out that pairs of identical twins may vary widely in their attitude towards each other, and that whereas one type apparently rejoice in twinship and never want to be separated, another type, the 'reluctant' twins, resent the fact that they are alike and do everything to make themselves different. This latter type, Dr Newman suggested, could be separated to advantage. 'Whether any harm would ensue from separating the former type,' he added, 'may be determined only by actually separating them and seeing.'

This advice might still seem worth following not only for identical twins but for fraternals as well. In many – if not most – communities, however, the actual decision as to where twins will be placed in school does not rest with the parents. Outside of the large cities, schools usually do not have more than one class for each grade or half grade, and twins must be kept together, willy-nilly. (Let us not forget that whole generations of Americans grew up attending 'little red schoolhouses' – where not only twins but siblings of different ages from the same families were in the same classroom.) But the new factor in the situation is that many of today's larger public and private schools do have two or more classrooms for each grade, and that in some it is the official policy to separate twins, while in others the choice is left to the parents.

In the huge New York City public school system, for example, there is no fixed official policy regarding twins. Sometimes, I learned, individual principals with strong 'separationist' convictions may prevail on parents to put their twins in different classrooms. There are situations, though, where this may be inconvenient or impractical, as in schools where the two or more classes in a grade (usually for the first years) have different hours (early and late shifts), and separating twins would require their mothers to take them to and from school, and fix lunch for them, at different times.

But if and when the decisions and opportunities for separating twins in school are freely left to parents, how do they, or should they, decide? This is another of the questions which I put to hundreds of mothers of twins. Their answers were in marked contrast to the overwhelming vote for dressing twins alike, at least until the twins can choose for themselves. On the school question, 62 per cent of the mothers are for separating their twins from the first grade on, if not earlier in nursery school or kindergarten. Only 31 per cent would like to see them together in school as long and as far as possible. Seven per cent were undecided, or, if their twins were very young, wanted to 'wait and see'. The decisions seemed very little influenced by whether the twins were identical or fraternal, or boys or girls.

How far this heavy vote for separation is representative of the true sentiments of parents of twins in general is a moot question. In fact, there is reason to believe that members of most Mothers of Twins clubs have been more than ordinarily exposed to the current 'twin-individualizing' theories through books, articles, and their

SCHOOL: TOGETHER OR APART?

Percentages of mothers who favour (a) having their twins in the same classrooms or (b) separated, and (c) those undecided. Classification as to 'identical' and 'fraternal' is according to what mothers believe and report their twins to be.

Type of twins	Same classroom (or until twins or events decide)	Different classrooms (from the start)	Undecided (not clear as yet or no opinion)
Identical pairs	33%	65%	2%
Fraternal pairs (of same sex)	32%	62%	6%
Male–Female pairs	29%	59%	12%
All twins together (Average)	31%	62%	7%

Based on replies from 320 mothers of twins

own club booklets, through lectures and discussions at their meetings, or because of the fact that in some of the communities 'twin separation' is the policy of the schools. One also must keep in mind that about half the mothers from whom we heard had twins not yet of school age, and derived their views not from what had happened with their twins but from what they expected to happen.

The 'pro-separation' arguments can be summed up as follows:

– If twins are put in the same class, comparisons will constantly be made between them; jealousy and friction will develop; and should one twin lag behind the other in classwork, he will have a feeling of inferiority which will hold him back still further.

– Look-alike twins in the same room may be confusing and disturbing to teachers and classmates, so that neither twin may get the proper attention. Also, some twins tend to exploit their likeness by cheating for each other and getting into various kinds of mischief.

– Keeping twins together prevents them from making friends on their own, narrows their thinking horizons, and inhibits their freedom to become individuals and to develop their personal interests and aptitudes.

Supporting the arguments for separation as applied in specific cases is this statement by a Chicago mother of nine-year-old fraternal girls: 'My twins are very different. The girls in school were constantly comparing them – "which is prettier? which is smarter?" The one who was behind in the classroom became so afraid of doing worse than her sister, she'd shake like she had the palsy when she was called on. After she was put in another classroom she began to do much better, and now both are much happier.' Again, a New York mother of six-year-old identical girls said, 'Because my twins are so very identical, we were worried about separating them in school. But it has worked. They love comparing notes about their schoolwork, teachers and classmates.'

But most mothers who favour school separation for twins suggest that it should not be too immediate or abrupt, as in this comment: 'My twins were not put together in kindergarten. They cried and cried at being separated. School is a whole new experience to any child, and to have two tots who had been constantly together in their first five years suddenly pulled apart isn't right.' Affirming this is a mother of twelve-year-old identical girls: 'My twins weren't separated until the third grade and it worked out fine. I think having kept them together at the beginning helped to make them well adjusted to other children, so they didn't mind the separation later.'

That any parent would even *want* to have twins together in school seems surprising to some who have been strongly conditioned by the 'separation' views. Here is how one such mother reacted: 'My identical boys, twelve and one-half, had been separated in the lower grades in a school where that was the policy, and which we favoured too. So when they started Junior High we were amazed to find there were many twins there who, at their parents' request, were being kept together. The dean said apologetically he didn't know I had twins, and why hadn't I made the same request. I've been puzzled by the difference in thinking.'

What, then, are the reasons for wanting to keep twins together in school as long as possible? Among the mothers who favoured this plan, the main arguments were these:

– Our twins have shown they are much happier together in school than separated. They enjoy their uniqueness and the attention it brings. Because of this they are stimulated to try to do better and to behave better when they are in the same classroom.

– Twins work and study better as a team than individually ('two heads are better than one'), and they provide incentives to each other.

– If twins are about equal in intelligence, and not too dependent, why should there be worry about comparisons if they are in the same class? Comparisons may well stimulate each to greater effort.

In most cases, the arguments for keeping twins together in school are applied to the identicals. Here, for example, is the statement by a mother of identical boys who were almost through high school: 'My twins were together in school until the fifth grade, and then separated as a matter of school policy. But although they had high grades while together, they went downhill after separation, until from the ninth and tenth grades on they again began being in some classes together. They not only did their classwork improve, but so did their relations with each other. When I asked them why, they said, "Because we are more together now." '

Fraternal twins, many mothers maintain, are usually so different anyway that there is no danger of their not being individuals, and thus it doesn't much matter whether they are in the same classroom or not. Boy–girl twins are regarded as posing the fewest school problems. Comparisons hardly bother them; since, if the girl excels in some subjects and activities, the boy usually is better at other things. In any event, there isn't likely to be too much conflict between them, or interference with forming their own friendships.

Looking back over all the pro and con school-separation arguments, parents may judge how these apply to their own twins. As in other phases of twin-rearing, it should be obvious, first, that there is no fixed rule about same or separate classes which holds equally for all twins; and, second, that even if there were such a rule, the choice of applying it is not, perhaps in most cases, in parents' hands. So now let us ask: How much harm, if any, will be done to twins either by (*a*) keeping them together in classrooms when the parents think they should be separated, or (*b*) separating them when the parents think they ought to be kept together? What, in short, do the experts – educators and psychologists – say about this?

Surprisingly, while many parents and teachers have assumed that the need for separating twins has long been established by scientific research, the fact is that no valid study on the point had been made prior to the very recent one by Dr Howard Mittman mentioned in the preceding chapter; and this study, as we said, *disputes the dogmatic assumptions* about separating twins and playing down twinship. Dr Mittman's study is still to be published at this writing, but he kindly provided me with the details. He had intensively questioned and tested three groups – 22 pairs of identical twins, 21 pairs of same-sex fraternals, and, for comparison, 21 pairs of same-sex singleton siblings – all attending high school, and with ages ranging from 15 to 18 years. The evidence led psychologist Mittman to this conclusion: 'While changes in personality development do accompany twinship, they are not, as many believe, necessarily detrimental to the child's life adjustments. On the contrary, twinship appears to be accompanied by a slightly superior social adjustment; harm, rather than help, is more likely to result if twins are separated in school or at home.'

Another widespread fallacy is that 'the experts all agree about separating twins'. This is far from the case. For example, the eminent Dr Benjamin Spock says in his famed book on child care: 'It seems foolish and cruel to have an arbitrary rule about separation of twins in school when there is no need.'

Especially significant is the statement by Dr John E. Anderson, Emeritus Professor of the University of Minnesota, who could speak not only as an outstanding authority on child psychology and development, but from personal experience as the father of two pairs of adult twins – an identical male pair and a male–female pair – and the grandfather of another twin pair. (The notable Anderson twins are dealt with again in Chapter 20.) Professor Anderson said:

The problem of separating or keeping twins together in school depends very greatly upon the characteristics of the individual twins themselves. If they are nearly equal in ability, have common interests and get along well together, I see no reason for separating them. But if they differ markedly in ability, so that one advances very rapidly whereas the other moves relatively slowly in grasping school content, it may be advisable to separate them or even to place them in separate schools. This also holds if there is a marked difference in the sociality and emotional life of the twins, and especially if one is developing a high degree of dependence upon the other.

In any event, none of the many educational authorities whom I queried were aware of any basis for a general policy of separating twins in school. For example, in the New York City school system, with close to ten thousand pairs of twins among the more than one million children enrolled at this writing, no evidence has been found to support such a policy, according to Dr Simon S. Silverman, Director of the Board of Education's Bureau of Child Guidance. Said Dr Silverman:

Most parents of twins have preferred to have them in the same classrooms, and we know of no reason why we should oppose this unless there is a marked difference in capacities between the twins, or some serious personality problem in one of them. Otherwise, we can hardly feel there is justification for pressuring parents into separating their twins, or creating worries that if the twins are kept together it will seriously impair their progress or threaten their emotional adjustment. Certainly, our records reveal no undue proportion of twins among the disturbed, maladjusted or delinquent pupils. Neither have we evidence that separating twins is ordinarily harmful.*

The foregoing views were fully supported by the late Professor Irving Lorge of Columbia University's famed Teachers College. He said:

*Among other large cities, according to information I received, Philadelphia and Chicago have no fixed policy for separating twins in public schools. In Chicago, however, the tendency in individual schools has been to separate twins if two equivalent classrooms are available in the same school, and if the parents agree.

I know of no evidence which would justify separating twins in school just because they are twins, and I am sure most schools in the country do not follow such a policy. Where twins are so identical in appearance as to confuse teachers, this may sometimes be a valid reason for separating them. But as to comparisons being made between twins in school, if they have a good emotional foundation, they will take such comparisons in their stride, as do well-adjusted singletons.

Thus one may gather that the question of whether or not to separate twins in school can best be decided in most cases by the personalities, capacities, and relationships of the twins themselves. In special situations, where mental differences or psychological conflicts between the twins are very great, separation may be the wise course to follow. (The advance signals for this are usually clear: If, in the home, one twin seems consistently brighter than the other; if they are unalike in various personality traits and in their ability to make friends; if there is bitterness and resentfulness between them, and one seems to be a bad influence on the other; if kindergarten and/or first-grade teachers find it difficult to handle them together, and so on.) On the other hand, if the twins are mentally and emotionally compatible, there may be no reason for separating them; but if they are separated, there is also no reason to assume that this will necessarily harm them.

Looking back over all that has been said about separateness and togetherness in twins in this and the preceding two chapters, we may wonder whether, in most cases, parents haven't been more stirred up about the problem than they need be. What may have been interpreted as rules for twin rearing can be seen as being based merely on impressions which often hold good for only a minority of twins. For example, fear that twins will become too closely attached applies as a rule mainly to the identicals, and then only to some of these pairs. The fraternals – and most definitely the boy–girl pairs – start out separated in many ways by nature, and tend more and more to pull apart despite efforts to keep them together. But for all twins, separation will come sooner or later, to one extent or another, through differences in experiences and social contacts, and ultimately through marriage and careers.

Yet we may also wonder whether, in the constant stress on

separating twins during childhood, there is not a tendency to over-look some of the advantages of togetherness. It is true that the individuality of twins – notably the identicals – may yield in some degree to mutual identification, or what some mothers call 'twindividuality'. But 'twindividuality' is a rare and precious thing, not to be lightly discarded. To repeat what we have said before, in a world where there is increasing personal isolation, it may be good to know that there is always someone with whom one is closely linked in thoughts, experiences, and mutual concern. To the degree that twins possess this feeling, they have an inbuilt insurance against loneliness. Here I will quote a veteran mother of twins – one whose identical twin sons are now grown up and married:

I think this swinging away from letting twins be twins – different clothes, separate rooms, separate friends, keeping them apart in school – can become just as much a fetish as making the twins one personality instead of two individuals. I think you should treat them as two individuals, which they are, but don't go overboard so that it becomes a mortal sin if they want to be together.

And here is another forthright statement by an Illinois mother of grown-up and married identical twin daughters:

It seems to me that parents who are given the privilege of having twins today are being conditioned to expect many problems far exceeding the necessity for such indoctrination. This overemphasis on twinship problems can lead to an overzealous analysis which itself can create problems.

These common-sense words perhaps sum up the whole situation with regard to policies for the psychological rearing of twins. Many theories of raising children in general, once accepted as almost gospel, have been deflated or tossed aside, and this may well be done with some of the pat twin-rearing theories which have plagued parents, particularly the one holding that 'twinship should be killed (or suppressed)' by keeping twins apart as much as possible. If twins are given the security of knowing that each has a full and equal measure of love and attention from the parents, and every opportunity for developing his individual resources, their twinship and attachment to each other can be an asset in their childhood and throughout life.

CHAPTER 12

Growing Pairs

———

How are they doing? This question trails along with twins from the moment they arrive and for years thereafter. Weights are carefully and continually watched. Successive pencil marks made on walls over little heads are eagerly measured. Behaviour is minutely observed. Pediatricians are frequently consulted. Reports from nursery school or kindergarten are pondered over.

Are the twins average for their age? – normal? – anxious parents ask or think. True, the question is also often asked about singletons. But it is asked far more often, and worried over much more, with respect to twins. Let's see what can be found in the way of answers.

There is no doubt that during infancy and in the pre-school ages, twins as a group tend to be smaller and somewhat frailer than singletons. This is in large part due to the fact that up to 60 per cent or more of the twins are born prematurely and undersized, as compared with only a fraction as many of the singletons (7 to 8 per cent). Also, as noted in Chapters 2 and 3, twins are more likely to suffer initially from prenatal food deficiencies, and from accidents before and during birth. But, if they have come through this period safely, do twins eventually catch up with singletons? And if so, when?

Taking first the 'preemie' twins, it has been found that the retarding or otherwise harmful effects of premature birth are seldom permanent, although to what extent and for how long they assert themselves depends considerably on how premature or undersized the baby was. On the average, 'preemies' usually catch up to the singleborn in health and height within a few years. This may hold especially for the twin 'preemies', who, as we noted in Chapter 3, when matched by period of gestation and/or weight, tend to be sturdier and healthier than the singleton 'preemies'. This, to repeat, is because it is quite natural for a twin to be born prematurely and underweight (as the majority are), whereas when this occurs with a singleton, it more often points to some deficiency in the mother or baby, or both.

Birth-Weight Differences Between Twins

	Per cent of twins with differences 0–5 oz.	Per cent of twins with differences 6 oz.–27 oz.	Per cent of twins with differences 28 oz. or over
Identicals	44%	51%	5%
Fraternals (*same-sex*)	33%	57%	10%
Male–Female pairs	23%	67%	10%

Based on data for 450 twin pairs

If one twin of a given pair is a great deal behind the other in weight and size at birth, there is an opportunity to see how soon the laggard catches up to the initially bigger twin. Among the hundreds of pairs of twins whose mothers reported to me, a great many had started off markedly different in size (in some cases up to 28 ounces or more) and often with one twin in the premature class who had to be kept in an incubator for a considerable time, while the other twin, a term baby, could be taken home almost at once. Yet, with few exceptions, the undersized twin usually had almost caught up with the other, and sometimes outdistanced him, within a year or two.

Parents should be especially cautious about going by standard tables of heights and weights for children in judging how their twins are growing, individually or in comparison with each other. First, taking all twins together, since the standard tables are compiled primarily for singletons, we must allow for the fact that most twins normally start off below the average in size and birth; so we must give twins a little more leeway at the low end of the table until there is time for them to catch up. Next, if the twins had a shorter than average gestation period – often by one to two months – they really are that much younger in physical development than are full-term children of the same calendar age.

Still another important point is that the height and weight tables have different meanings for identicals and fraternals. In the case of identical twins, while the tables may throw useful light on how well they are growing, it is the comparison between one and the other which is most significant. Remembering that identicals have the same hereditary growth tendencies, one may expect that any marked differences in size shown at birth will ordinarily be overcome within a year or two. If, after that, either twin is markedly shorter or is noticeably more underweight than the other, it is reasonable to suspect that something is not right organically, and a doctor should be consulted. For example, there was a medical report on two $4\frac{1}{2}$-year-old twin sisters, one so dwarfed by the other that no one would believe they were even twins, let alone being identical twins, as was established. A check-up showed that the undersized twin was suffering from a condition called *juvenile myxedema*. After being given thyroid treatment, she grew rapidly, adding nine inches to her height in nine months, and subsequently almost reached her twin's height.

With fraternals of the same sex, comparisons between the two have much less significance, for it is not unusual or abnormal for one to be near the low end of the range of average heights and weights for his or her age, and the other to be near the high end. In this respect their position is no different from that of two singletons of the same sex in a family.

At full maturity, twins can be expected to come very close to the stature they would have reached had they been singly born in the same family. As evidence, Swedish male twins called for army service in recent years have been found by Professor Thorsten Husen to average only one-half inch less in height than the single-born draftees. Among these twins themselves the identicals were somewhat shorter – by a third of an inch – than the fraternals. For the most part, however, twinship usually has much less effect on ultimate height than do the twins' hereditary factors – that is, their genes for tallness or shortness – interoperating with their environment. The best clue as to how tall any twins will become can thus be provided by looking at their older siblings, if any, and their parents and other close relatives.

Now for another familiar question: *Do twins tend to be more defective physically than singletons?* This depends mainly on whether or not the particular twins came into the world handicapped by prenatal and birth difficulties. Since so many twins, *as a group*, do meet with adversity before or during birth there will be an above-average incidence of defects among them. Thus congenital malformations are about twice as common among twins as among singletons; so, too, are some of the brain disorders due to injuries sustained during delivery. When twins are very premature, dangers of brain damage are increased, with the risk of incurring cerebral palsy being four to six times greater than in full-term babies. Again, certain eye defects may afflict twins more often than singletons. But here it is important to stress that perhaps most of the many twins who grew up with serious eye defects in former years were the unfortunate victims of incubator accidents *which very rarely occur today*.

Among the saddest cases was that of the Petraglia triplets, born in 1953 in New York City. All three emerged from their incubators incurably blind with the condition called *retrolental fibroplasia*, which also had produced blindness in thousands of other incubator babies, singletons as well as twins. The cause of the condition had been a mystery, but soon after the Petraglias were afflicted by it – and too late to save them – doctors found that it was the result of excessive dosages of artificially administered oxygen.* Almost as soon as such dosages were reduced, few cases of this blindness appeared. Today, when prematures have to be put in incubators, parents may be assured that every precaution is taken to avert damage, although, as Dr Leona Zacharias has warned, the risks cannot be entirely avoided when heavy oxygen therapy is necessary for the survival of some infants.

Various other kinds of afflictions and defects which are not due to twinship itself but to prenatal or delivery accidents can, un-

---

*The plight of the blind Petraglia triplets, two girls and a boy, brought an outpouring of sympathy in their community, and resulted in the building of a home for them in which they and their parents now live. Many organizations contributed funds, workers and craftsmen of every kind gave their services, and merchants donated all the furnishings of the triplets' 'dream house' – a modern ranch-type dwelling with no steps inside or out. At this writing the trio are attending a special school for the blind, and are reported as bright and well-adjusted children.

doubtedly, be much reduced or eliminated by advances in medical knowledge and techniques. Aiding further is the increasingly better preparation of mothers for twin-bearing. In fact, it can already be said that if a mother today is healthy and has received good pre-natal and delivery care, there is only a minimal risk that any pair of twins born to her will be defective. In support of this are findings that the incidence of prematurity, abnormality and defects is very much lower among twins born to mothers in the more favoured groups than among those born to mothers in underprivileged groups.

Once twins have safely come through the prenatal and birth ordeals, they can be expected to have the same chance for good health and normal growth as single born children. Occasionally twins who apparently seem quite sound in early childhood may later show the delayed reaction of some adverse initial experience, but this may apply mostly to minor orthopaedic abnormalities or structural defects which are not too serious. With these possible exceptions, parents can be assured, 'If your twins are all right now, you need have little worry they won't be so later.'

Some of the exaggerated fears about twins are due to the fact that the medical literature carries so many reports about twins with various diseases, defects and abnormalities. One must understand that twins are of special medical interest because (as will be fully explained in Chapter 23) their afflictions throw light on the relative influences of heredity and environment. While a given condition may be no more frequent in twins than in singletons, the mere fact that two members of a twin pair have the same disease or defect (especially some rare one) may be the occasion for a lengthy medical treatise, and thus will heighten the impression that twins generally tend to be sickly and defective.

Yet, on the favourable side, the attention given twins by medical scientists has been of great value to twins themselves. The knowl-edge of which diseases are hereditary can help to make clear whether or not, if one twin has an affliction, the other twin is also threatened by it, and to what extent. Following are some facts which parents of twins, and twins themselves, might well keep in mind.

The likelihood that both twins of a pair will be victims of the same disease or defect is governed, first, by whether it developed before birth or after birth. If a condition is due solely to something that was wrong in the prenatal environment – a germ disease, a chemical or nutritional deficiency in the mother, or some other interference with the twins' proper development – both twins can be born with the same defect or disease, regardless of whether they are *identicals or fraternals*. Likewise, following birth, any infectious or purely environmental disease, or the effects of malnutrition or unwholesome living conditions, can equally afflict both of a pair of twins, regardless of their type.

However, if heredity plays any part in the development or severity of a given disease or abnormality, the story may be quite different for identicals and for fraternals. The greater the role of heredity, the greater the chance that both twins of an identical pair will be similarly afflicted. But with fraternal twins, the more that heredity is involved in a given condition, the less the chance that both will be afflicted in the same way. To go into more detail, here is how the facts in specific cases may be governed by the type and sex of twins:

Identical twins. Since these twins have exactly the same hereditary factors, any defect-producing gene or genes in one which might lead to the production of any hereditary disease, defect or weakness will also be found in the other. If a condition is predominantly due to heredity (for example: colour blindness, albinism, haemophilia), its occurrence in one of identical twins means it will almost invariably also occur in the other. If a condition is largely but not entirely due to heredity (for example, diabetes), environmental differences may occasionally cause the disease to show in one identical but not the other, or in one earlier than in the other. If a condition involves some clear hereditary tendency or susceptibility but depends a good deal for its expression on adverse environmental factors, there is a considerable chance that one identical will show the affliction and the other will not (as with various allergies, some types of mental disease, certain heart conditions, and so on). However, the chance that any genetically influenced condition will equally afflict both members of a twin pair is always very much greater if they are identicals than if they are fraternals.

Fraternal twins. The fact that these twins may have differences in many of their hereditary factors does not mean that they cannot sometimes have the same hereditary afflictions. One must remember that *on the average* fraternal twins have about half of their genes in common, as do any two single children of the same two parents. By and large, then, there are many instances where fraternal twins both carry genes leading to or exposing them to the same defect; and, depending on how the genes work and what the influences of environment are, the same affliction or abnormality may often appear in both members of a fraternal pair. But, again, in comparing large groups of identical and fraternal twins, one is certain to find that any condition which is wholly, largely, or partly due to heredity will appear simultaneously in both members of a fraternal pair far less often than in both members of an identical pair.

Boy–boy and girl–girl twins. Whether twins are identical or fraternal, their sex may have much to do with the chance that any of a variety of abnormalities or defects will appear in either or both. Generally, boy twins are more likely to be born defective or subsequently develop diseases and defects to a greater extent than are girl twins. Further widening this difference between the sexes is the fact that 'boys will be boys' – that is, as boy twins grow, they tend to be more active and exposed to more environmental mishaps than are girl twins. Altogether, both nature and environment combine to discriminate against males in the matter of disease and abnormality.

Boy–girl twins. How the foregoing facts apply may often be seen most dramatically when comparing medical histories of the boy and girl of an opposite-sex twin pair. If only one of the two was sickly or defective at birth or in early infancy, it will most often have been the boy; if both are afflicted by the same infectious or other environmental disease, the boy is apt to be hit hardest; and in a number of hereditary conditions (called 'sex-linked'), such as colour blindness, haemophilia and certain structural, muscular and eye defects, the boy alone may be singled out. Only in a minority of diseases (primarily glandular conditions) is the girl twin more apt to be the major sufferer. Why all this is so will be told in detail in Chapter 18. At this point we would merely caution parents of a boy–girl twin pair to set aside any previous notion that little boys are the sturdiest and the girls the frailest; rather, while one should always keep a watchful eye on both, it may be wise to have the eye just a little more widely open for the boy twin.

A final worry about twins to be set at rest is that even if they are healthy, they are not likely to be able to compete physically with the presumably sturdier singleborns. This notion can be challenged by a long list of twins outstanding in athletics. Among identical twins alone, here are some recent examples:

At the Rensselaer Polytechnic Institute (Troy, New York), the Wollkind identical-twin track stars, David and Robert, in 1964 set records as the foremost runners in the school's 62-year-old track history. (The Wollkinds also were outstanding in scholarship, scoring nearly perfect averages as maths majors.) At Northeast Louisiana State College, in 1960, Don Styron – who, with his twin, David, had made up a starring sprinting and hurdling team – broke the world's record for the 220-yard low hurdles. Some years earlier, at the University of Michigan, the identical twins Ross and Bob Hume were co-holders of the Western Conference indoor and outdoor mile crowns, their joint titles having been achieved by the unusual practice of finishing their races in a deliberate dead heat, holding clasped hands. In football, during 1964, the Feldman identicals, Barry and Joe, were varsity stars at two different colleges, Barry at St Lawrence University, as quarterback, and Joe at Dartmouth, as fullback. Other football greats of recent years were the University of Southern California identical-twin tackles, Mike and Marlin McKeever.

Basketball, too, has numbered among its twin college stars the Van Arsdale identicals, Tom and Dick, of Indiana University, and the O'Brien twins, Eddie and John, of the University of Seattle. In the women's contingent, America's top squash tennis stars for years were the Howe twins, Betty (Mrs W. Pepper Constable), and Peggy (Mrs Robert White), both wives of surgeons.

That their matching genes may have much to do with the similar athletic prowess of identical twins, such as those mentioned, has been suggested by Professor Logan Wright (Purdue University). He pointed out that marked similarity in reaction time, agility and co-ordination – all essential to athletic achievement – has been found in identical twins (even those reared apart), indicating that heredity lays down a pattern of physical development and functional equipment which permits athletic ability to manifest itself in given ways and degrees, according to the type of training. A further possibility is that the inclination towards a particular sport may be governed by traits of mind and personality which, in turn, are also influenced by heredity; so in this way, too, identical twins may be led into similar athletic channels.

CHAPTER 13

The Minds of Twins

'THEY'RE *twins* – don't expect them to be bright.' A public-school teacher was overheard saying this to a colleague who had been discussing the backwardness of two little boys in her second-grade class. The fact that there were some singly born children in the same class who were even more backward than the twins was overlooked. For, going with the belief that twins tend to be sicklier and physically more defective than the singleborn, there is the long-standing notion that *twinship of itself* carries with it a high risk of being mentally retarded or unbalanced. How much truth is there in this?

When discussing mental traits of twins – as in our previous discussion of their physical defects – one must distinguish between different kinds of twins. There are those born prematurely and with initial handicaps, and also some full-term twins who sustain injuries and impairments in pre-birth accidents. These must be distinguished from the twins who enter the world just as fully developed, healthy and sturdy as the average singleborn. Further, there may be differences between the identical and fraternal twins, and between male and female twins, which must be considered in discussing their mental traits.

Let us start with the *intelligence* of twins. If we take all twins together, it does appear from many studies that their intelligence test scores collectively may be from 5 to 9 points below the average for singletons of the same ages and backgrounds. But, upon looking at the twins more closely, we find that they fall into two almost distinct groups – one group fully up to singletons in IQ, and the other considerably behind. This trailing group is made up largely of those who had been 'preemies', or who were born with some sort of impairment. And it is these, mainly, who lower the average for all twins.

In most cases, any twin deficiencies are likely to show up during

141

the first years of childhood. Prematurely born twins (or singletons) are particularly apt to start out well behind full-termers in mental performance, just as they also tend to lag behind in physical development. But follow-up studies indicate that the initial retarding effects are seldom permanent. Physically, the prematurely born children tend to catch up to the average in growth by about age eight or so. This also happens with their mental development in most cases; and often the mental catching-up may take place even sooner. However, the time at which 'preemies' catch up mentally has been shown to be much influenced by their home conditions and the opportunities given them for developing their minds.

The chief causes of any I Q deficiences or school backwardness among young twins – where not traceable to some inborn or prenatally caused impairment – usually lie in speech and language deficiencies, which are considered as resulting if twins are left to themselves too much. One evidence of this, it is held, may be the habit many twins get into of using a special '*twin language*', consisting of twisted or made-up words and peculiar sounds, gestures expressions, and so on, intelligible just to themselves. (However, only a minority of the mothers reporting to me said that their twins used this 'language', and that when they did, it was usually for a short period – seldom more than a year or so.) Going with this habit – and helping to develop it – is the further fact that twins may have less chance than singletons to converse with other children, and perhaps with adults as well. These effects are apt to be most pronounced in families with no other children, and particularly in the poorer and less favoured groups, where mothers are hard-pressed for time and may be especially inclined to leave twins to themselves as much as possible.

While there would seem to be logical reasons, therefore, why many twins should be held back in speech and language development, one may question whether the factors mentioned are actually as serious as they are assumed to be. For one thing, the special 'twin language' may not be entirely a hindrance. The purpose of any language is communication, and it is possible that by using their own made-up words, sounds and gestures – not really so different from what teenagers and adults often use – many twins being developing this art, and sharpening their wits, sooner than do many singletons. Actually, there is no real evidence that the use of 'twin language' for a while produces any lasting learning drawbacks. (No one, to my knowledge as of now, has divided twins into two groups – those who used 'twin language' and those who did not – and checked to see whether the first group continued to be academically retarded in any way.)

Another common belief is that twins are far likelier than single children to develop speech defects, such as stuttering, and that this also goes somehow with left-handedness among twins (which, as we reported in Chapter 4, is not very much higher in twins than in singletons). But when I checked with one of the leading experts in the field, Dr Godfrey Arnold, clinical director of the big National Hospital for Speech Disorders in New York, he told me, 'From my own experience in examining more than 50,000 persons with speech defects, I would say there definitely is no special association between twins and speech defects. In other words, among the vast numbers of speech-defective individuals whom I observed, the proportion of twins was not only no higher than their proportion in the general population but may even have been less.'

What about the general level of *mental performance* in twins? Here, again, leaving aside the small proportion with some permanent impairment, there is no reason to believe that normal twins will lag for long behind singletons in their schoolwork. A number of studies have indicated that such early IQ deficiencies as there may be in twins – as previously noted – tend to decrease or disappear in time; and following through into the late ages, Dr Lissy F. Jarvik found that twins over sixty years old scored as high on psychological tests as did singleton oldsters, and showed even less mental decline than the average for persons of their age. Our own reports from parents of twins well along in childhood would offer confirmation that their school records compare favourably with those of the single children in their families.

What can also be shown is that twinship need be no barrier to high intelligence and achievement. Innumerable twins with high IQs and top grades are listed in schools everywhere. Among the most striking examples are the Schaefer twins, Philip and Elmer, of Elmhurst, Illinois, winners in the 1958 National Merit Scholarship contests for the cream of the U.S.A.'s high-school students, who were found to have two of the highest IQs ever recorded. In fact, when at age twelve they were studied by Dr Paul Witty of Northwestern University, they 'broke the IQ thermometer' – that is, their scores for their age went beyond anything the tests could measure. (While very similar in appearance and capacities, the Schaefer twins are fraternals.) *And* – to confound many theorists – the Schaefer twins had been premature babies, and for several years in early childhood *had used their own twin language.**

Unfortunately we cannot ignore the fact that many twins do not have good minds, and that the proportion of mental defectives among twins is relatively higher than it is among singletons. (In a New York State institution for mental defectives, twins constituted about 3 per cent of all admissions, whereas there should have been no more than 2 per cent on the basis of their numbers in the general population.) Much of this excess of twins could be explained by factors already discussed: Prenatal deficiencies, accidents at birth, and effects of prematurity ('preemies', whether twins or singletons, having about twice the rate of mental deficiency of full-term babies). But some experts believe there is a special likelihood that defective twins will attract attention and be institutionalized more readily than will singleton defectives, which may make the relative recorded incidence of mental defects in twins seem larger than it really is.

Of particular interest in the case of twins is *mongoloid idiocy* (or Down's syndrome). Accounting for about 5 to 10 per cent of all serious mental retardation, this defect may have a relatively higher incidence among twins than among singletons mainly for this reason: The risk of bearing a mongoloid child goes up sharply among older mothers, who, in turn, produce above average numbers of twins (as explained in Chapter 5). Another unusual aspect of mongoloid idiocy is that if one of a pair of identicals is a mongoloid, so is the other (in all cases known to date); whereas, among fraternals, if one is a mongoloid, the other will be so only rarely – not more than one in twenty-five cases. The explanation is that this

*That prematurity of itself, whether in twins or singletons, need not prevent the development of genius is proved by the many cases of famous men who started life as premature babies. Among these were Newton, Darwin, Napoleon, Voltaire, Rousseau, Victor Hugo, Lamartine and Renan.

type of idiocy is caused by a chromosome abnormality (an extra chromosome) in a fertilized egg which throws the development out of gear. Thus, if an egg with the abnormality gives rise to identical twins, both will be mongoloid. However, when there are two fertilized eggs in the mother at the same time, leading to fraternal twins, the odds are heavily against both eggs having the same abnormality. (Among other inborn human defects traced to abnormal chromosome numbers are the 'Klinefelter' syndrome in males, and the 'Turner' syndrome in females – both involving defective sexual development and often, also, mental retardation. As with mongoloid idiocy, in the rare instances when either of these abnormalities is found in twins, it will almost invariably afflict both if they are identical, but probably only one if they are fraternal.)

In various other types of mental defect the chance that both members of a twin pair will be affected depends upon the extent to which the particular condition is due to environment, heredity, or a combination of the two. For example, *cretinism*, another common form of idiocy, is found chiefly in babies whose mothers have a thyroid deficiency (often linked with goitre). In this case the defect occurs almost as often in fraternal as identical twins. So, too, any mental defects due purely to prenatal or birth accidents can almost as readily affect paired twins of either type simultaneously. The situation is entirely different with mental defects which are hereditary, such as *amaurotic family idiocy* or *phenylpyruvic idiocy* (phenylketonuria). If these conditions (due to recessive genes) occur among twins, both will always be affected if the twins are identical; but in a fraternal pair, if one is affected, there is only a 25 per cent chance that the other also will be.

Defectiveness in the 'slow mind' category – where the individual is of the 'moron' type, with an IQ much below average (ranging from below 70 down to about 50) – is sometimes chiefly environmental, and sometimes wholly or partly hereditary. In most (but by no means all) cases, when one of a pair of identical twins is a moron, the other is also; among fraternal twins, this double moron situation occurs in less than half, or perhaps only a quarter, of the cases.

When we come to *mental diseases*, or various types of 'insanity', in twins (or singletons) it should first be clear that these conditions are distinct from the mental deficiencies we have just discussed. The deficiencies are all due to impairments of the brain which slow it down or otherwise prevent it from functioning at a normal level of intelligence; moreover, they are almost invariably *congenital* – present when the baby is born, even though they may not be detected at once. The mental diseases, on the other hand, are quite different in nature. First, they may go with any degree of intelligence – high or low. Second, very few babies, if any, are born 'insane', although tendencies towards developing mental disease later may be present in one degree or another. Third, none of the special hazards besetting twins before or during birth – prematurity, accidents, etc. – have been found to make them any more susceptible to insanity than are singletons. In other words, while twins are proportionately more likely than singletons to be born with mental *defect* or *retardation,* they are not more likely to be born with any greater predisposition to mental *disorder* or *insanity.*

What, then, of the possibility that twins have a higher risk of being 'pushed into insanity' by the special psychological stresses to which they may be subjected – twin rivalries, conflicts, jealousies, comparisons, and so on? Whatever effects these may have on the personalities and problems of twins, there is no evidence that they have any serious unbalancing effects on their minds. This is shown by the fact that there are relatively no more twins than singletons in mental institutions – that is, in proportion to their numbers in the total population. Dr Eliot Slater has found this so in an extensive study in England, and Dr Kallmann found this to be true also in the United States.

Further, if undue numbers of twins were emotionally disturbed, the evidence should appear during childhood or adolescence. But when I personally checked with the New York school system, and with several of the city's large child guidance agencies, I found no record of any disproportionate number of twins among the problem cases. At one of these agencies, the Jewish Child Care Association of New York, which has dealt with many thousands of disturbed children, the research analyst, Mrs Dorothy Foote Tate, told me the incidence of twins among these youngsters was almost exactly the same as their ratio in the population – that is, about one twin pair in 100 children, or one single twin for every 50 children.

Mrs Tate said, 'Neither our records, nor the conclusions of our staff psychologists, would point to the likelihood that twins run any greater risk of becoming mentally or emotionally disturbed than single children of the same families and in similar environments.'

One aspect of twinship that does enter into most of the common mental diseases is that the chance of 'double insanity' in a twin pair is very much greater for identicals than fraternals. In this instance there seems little doubt that heredity plays a major part. This does not mean that in any of the commoner mental diseases, such as schizophrenia or manic-depressive psychosis, heredity need be the sole or direct cause. Heredity may create the susceptibility; environment, in the form of special emotional stresses, may provide the extra push over the brink of sanity. The same push, however – sometimes a very light push – would not unbalance a person without the inborn susceptibility. Thus, any such inherited predisposition in one of a pair of identical twins would also be present in the other, and if one developed a mental disease, so, ordinarily, would the other under similar conditions. With fraternal twins, on the other hand, the chance is great that only one of a pair will have the inborn tendency; so, even though exposed to the same environmental stresses, when one of a fraternal pair becomes mentally diseased, the other usually does not.

The possibility that 'double insanity' occurring in identical twins could be due to their closeness, and the one 'catching' insanity from the other (technically referred to as *folie à deux*) was discounted by the late Dr Kallmann. He noted there have been many cases in which both members of an identical pair had been separated for a long time, or had had very different environments, and yet when one developed a mental disease, so did the other. Drs E. J. Gardner and F. E. Stephens cited such a case involving identical-twin young men who, after living apart for years, developed schizophrenia within a short time of each other, landed in the same mental institution, and showed psychotic behaviour so remarkably similar that doctors could easily have confused their charts. Contrariwise, in the great majority of cases when fraternal twins have shared the same environment, and one has developed schizophrenia, the other has remained free of the disease. Similarly, both of an identical pair are afflicted much more often than are both of a fraternal pair by various of the other, more common mental diseases, including *manic-depressive psychosis*, *involutional psychosis* (the latter usually developing during or after middle age) and *psychopathic personality* (an elusive mental abnormality in which the afflicted person, while seemingly rational, is peculiarly cold, deceitful and sometimes vicious and criminal).

Having given much attention to mental defects and mental ailments in twins, we should again stress the fact that the great majority of twins are in the normal range, and that, as in athletics, a good many have made distinguished records in the intellectual and professional fields. This latter point, incidentally, can help to answer the question, 'Have there been any truly *notable* twins?' which is asked frequently – and anxiously – by parents of twins, and by twins themselves. The implied concern behind the question is that there may be something in twinship which inhibits twins from achieving great success. So we may say, first, that while history tells of no twins in the top genius class, there have been many, in pairs or individually, who have reached high levels in various fields. And it may well be that some geniuses of the past, or some in the highest ranks of notables, started out as twins but left no record of their biological mates. In any case, the statistical odds that *both* of a twin pair will win equal great fame were and are always small.

In recent times twins have been listed among leaders in many areas. Among them have been the identical-twin Picards, Jean and Auguste of France, pioneers in undersea exploration; the noted American identical-twin scientists, Robert Brode, physicist, and Wallace Brode, chemist; and, in medicine, the distinguished Guttmachers – Alan, obstetrician and expert on twins (whom we quoted in early chapters) and Manfred, psychiatrist, of Baltimore's Johns Hopkins University. The late Professor Horatio H. Newman, who pioneered in twin research (to be discussed in Chapter 16), was a twin himself. In industry, the historic Stanley Steamer of early automotive fame was the product of twins, F. E. and F. O. Stanley. The arts boast quite a number of notable twins. Thornton Wilder, author of many great books and dramas (among them, *The Bridge of San Luis Rey*, in which identical twins are important characters), was one of a twin pair. In American painting there are the identical-twin Albrights, Iva Le Lorraine and Malvin Marr, and Soyers, Raphael and Moses.

The music world, so far as I could learn, has had no famous twins – at least as a pair. True, in the seventeenth century there were the Bach twins, Johann Ambrosius and Johann Christophe, but these two are less distinguished by their own achievements than by having been the father and uncle, respectively, of the great Johann Sebastian Bach, a singleton. On the stage, screen and TV, there have been many well-known twin actresses or dancers (such as the Dolly Sisters and the Fairbank Twins of former years), but their celebrity may have stemmed mainly from their uniqueness as twin performers.

In American journalism, two of the best known columnists are the identical twins 'Abigail Van Buren' and 'Ann Landers' (born as Pauline Esther and Esther Pauline Friedman, in Sioux City, Iowa). Their rival daily advice columns appear in hundreds of newspapers – often in competing newspapers of the same city. (Reports of a feud between the twins, which began when one started doing her column and the other followed with a competing one, have been given wide circulation.) Another pair of twin journalists were the noted Egyptian identicals, Mustafa and Ali Amin, co-editors and co-publishers of Cairo's largest newspaper, *Al Akhbar*, until charges of espionage were brought against them in 1965.

In military ranks there have been three outstanding pairs of twin generals in recent times. The United States, during World War II, had the identical-twin Air Force generals Barney McKinney Giles (who rose to be chief of Air Staff) and Benjamin Franklin Giles (who was made commanding general of the U.S. Air Forces in the Middle East). Their counterparts in Britain were the identical-twin Air Vice Marshals Richard and David Acherly. The French Army, during World War I, had the twin generals Felix and Theodore Brett, who not only looked and acted amazingly alike but were so similar in their thinking that when they were military students, the then head of the French War College, famed General 'Papa' Joffre, became so suspicious about their almost identical examination papers that he ordered an official inquiry. (It cleared the twins.)

As we look back over this chapter and the preceding one, we can see that the answer to the question, 'How *normal* are twins?' depends always on whether one is thinking of twins as a group, or of a given pair of twins – say, *your* twins (or you yourself, if you are one of twins).

Taking all twins together, it has also been shown that because of the extra hazards of birth which so many of them undergo, a higher percentage of twins than of singletons start out with defects, abnormalities or other handicaps. Nevertheless, in most cases the initial impairments and disadvantages – particularly those resulting from prematurity – are overcome before very long. While the percentage of twins who remain defective or retarded might still be above average, these none the less make up only a small proportion of the twin population, and, with continued improvement in the conditions under which twins enter the world, even this small proportion of defectives among them will be steadily reduced.

In other words, *the overwhelming majority of twins are destined to be fully as normal as are singly born persons, during childhood and throughout life.* Except for the relatively few unlucky ones, twins on the average can count on being just as healthy, bright and mentally alert, and just as sane, well-adjusted and successful, as the average singleborn.

CHAPTER 14

Identical Twins
I: Physical Traits

▬▬▬

O F all human phenomena, nothing could be more remarkable than identical twins. The wonder of such twins may not be fully appreciated, even by their parents, or by the twins themselves. For think what it means that starting from a single, tiny fertilized egg, there can evolve two human beings who, from birth until the day they die, may be almost exact copies of each other in a myriad of details, inside and out.

The development of just one person from a speck of living substance smaller than a period on this page is remarkable enough. That speck must go through countless orderly changes until there results a living mechanism infinitely more complex and efficient than the most stupendous contrivance human beings can fashion for themselves. Yet how much more fantastic is it that from the very same droplet of substance *two persons* can evolve side by side, virtually paralleling and synchronizing every stage in their development. You who have or are identical twins, take a bow!

The fact that twins duplicate each other to such an extent proves, for one thing, that no baby – singleton or twin – is a haphazard product. Quite the contrary, each child is the end result of the most painstaking carrying out of precisely detailed 'blueprints' drawn up by his or her unique hereditary factors. And what we see in identical twins is merely (or can we say 'merely'?) the fact that the very same gene blueprints that had been prepared for a single child were used to produce two children. Only to the extent that environmental factors can induce deviations from the blueprints – sometimes minute, sometimes marked, just as with a single baby – will identical twins be different. But no matter what their external or internal differences may be, identical twins will carry the same *inbuilt* gene blueprints throughout their lives, and their destinies

151

will be guided or influenced in innumerable ways by these matching hereditary factors.

The question arises: 'Why is it so important to know that identical twins have the same hereditary makeup, whereas fraternal
twins do not? How can this affect the health and well-being of
identical twins – their education, social relationships, future adjustment, happiness?' Some of the answers already have been
suggested in preceding pages. Here, and in following chapters,
more specific and detailed answers will be given.

Let us begin, first, with this fact: No identical twins are ever
exactly alike. As we have stressed before, the term 'identical' refers
only to their genes, and not to their traits, which can develop quite
differently under varied environmental conditions. Moreover, the
effects of environment may be greater on one twin than another, or
on one pair of identicals than another pair. Thus, even among
identical twins as a group one can find various degrees of likeness
or unlikeness between partners, not only in looks but in other
characteristics as well. Some of the reasons for this may go back to
the way in which the twins were conceived, and how they developed
prenatally. In other words, scientists now recognize that identical
(one-egg) twins may be of several types, as determined by the
following circumstances:

(a) Identical twins produced when the original egg divided immediately after fertilization, with the two halves pulling apart almost at once and moving on to become implanted in different sites
in the womb. The twins then develop as separately from one
another as if they were fraternals. Each twin has its own placenta,
sac and bag. (As noted in Chapter 4, up to 30 per cent of the
identical pairs develop in this way.)

(b) Identical twins produced when their egg divided after it had
begun to develop, and the two parts, although separate, stayed
close enough together to become implanted and to grow within the
same outer bag, attached to the same placenta. (This is true of the
majority of identicals.)

(c) Identical twins whose separation did not come until some
days after the egg's growth and implantation, so that they developed thereafter within *one inner sac*, encased in the one
outer bag. (This happens with only a small number of identicals,

and, as explained in Chapter 2, may often prove dangerous.)

(*d*) Identical twins of the Siamese type, whose separation came so late that it was not complete, causing them to remain joined to one another at some part of their bodies. (Discussed in Chapter 2, and further in Chapter 20.)

Rarest and most amazing of all 'identical' twins are 'identicals' of *opposite sex*. (That's right – a boy–girl pair coming from the same egg!) Such cases, only a few of which have been discovered in recent years, result from an abnormality during the egg division involving the X Y pair of sex chromosomes. As was explained in Chapter 1, when an X Y egg divides to form identical twins, each half normally receives the Y chromosome paired with an X, and develops into a boy. But in the exceptional cases mentioned, the Y drops out from one of the halves, and, since a Y must be present to produce a boy, this twin develops into an abnormal girl of the XO *Turner syndrome* type (with many abnormalities, including ovaries rudimentary or absent, and usually mental retardation). The other twin, receiving the Y plus the X, develops into a normal boy.

Looking over the foregoing possibilities, it might be supposed that the identical twins who are most alike would be the ones whose separation took place latest, and who developed most closely together in the womb. The truth, however, may be quite the reverse. It is when the twins are completely separated at the earliest (two- or four-cell) stage, and grow with separate placentas, bags and sacs, that they have the fullest freedom to develop in the same way, according to their duplicated gene blueprints. But if they are close together in the same bag, attached to the same placenta, the crowding and the competition for the common food source may lead to inequalities in development which may, in turn, prove detrimental or injurious to one or the other. The results can often be seen at birth when there may be marked differences in the size and weight of identical twins, or one may be defective and the other normal, or one is stillborn while the other survives.

Another interesting initial difference in identical twins sometimes is the well-known 'mirror-imaging' discussed in Chapter 4. But there may be an additional effect if the embryonic separation does not come until after the right and left sides of what otherwise would have been a single individual have been laid out. One twin may then carry the stamp of certain 'right-side' traits, the other twin of 'left-side' traits. To understand this better, keep in mind that in the two sides of your own face and body, even though they were laid out by the same genes, there were differences when you were born, and these differences increased as time went on. Now imagine yourself being cut in half, and each half regrowing into a complete person. The two 'you's' would then be different, because the one would be a doubling up of your right half, the other of your left half. The later in your life this division and doubling had taken place, the more different the two 'you's' would be. Similarly, then, the later the embryonic stage when twins are formed, the more different they're apt to be, and the more likely they also are to show 'mirror-imaging'.

Here we can see how some of the most important influences determining the degree of similarity between identical twins may occur before they are born. In fact, although it was formerly assumed that the prenatal environments were most different for fraternal twins, it is now apparent that the opposite is true – that the environmental differences in the womb tend to be greatest for identicals. One result is that identical twins may be more unalike at birth than they are later. (For example, take the cases cited where one newborn identical is very much bigger and heavier than his partner, or where one is normal and the other defective.) On the other hand, fraternal twins may come into the world looking more alike than they ever will thereafter.

Thus, with some identicals looking least alike in infancy, and some fraternals most alike, confusion as to twin types may be greatest in the early years. But after a while the situation reverses: The initial birth differences between identical twins usually smooth out as their duplicated genes assert themselves more and more. The twin who was much smaller and punier usually catches up with his mate in time, and the likeness in their features and in many other traits becomes more apparent. (As an added factor, many genes work according to a sort of time-clock mechanism, not making their effects felt until given stages of life, so that new *similarities* between identicals may crop out at successive ages.) On the other hand, in fraternal twins the hereditary *differences* show up increasingly as time goes on, and there is less and less likelihood of mistaking them for identicals.

How extensive can be the similarities in identical twins is becoming ever clearer as scientists pursue their studies. Looking beneath the surface likenesses of identicals, one finds that these exist in large measure because the parts are modelled over very similar underlying tissues, muscles and skeletal structures, and also arise from the closely duplicated chemical and organic functioning of the twins. Some of the important ways in which the physical resemblances between identicals assert themselves were discussed in Chapter 4. Let us now look a little closer at the details.

The amazing likeness in appearance of most identical twins shows with what fidelity their innumerable matching genes work in conformity with their genetic blueprints to construct countless details of the face and body: The *nose*, and its separate parts – bridge, nostrils, junction with the upper lip, and so on; the *ear shapes*, and whether the lobes are loose and free of the face, or attached; the shapes of the *eyes, eyebrows, eyelashes, mouth, lips* and *chin;* the *teeth* formations and *jaw* structure; the *hair* forms (straight, wavy or curly). All these parts, as a rule, are usually very close to being duplicates in identical twins – any great differences being caused by purely environmental factors such as diseases, accidents, habits. The *colouring* of identical twins – in their eyes and iris patterns, and their hair and skin – will also match remarkably in all cases except in the rare instances where environmental mishaps have disrupted the normal pigmenting processes. Further, any changes in the colouring of the hair with age will very likely be the same and will follow the same time schedule in these twins.

Looking below the surface, many additional similarities in identical twins can be found throughout their bodies. An American popular song tells of 'The head-bone connected to the neck-bone, the neck-bone connected to the collar-bone, the collar-bone connected to the breast-bone', and so on. In identical twins, all the way from head to toe, the hundreds of bones are highly similar (barring the effect of accident or disease in one and not the other).

Some parents may ask: 'Suppose our identical twins weren't brought up together, but that each was reared in a different home

CHANGES IN TWINS

IDENTICAL TWINS

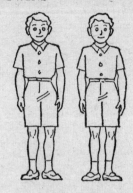

Often look least alike
at birth and in infancy

... but resemblances increase
as times goes on

FRATERNAL TWINS

Often look *most alike*
at birth and in infancy

... but resemblances diminish
as time goes on

and manner – would they still be so much alike?' As it happens,
scientists have studied scores of twins who were indeed separated
when very young – often shortly after birth – and adopted and
brought up in separate homes under different conditions. No
matter how early and for how long identical twins had been

separated, in all but a few cases *these twins had continued to resemble each other physically* almost as much as identical twins reared together. In fact, it was usually the striking resemblance between two such twins (who sometimes did not even know of each other's existence) that led to their being reunited again.

Some of the most fascinating stories of how long-separated identical twins had been brought together were reported by the late Professor Horatio H. Newman, who studied many of these cases. One day a twenty-year-old girl, Eleanor —, was taking a bus trip in Michigan. The bus stopped at a convent and a nun she did not know got on board and sat down beside her, greeting her smilingly as 'Georgiana'. When Eleanor said there must be some mistake, the nun, in amazement, told her of a pupil at the convent school who was her exact image. The two girls met, and it was eventually learned that they had been separated while infants and adopted by two different couples – who did not know one another, nor know that their foster child had a twin.

In another case two boys, Kenneth and Jerry, were being reared in different homes in the same city. One day a schoolteacher who had Kenneth in her class happened to visit another school. In one of the classes, a 'Jerry' was called upon to recite, and the visiting teacher was astonished to see a boy she was certain was her own pupil, Kenneth. Again the mystery was soon cleared up by finding that identical twins were involved.

Still another case was that of two attractive eighteen-year-old girls with different surnames, who some years ago entered Baylor University, in Texas. No one could mistake them for anything but identical twins. As the facts showed, they had been separated when a week old, had been raised by different foster parents and, except for a few brief meetings in their teens, had not been together until they entered college. Yet, despite all the differences in environment, their duplicated genes had worked through the years fashioning them almost into images of each other in their lovely faces and figures.

(How remarkable similarities in psychological traits have also been found in many pairs of long-separated identical twins will be told in Chapter 16.)

CHAPTER 15

Identical Twins
II: In Sickness and Health

THE first twins I ever knew were an identical boy pair, Elias and Harry, who lived a few doors from the house in Milwaukee where I grew up.

A few years ago these twins dropped in to visit me in New York. In the long intervening period they had become doctors (one a surgeon, the other an internee). But, after some three decades of successful practice in Wisconsin, both had been forced to retire at about the same time because of exactly the same disabling ailment – bleeding duodenal ulcers – which had required each to undergo the same operation, a partial gastrectomy (removal of a portion of the stomach).

As they told me of all that had happened to them since our boyhood days, most striking were the many similarities in their medical histories, which, as doctors, they were in a special position to note and discuss. Moreover, because of their sincere desire to add to the scientific knowledge about twins, they permitted me to tell their story in this book. In many ways it throws light on how identical twinship can affect the destinies of two individuals. (Both of these twins died in 1964, a few months apart.)

But before telling more about Drs Elias and Harry, let us consider certain general facts. In the preceding chapter we dealt mainly with the surface resemblances between identicals. These, however, like the proverbial tops of icebergs, are only a fractional representation of the innumerable similarities inside their bodies, in their organs, tissues, muscles and bones, and in their bodily functioning. As one result, in the sense that every person is a 'chemical factory', identical twins represent two almost duplicated chemical factories, constructed and equipped according to the same plans, and capable of working and producing almost identical substances – that is, if they are given the same raw materials and are operated in the same way. As noted in Chapter 4, identical twins are alike not only in all their blood groups but also in hormones, serum proteins, serum lipids, and in various other secretions. Furthermore, throughout their lives their developmental patterns – the onset of puberty (and, in female identical twins, of menstruation and the menopause) – usually follow the same time schedule; and, not least, the identicals tend to be much alike in their heartbeat rate, blood pressure, brain waves, respiratory rate, digestive process, and other functions. Only to the extent that outside influences interfere will identical twins be found to differ to any great extent in their bodily makeup and physiological processes.

With this in mind, it is hardly surprising that the medical histories of identical twins are so often the same in important respects. Coming back, then, to my twin friends, Drs Elias and Harry, we find dramatic corroboration in their own medical story, as shown in the accompanying chart which they helped to prepare. Here we see how their similar afflictions extended to many varied conditions, appearing in both at about the same time from birth through the adult years. One congenital condition was a slight spinal abnormality. Later both were plagued by the same chronic eyelid condition, slight visual defects, sensitivity to heat, quinsy, specific tooth loss, hair loss, bursitis, and their truly serious afflictions – the bleeding duodenal ulcers and, finally, heart and arterial disorders. The ulcer condition, while often apparently environmental, in their cases seems to have been hereditary, inasmuch as the same condition afflicted and/or caused the death of their father, a sister, and several other close relatives. Despite their burden of ills these doctor twins were extremely cheerful, alert and jaunty individuals until the very end.

Early in June 1964, while Harry was visiting in New York, he called to give me added details on the strangely similar medical histories of his twin and himself. A few days later Harry died of an attack of arteriosclerotic artery disease, and just seven weeks later Elias was carried off by precisely the same cause.

What can we make of the story of these identical twin doctors? There is little question that their common pool of genes had much

MEDICAL CHART OF IDENTICAL-TWIN DOCTORS

'Elias' and 'Harry', born 12 January 1899

BOTH HAD

Spina bifida occulta

Slight opening in the lower spine, with hairiness above. Present from birth.

Quinsy

An abscess behind the tonsils, which had to be incised in both at about age 23.

Kidney stones (renal calculus)

At age 45, each passed a kidney stone without awareness that the same thing was happening to the other. (Harry, then an Army medical major, was hospitalized for the condition while in New Guinea. Several weeks later he found out that Elias had passed a stone at about the same time in a Milwaukee hospital.)

Bursitis (acute bilateral)

Each has calcific deposits on the upper arm muscles, in the subdeltoid bursae.

Arthritis (hypertrophic-osteo)

The condition produced small nodules on the little fingers of each hand in both; termed 'Heberden's nodes'.

Bleeding duodenal ulcers (recurrent)

Both underwent the same operation, a gastrectomy (removal of portion of the stomach), Elias in 1955, Harry in 1958.

Eyelid inflammation

Slightly inflamed margins of upper and lower eyelids, with scanty eyelashes, long present in both. Very susceptible to wind irritation, and their eyes inflame easily.

Eyesight

Both have the same degree of myopia, and astigmatism in the same axes. Their eyeglasses are interchangeable.

Heat sensitivity

Both are equally sensitive to heat and dislike excessive exposure to the sun. At the same time, both like cold weather – even what others call bad weather.

Receding hairline

The pattern of hair loss is the same in both, with the degree of thinning only slightly greater in Elias.

Teeth

Loss of the same matching teeth have occurred in both, but on reverse sides ('mirror-imaging').

Heart and arterial ailments

Harry had attack of angina pectoris, December 1962, and was hospitalized. Elias had a coronary occlusion a few months later. Electrocardiograms of both showed similar changes in myocardial hypertrophy. (St and T waves).

DEATHS

Both twins died in 1964, within seven weeks of each other, of the same cause – arteriosclerotic artery disease. Harry died in New York City, on 10 June 1964; Elias, in Miami, Florida, on 1 August 1964.

---

to do with their similar medical histories. While they shared much the same environment when growing up, thereafter they were apart most of the time, attending different medical colleges and practising different specialities in different cities, and during World War II one served in the Army, the other did not. Only in later years, after both were forced to retire, did they live together much of the time. (Neither twin married, for despite similar romantic interests in women, both were held back from embarking on family life by the uncertainties about their health and future.) On the whole one could argue that their environments were not too different, basically, and therefore possibly accountable in considerable degree for some of their similarities in temperament, behaviour and habits – although how far these similarities could have contributed to their matching medical histories is debatable.

In any event it should be emphasized that while identical twin-ship may have caused the similarities in the ailments of these two doctors, the *twinship of itself* did not cause any of the conditions, or make these two any more sickly than they might have been if they had been singletons with similar hereditary makeups. Further, while similarities in the environment of identical twins can contri-bute to similarities in their medical histories, there is nothing about their circumstances after birth that can produce specific ailments in them which would be any different from the ailments produced in the singly born under the same conditions. But it is obvious that if identical twins stay close together, infectious or other environ-mental diseases may hit them both at about the same time. Yet it is also possible that because their constitutions are so much the same, the chances that both of an identical-twin pair will be affected by even a non-hereditary disease, or will be susceptible to its development in the same way and same degree, are considerably greater than for both members of a fraternal pair, or for two single-tons in a family. This has been shown to apply in tuberculosis and polio, for example.

When we come to the major organic diseases, however, some-thing of great importance can be said on the optimistic side: Once safely through infancy, *it is the big exception for both members of an identical-twin pair to develop the same serious ailment* at the same time or soon thereafter (as happened with our doctor twins). Of particular interest to grown-up twins, that statement applies to the major heart diseases, common cancer, brain haemorrhage (vascular lesions or 'stroke'), pneumonia, arteriosclerosis, cirrho-sis of the liver, and kidney disease. In all these conditions any effects of heredity are overshadowed by environmental influences, and not one of these major conditions, if bringing death to one identical twin, is necessarily or even usually destined to afflict or bring death to the other because of the twinship. An exception among the principal diseases is *diabetes*, the development of which is strongly influenced by heredity, and thus, where appearing in one twin of an identical pair (especially in early life), it is very likely to occur in the other twin as well.

Among less prevalent diseases and defects there are scores which are markedly hereditary. If any of these conditions is present or developing in one of an identical pair, it is almost certain to afflict the other. The list includes some of the blood diseases – haemophilia, Cooley's (Mediterranean) anaemia, and 'sickle-cell' anaemia; cystic fibrosis of the pancreas; certain muscle and neurological disorders, including some rare types of ataxia, muscular dystrophy, and paralysis; and a considerable number of eye defects, among them colour blindness, night blindness, and often (but not always) glaucoma and cataract. Deafness, when present at birth, usually afflicts both twins of an identical pair; but when it develops in adult life, and is of such hereditarily influenced types as middle-ear deafness (or otosclerosis) and inner-ear (or nerve) deafness, it may or may not afflict both twins in the same way. Not infrequently deafness occurs in only one. Gout may work similarly as may also certain forms of goitre, and certain types of allergy.

(Detailed facts regarding the foregoing and many other hereditary or hereditarily influenced diseases and defects, and their chances of afflicting both or only one of an identical-twin pair, will be found in the author's comprehensive work, *Your Heredity and Environment*, and in some other books listed in its Bibliography. In all cases, however, it is wise not to draw conclusions about the threat of any given disease or defect to twins or to others without first obtaining accurate medical diagnosis and/or consultation with competent authorities who may be suggested by one's doctor.)

We have gone into such length about 'dual threat' diseases and defects in identical twins because there are many ways in which the knowledge regarding them can serve a useful, and sometimes even life-saving, purpose. For one thing, much worry can be eliminated by knowing which ailments, if occurring in one of an identical-twin pair, *do not* necessarily menace the other twin. But where a condition in one identical *does* carry a threat for the other, it is highly important that there should be concern. With respect to many ailments, the warning signal provided by one identical twin's affliction can and should lead to prompt medical examination of the other, and thus make possible timely precautionary measures or treatment. This holds good for diabetes, ulcers, heart diseases, various eye and ear defects, many of the nervous and mental disorders, and possibly tuberculosis. At the same time, the fact that one identical twin has an ailment and the other does not may often help the doctor to discover *why* the first twin was afflicted, and so aid in his or her ultimate recovery.

Another important way in which identical twins can benefit each other is with respect to their identical blood type. Whenever blood transfusions are required, it can be known immediately that either twin is a 'walking blood bank' for his or her partner. Again and again this fact has proved invaluable in emergencies. Such an advantage usually does not exist for fraternal twins, or for two singleton siblings, or for a parent and child (and obviously not for unrelated persons), because there is always the risk that their blood may be carrying clashing substances.

Most remarkable of the medical advantages which identical twins can have for each other are those in connection with *skin grafts* or *whole organ transplants*. In Chapter 4 we told how the interchangeability of the body tissues of identical twins can serve in making 'twin-type' tests. This knowledge has led to increasingly important practical applications. First, with respect to skin grafts, serious situations may arise when a person has been badly burned or disfigured, and new skin is urgently needed for repairs. With anyone who does not have an identical twin, only skin from some-where else on his own body can be transplanted with permanency, although if such a graft is not possible, skin from another person may help for a while. But identical twins, in addition to being 'walking blood banks', are also 'walking skin banks' for each other. As one striking example, a few years ago an airman in a United States Air Force hospital in Germany was in a critical condition with third-degree burns. A surgeon hurrying to the patient happened to spot the man's identical-twin brother. The latter promptly volunteered for a skin graft, and this saved his twin's life.

The identical-twin medical drama has reached its highest points in the cases where one twin, facing death as a result of serious disease in both kidneys, has been saved through the transplantation of a healthy kidney from the other twin. (Each twin, as well as any other person, can ordinarily get along quite well with a single kidney.) The first of these operations was successfully performed in 1954 by a team of Harvard Medical School surgeons (Drs

Joseph E. Murray, John P. Merrill and J. Hartwell Harrison), and involved the twenty-three-year-old twins, Richard Herrick (the recipient) and Ronald (the donor of a kidney). At this writing, many additional successful kidney transplants between identical twins have been made. The likelihood that even fraternal twins or singleton siblings, or a parent and child, may successfully transfer kidneys under certain conditions has also arisen as the result of new techniques being employed to alter the recipient's tissues sufficiently so that the graft of the donor's kidney will take. The further possibility that organ and tissue transplants may eventually be made between unrelated persons as well is also being held out by medical scientists. It is unlikely, however, that such transplants will ever be made as easily or safely as those between identical twins.

Apart from the not too infrequent cases where one identical twin may be called upon to make a physical sacrifice for the other, the very knowledge that their bodies and functions are duplicated in innumerable ways can be mutually beneficial throughout their lives. For, in almost every aspect of their health, their development and their functioning, if one identical falls behind the other in any significant degree, it will be at once apparent – since their heredity is the same – that something in the environment is responsible. Comparisons between identical twins may at times be decried. Yet, just as an individual person may compare his weight, physical well-being, and performance from one day to the next and draw helpful conclusions, so one identical twin can also benefit by comparisons with his genetically 'other self'.

Whether the resemblances between identical twins grow smaller or greater as time goes on, the underlying hereditary likenesses permeating their bodies will never be erased. The same tests – of blood groups, colouring, and other physical traits – which can be used in infancy or childhood to prove that twins are identical can be made when they are in their oldest years, and regardless of whether they have always stayed together or have long been separated. In fact, as identical twins grow older, new evidences of their identical relationship may continually crop out, especially in the forms of those diseases, defects or bodily quirks which have a 'time-clock' mechanism for later onset. Often, too, hereditary characteristics of facial details and body form become more marked as the years go on, and likenesses between many identical twins may actually increase.

Yet we must not overstress the similarities between identicals. For always there is the fact that at no time, from before birth onwards, are they ever completely the same. If heredity produces innumerable likenesses, environment may equally create innumerable differences, sometimes very great ones. We have seen how, at the very beginning, one identical twin can be much sicklier or more defective than the other, or one can be born alive, the other dead. As the years go on, almost never do the physical lives of identical twins follow precisely the same course.

What has been said so far about the physical makeup and health of identical twins leads to another question: Are their *psychological* traits – ways of thinking, mental performance, social behaviour, and so on – also similarly conditioned by their matching hereditary makeup? For the answers we go on to our next chapter.

CHAPTER 16

Identical Twins
III: Mental Traits

JOEY and Jimmy, age 3½, are typical peas-in-a-pod look-alikes. But their worried mother writes me, 'At the nursery school I was told that Joey has an IQ of 112, Jimmy only 106. How can this be if they're *identical* twins?'

As we saw in earlier chapters, it is the comparison between twins, especially with respect to mental traits, that worries many parents. Suppose, then, we do make comparisons: If *you* have identical twins, should you expect their minds, school achievements, and personalities to be alike? And if not, what can cause the differences, and how far can these go?

Since identical twins have exactly the same hereditary equipment for mental as well as all other traits, the question goes beyond their relationship and into a much wider area: To what extent are the mental traits of human beings in general produced by their hereditary makeup, and to what extent by their rearing, experience and education? We will find no easy answers. Despite decades of study by psychologists, there is agreement only that whatever the *inborn* mental capacities of people may be, their mental performance – including their scores on intelligence tests – may be much influenced by their environments and training. Most interesting for us, some of the best studies on the 'heredity *v.* environment' question have centred on identical and fraternal twins, in comparison with each other and with single siblings.

The IQs of identical twins of a pair usually tend to be very close together, although seldom exactly alike. In most cases their IQ difference is small – averaging little more than 5 points. This is considerably less than the usual IQ difference between members of a fraternal pair, which averages about 8·5 points, and is much smaller than the average difference between any two single children in a family, which may be from 10 to 14 points.

What are we to make of these figures? Are the IQs of identical twins so much more alike as a rule than those of two fraternal twins or two single siblings because they have identical hereditary factors and the others do not? Or is it because identical twins are reared more closely together and in the same way?

A first thing to note is that fraternal twins, too, are usually closer in their IQs than are two singletons in a family, even though the fraternals may have just as much difference in their 'mental' genes. This shows that the similar environment and training of twins do help to make their minds work more alike. It might be argued, then, that identical twins are most alike in IQ because they are most alike in training. So let's ask: 'Suppose a pair of identical twins (yours, for example), were *not* reared together – that they were completely separated, not only in school, but were also raised in different homes? How would their IQs compare under those circumstances?'

The question has an answer in the cases of the separated twins we discussed in Chapters 14 and 15. Tests of these identicals who had been reared apart from infancy onward showed that their IQs differed on the average by only a few points more than those of identicals who had been reared together. Drs L. Erlenmeyer-Kimling and Lissy F. Jarvik have gone over the combined studies of IQs of thousands of twins and singletons, and have analysed the 'correlations' (statistical relationships) between the IQs of identicals reared together and apart, as well as of fraternals twins, pairs of single siblings, and pairs of unrelated children brought up together in foster homes or institutions.* The results, shown in

* 'Correlations' are degrees of closeness as measured by certain standards. If in a group of paired individuals – twins or others – the IQ of one member of a pair is always matched exactly by that of the other, this is a correlation of '100' (or ' +1·00'). If no consistent relationship at all is found between the IQs of paired members in the group (for instance, if in one pair one member has an IQ of 110, the other of 90; in the next pair, one an IQ of 85, the other of 130, and so on) this would be a correlation of 'zero'. In between the 100 and zero extremes, the more or less often the IQs of members of pairs match each other or come close together, the higher or the lower would be the average correlation for the group as a whole.

HOW CLOSE ARE TWINS' IQs?

Here are the IQ correlations (degrees of closeness) between pairs of twins of different kinds, as compared with those of other paired children.*

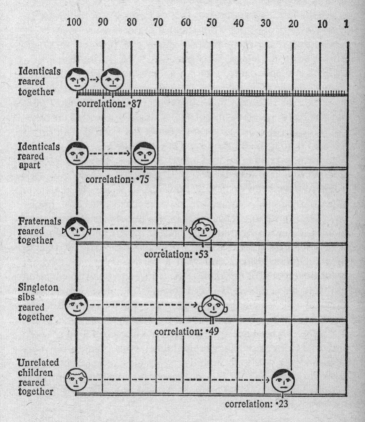

*Figures given are averages derived from an analysis of intelligence-test scores in 52 studies, covering thousands of twins and non-twin children, as reported by Drs L. Erlenmeyer-Kimling and Lissy F. Jarvik. (*Science*, 142, 12 Dec. 1963.) 'Unrelated children' refers to foster children of different parents reared in the same home. 'Correlation' is further explained in the text.

the illustration (p. 169) were considered evidence that the minds of identical twins do tend to be geared by their matching genes to perform in much the same way, even under different conditions.

A striking case in point was that of the identical British twins, sons of an Oxford tutor who had died just before they were born. The mother could keep only one, and so gave the other for adoption. The twin George, who remained with his mother, had a brilliant academic career. One day a former teacher of his, seeing a man whom he assumed to be George, greeted him heartily. Surprisingly, there came a puzzled answer in a strong, uncultured Welsh accent. It turned out, of course, that the man was the other twin, Llewellyn, who had been reared by his foster parents on an isolated farm in Wales. Yet when tested, while he was found very backward in reading and verbal performance, his IQ was 137 – fully up to that of his educated twin, George.

There have been instances, however, in which the matching genes of separated identicals did not rule the mental roost. In one case there was a difference of 24 points in the IQs of two young women identicals separately adopted as infants and raised under very different conditions. Gladys, brought up in an isolated Canadian mountain district and with a back-country grade-school education, scored only 92 in IQ. Her twin, Helen, college-educated and a teacher, scored 116. But this was the most extreme case discovered. At that, the IQ difference – quite likely due to the markedly superior education, and training in taking tests, of the one twin – was not nearly so great as can often be found between fraternal twins or singletons raised together in a family.

In another well-known study, two Yale experts, the late Dr Arnold Gesell, and Dr Helen Thompson, sought to learn what would happen if two highly similar $3\frac{1}{2}$-year-old girl identicals were conditioned in very different ways. Accordingly one of the twins was given intensive special training for a long period, while the other was not. But when the separate training of the one twin ceased, and both were left to their own devices, it was not long before they bounced back together in performance. So it would appear that *under the same conditions* the minds of identical twins can be expected to work in about the same way; and it is only under extraordinary circumstances that they will show any great difference in mental performance.

Yet even small differences between identical twins as they grow up may perplex and worry parents or the twins concerned. The first thing to explain, then, is that intelligence tests or personal observations of young children may be very unreliable (and under age 2 are often meaningless). Except where there are clearly established mental defects, one may have to wait until twins are about six years old before their IQs can be considered indicative of their future mental performance, either as a pair or in relation to each other. This is especially so if the twins were premature, and most certainly true if one was much behind the other in development at birth. In most cases (as noted in Chapter 13) where both twins seem somewhat backward in early childhood (but are not defective) they may be expected to achieve average IQs later. Similarly, when one twin has been behind the other in IQ, he may catch up before long and sometimes – like the tortoise and the hare – come out ahead.

Also to be considered is the fact that the IQ lumps together the scores on various types of mental performance – language, numbers, abstract reasoning, and so on. While one twin may have a total IQ score higher than the other, his twin may do better on some parts of the test. The twin who talks more fluently may not be as good at working out problems as his twin, and vice versa. Or, again, both twins may end up with almost the same IQ totals, but may have reached their scores in different ways. Thus it has been found that while the IQs of identical twins may be very similar, their school achievements may be less similar; and the more the twins have been separated, the less similarity there is apt to be in their scores in such subjects as reading, spelling and arithmetic. However, there does appear to be a strong hereditary component in *mathematical ability*, and in *musical talent*, and perhaps also in aptitude for *science*; so, if two identical twins differ greatly in achievement in these areas, there may be special reason to assume that one is lagging behind his capacities.

Now suppose there is an unmistakable and large disparity in the whole intelligence of one identical twin as compared with the other. What can account for it? Sometimes this may be traced to physical factors – perhaps to some injury or deficiency which the lagging twin had suffered before or during birth, or to some disease or mishap in infancy. Some – but not all – types of epilepsy and cerebral palsy may cause mental retardation, and may occur in one identical twin and not in the other. Also, in former years, excess oxygen in incubators may have affected the intelligence (as well as the eyes) of many prematurely born twins, and perhaps one more than the other. More often, any significant lag on the part of one identical twin either in IQ or in a particular subject can be traced to psychological factors. Remembering that Jimmy has in all probability the same basic mental equipment as Joey, the reasons he's not using it as fully may be much like those which inhibit any child from doing as well as he might: shyness when called on to recite; lack of drive or interest; a fancied resentment. In many cases alert parents and/or teachers may be able to detect or guess what's wrong. If not, and should a paediatrician find nothing physically wrong with the lagging twin, it may be well to consult a psychologist either in the school system or outside.

Relationships between the twins can affect their relative mental performances and should not be overlooked. One factor may be the frequently observed tendency among twins for one to be dominant, and the other to take a back seat. Sometimes this may lead to the dominant twin being more aggressive, enterprising and successful in school, and more popular with teachers and classmates. But not infrequently the twin who is less successful in social relationships or in physical feats may seek an outlet in his studies and do better in his schoolwork. This type of compensation may tend to keep the twins in balance with each other – which is just what their parents may wish most.

In fact, it is not necessary that identical twins should be equally successful in everything. So long as each is helped to develop his mental capacities as fully as he wishes, and in a way to bring him happiness, there is no reason why differences in school performance or in various competitive areas should keep twins from being well-adjusted to each other and later becoming well-adjusted adults. Nevertheless, while up to a point differences in identical twins in given subjects, aptitudes or interests may be encouraged as leading to individuality development, there is danger if they do not keep fairly abreast of each other in their total school averages and relative achievements. If one twin consistently falls behind the other to any marked degree, the situation may become serious with the approach of maturity and/or the college years. One twin may miss out on entrance to a preferred college, or fail to have equal opportunity for getting a job or attaining success and happiness. So, as a preventive measure, beginning with the twins' early school years, parents should make every effort to see that the achievements of one twin – scholastic, social, athletic – come up to and average out fairly closely to those of the other.

This brings us to the next question: How alike can one expect identical twins to be in *personality*? Often when this is asked we find an interesting psychological quirk – not in the twins, but in their parents. For, in many cases, when comparisons are resented with respect to school performances, and mental differences are deplored, parents don't seem to feel the same way about comparing twins' personalities. Indeed, many mothers, either because of desire to distinguish between their identical twins or to secure assurance that the twins' individualities are developing, seem eager to detect differences in personality as soon as possible. Thus one of the Mothers of Twins clubs routinely queried enrolling members – many of whose twins were mere infants – as to which twin was 'dominant' or 'submissive'. Among the many mothers reporting such a distinction was one whose twin boys were *seven months old*. (One wonders in what sort of conflict – perhaps a 'bottle battle'? – these teensie-weensies had settled the question of supremacy.) Also, in statements to me, a mother of sixteen-month-old girl twins labelled one an extrovert, the other an introvert, the mother of eight-month-old boy twins said one was a real 'he-man', the other 'more of the reflective and delicate type'; and various other parents have professed to see in identical twins who were anywhere from four months to a year old such personality contrasts as 'bravery' versus 'timidity', 'sociability' versus 'aloofness', 'flirtiness' versus 'prissiness' – and indeed almost any contrasting traits one can think of.

The fact is, of course, that professional psychologists would hesitate to make such definite decisions about the personalities of any two very young children, for personality tests in the pre-school years may be even less reliable than are the intelligence tests. To be sure, at any given time certain differences in personality can be detected in young identicals, but these are usually minor and apparent mainly to their parents, siblings or intimate friends. Moreover, many parents report the familiar seesaw effect of a given trait shifting from one twin to the other at various times, and quite often it is merely an illusion that the contrasts exist at all.

When identical twins do reach the age when their personalities can be judged with any degree of reliability, the findings of many studies show this: In almost all basic personality traits identical twins tend to be much more alike than do fraternal twins of the same sex, or two single siblings in a family. For example, in one study of twins at ages 11 to 15, by Drs Raymond B. Cattell, Duncan B. Blewett, and John R. Beloff, such traits as being easygoing, sociable and warmhearted or bold and outgoing were shown as appearing together in both members of an identical pair much more often than in both twins of a fraternal pair or in two single siblings. In another study, Dr Steven G. Vandenberg (University of Louisville) found much more similarity between the identicals than between the fraternals in such traits as response to music and colour, and in degrees of self-confidence and stubbornness.

Food preferences are of special interest in identicals. As a rule, both will go for or reject much the same foods and beverages, sometimes from their earliest years. In the case of my identical-twin doctor friends, told about in the previous chapter, it was fascinating to hear them discuss their likes and dislikes. Throughout their lives they had found that if one didn't like something, the other usually didn't, either. For instance, both had discovered separately that they disliked peppermint, grapefruit, tomato soup, fruit juices, and cocktails.

That there may be an inborn basis for food and drink preferences or aversions in identical twins, arising from their biochemical functioning, has been previously suggested (Chapter 4). Again, we noted (Chapter 15) that allergic reactions of identicals to various specific substances may be much the same. Among other things, biochemist Roger J. Williams has maintained that a craving for alcohol by some individuals, or a dislike for it or inability to tolerate it by others, may be linked with inherent characteristics of the body chemistry. If so, there would be a special reason why the drinking habits or aversions of identical twins should tend to be the same. Similarities in the smoking habits of identical twins – indulgence or abstinence – were also reported by the late British geneticist, Sir Ronald Fisher, as pointing to hereditary influences.

But the question always pops up: 'Doesn't the fact that the *environments* of identical twins are so much the same account for their similarities in personality?' To a considerable extent this may be so, as it applies to their early closeness and training. But it is important to note that identical twins themselves *create* similarities in their 'personality environment' by looking so much alike and functioning alike in so many ways. In other words, whether they are both good-looking or homely, robust or sickly, bright or dull, talented or unartistic, identical twins tend to inspire much the same reactions from other people, and this in itself is a great influence in moulding their personalities along similar lines.

Thus it is again not surprising that even among the twins who are separated in infancy and reared apart, close resemblances in personality often develop. One of the most striking cases on record was that of the twins Millan and George, born in Salt Lake City, who had been separated almost immediately after birth and brought up far apart by foster parents of different types, under quite different conditions. When they came together, at age 19, they were found to be remarkably alike not only in looks but also in intelligence, temperament, and achievement. Both had artistic leanings, one towards music, the other towards drawing; and both had won amateur boxing championships. (Their twinship further asserted itself in a sad way when, while serving apart in the Army, they both developed – almost simultaneously – the same rare crippling disease of *spondylitis*.) Also, there were the Baylor University twins, Louise and Lola, whose amazing physical similarity after years of separation was mentioned in a previous chapter. These twins, too, on being reunited as young women, were found to be closely matched not only in IQs but also in many abilities (both were artistic) and in personality traits.

Added to the accounts of American reared-apart twins is that of the two male identicals given the names of Tony Milasi and Roger

Brooks after their separation in infancy and adoption by two quite different couples, one Italian, the other Jewish. With Tony raised in New York State and Roger in Florida, these twins knew nothing of each other's existence until, through the now familiar coincidence of mistaken identity, they finally were brought together at age 23 (in 1964). Though psychological tests by Dr Syvil Marquit of Miami showed that they had nearly the same IQs and basic aptitudes, their personalities were apparently very different (not surprising in view of how different had been their home lives and rearing), Roger being rated as 'more sensitive and impressionable', Tony as 'more extroverted and self-assured'. (None the less, the twins were so drawn together that Roger moved to Tony's city to live with him.)

Other studies of identical twins reared apart, made in Denmark by Dr N. Jule-Nielsen, give further evidence of how matching hereditary factors can lead to the development of great similarities in twins' personalities, even when there have been great environmental differences. The Danish group comprised twelve pairs of adult identical twins, ranging in age from twenty-two to seventy-seven, who had been separated in early childhood and not reunited until much later – in many cases, as with twins previously mentioned, because one was repeatedly mistaken for the other. One pair, the male identicals Palle and Peter, had been raised from infancy in very different homes in Copenhagen, and had quite marked differences in education (one had only an elementary schooling, while the other was studying medicine); but, when brought together at age 22, they proved to be remarkably similar in mental development and personality. As Dr Jule-Nielsen reported: 'Both seemed introspective, lacked self-confidence, found it difficult to achieve emotional contact with other persons, and presented similar neurotic, hypochondriacal symptoms.' Despite this, they took to each other so well that they left their respective homes and thereafter kept closely together.

Not so successful was the reunion of another identical male twin pair, Kaj and Robert, who had been apart from infancy until the age of 40. Kaj, raised in a village by a poor couple, had a jail record and an erratic history. Robert, who grew up and was educated under favourable conditions, had become a technician. But he too, though never in direct conflict with the law, had, like his twin, shown an antisocial streak, was maladjusted, and had sought psychiatric help. Tests showed them to be much alike in basic personality and with much the same problems – work, money and women. (Each had been married three times.) Before long they broke off relations with each other.

Also unsuccessful was the reunion of two women identicals, Ingrid and Olga, who had been separated when only eight weeks old. Ingrid was reared on a farm in one part of Jutland, Olga in a children's home in another part. When brought together again at age 35, they found that although they had similar personalities, they were too different in background and views to provide any basis for a continuing close relationship.

Of special interest are the brain-wave recordings (electro-encephalograms) of the group of separated Danish twins which were made by Dr N. Jule-Nielsen in association with Dr Bent Harvald. The 'EEGs' of the two members of each pair were found to be almost completely alike in all significant aspects (as are those of Ingrid and Olga, which are reproduced here). This led to the conclusion that brain waves in individuals generally are primarily

BRAIN WAVES OF SEPARATED IDENTICAL TWINS

Ingrid's EEGs   *Olga's EEGs*

The above amazingly similar brain-wave patterns (encephalograms, or 'EEGs') are those of the two thirty-seven-year-old Danish identical twins, Ingrid and Olga (referred to in the text), who had been separated at the age of eight weeks, reared apart under very different conditions, and not re-united until about a year before the recordings were made by Drs N. Jule-Nielsen and Bent Harvald.

determined by hereditary factors which continue to assert themselves throughout life.

We do not wish to leave readers with the impression that the personality patterns of identical twins (or of single individuals, for that matter) are unalterably set for life by their genes, and that environmental influences play only a small part. The cases usually dwelt on (because they may be the most interesting) are mainly those of twins whose personalities developed similarly despite differences in environment. But one could also give many instances in which identical twins, separated or not, showed considerable differences in personality (as was true with Tony and Roger, previously mentioned). In a later chapter we will tell of some extreme cases, in which one twin became a criminal or was a suicide, or the behaviour paths diverged sharply in some other respect. Perhaps, just as parents may look for and emphasize very small differences between their identical twins, many scientists in studying twins may have been inclined to look for and emphasize similarities.

Regretfully for scientific study but happily for twins, the cases of those separated from infancy onwards are becoming increasingly rare. The sharp decline in parental mortality has greatly reduced the chance of twins being orphaned in infancy; public aid has enabled impoverished parents to keep their twins; and also, when twins have had to be given out for adoption, the demand for these babies (at least in the United States, and in other advanced countries) has become so great that any twins offered are eagerly snapped up as a pair. (Among the 500 or so pairs of twins reported on in the questionnaires filled out for me, at least six pairs, to my knowledge, were adopted. In another case, reported to me, a Los Angeles couple, in 1960, adopted a set of triplets.) However, the stories already available of twins separated in the past, and other evidence brought out in this chapter, should help to give parents a good idea of what can be looked for in the way of mental and personality differences or likenesses in their own identicals, and what practical value this knowledge can have.

Above all, one should keep in mind that identical twins are in a unique position in relation to themselves, and in the way other people react to them. Comparisons between the twins – no matter what the parents may feel or do – are unavoidable. These will be made not only by other people but also by the twins themselves throughout their lives. If comparisons merely reveal interesting differences between the twins, this may be all to the good. Harm can be done only if the comparisons are consistently unfavourable to one twin and show him or her at a marked disadvantage in relation to the other. It is mainly for this reason that the strongest efforts should be made to keep identical twins in balance – physically, mentally, emotionally, socially, and in their achievements – to a greater extent than is ordinarily necessary or possible with two fraternal twins, or with any two singletons in a family.

CHAPTER 17

Fraternal Twins
I: Boy–Boy and Girl–Girl Pairs

———

SOME years ago, while in the club car of a train, I got into conversation with two men who said they were fraternal twins (although no one would ever have suspected it from their appearance). Soon the three of us learned that we were linked by an odd coincidence. We had all been born in Louisville, Kentucky, at about the same time; our respective families had moved to other cities when we were children, and – most interestingly – there were no official records of our birth, since, apparently, we were born just before such records began to be kept in Louisville. But the effect of this official negligence had been quite different for the twins and for me.

My father, while I was quite young, had had the foresight to obtain from the family doctor who ushered me into the world an affidavit which ever since has served me in lieu of a birth certificate. But the fraternal twins had not been so lucky. By the time there was need for their birth records, their parents had died in an accident, no one could recall the name of the doctor who delivered them, and the best that could be produced was a statement from an aunt attesting from memory to their birth date and the fact that they were twins. Over the years they had had repeated difficulties whenever this was offered for official purposes.

We've told this story to emphasize the fact, previously brought out, that whereas the twinship of identical twins is *inborn*, and the evidence is carried on their faces and inside their bodies wherever they go, the situation with fraternals is radically different. These twins, whether of the same sex or of opposite sex, can prove their relationship *only by their birth certificates or other documentary evidence*. One can't tell that fraternals are twins by looking at them or testing them. Once they've achieved birth, they are no more linked biologically than are any two single siblings. Any special

180

relationship between them thereafter can derive only from the extent to which they are reared as twins and continue to be conscious of their twinship. This is not to imply that the relationship between fraternals can be lightly dismissed. Even the bond that is felt between two identicals is primarily psychological. And if single brothers and sisters in a family can preserve a lifelong attachment, there is every reason for the bond between two members of a fraternal pair to be more than ordinarily strong, meaningful and enduring.

Previously we have dealt with many aspects of the fraternal-twin relationship as it contrasts with that of identical twins. In this chapter we will go into more details about fraternals of the same sex, illustrating the facts with close-ups of actual pairs as described to us by their parents. In the next chapter we will deal with fraternals of opposite sex, whose relationship is very different in a great many ways from that of other twins.

Starting, then, with the boy—boy and girl—girl pairs, one must first be certain that the twins who are assumed to be fraternal really are of this type. As stated in Chapters 2 and 4, there may have been a wrong diagnosis (in up to one in five or six cases of like-sex pairs) if the decision as to their type was hurriedly rendered on the basis of the twins' afterbirths; for it may be recalled that two placentas can often go with identical twins, and a single placenta with twins who are fraternal. Again and again the failure to recognize this has led to confusion and later annoyance or grief, when twins who were being raised as identicals turned out to be fraternals, or vice versa. In most instances the error is cleared up after the twins have passed through infancy, and especially when differences in hereditary traits, such as in eye and hair colour, definitely stamp a pair as fraternal; or, contrariwise, when twins continue to look so startlingly alike that, as one New Jersey mother observed, 'The two placentas may have said "fraternal", but my eyes tell me plainly they're identical.' Whenever doubt still remains, there are the twin-typing tests which we discussed in Chapter 4.

Once the reader is clear that the twins he or she has in mind are indeed fraternal, the next important point to consider is how similar or dissimilar they may be. For, while all fraternal twins differ in their hereditary makeup, the *amount* of difference can be much greater in one pair than in another pair, and can have an important bearing on everything concerning them. Here, for example, are contrasting descriptions of two pairs of fraternals, living in the same community, as given by their mothers. First, a pair who are extremely different:

My three-year-old twin boys are so unlike you wouldn't believe they're brothers. Twin A has brown eyes and dark skin, while Twin B is blue-eyed and blond. Twin A was bigger at birth, and has kept his edge in height by about two and one-half inches, and also is several pounds heavier and more huskily built, while Twin B has a smaller build, with tiny bones. Twin A was born with hydroceles (fluid in the testes), and Twin B had defective, turned-in feet (corrected by plaster casts and special shoes) and two hernias (which have been operated on). Twin A is more easy-going, more cheerful and friendlier with strangers, yet is very emotional and cries easily, not defending himself when he is attacked by his smaller twin, who is a little roughneck and is constantly getting into fights. Twin A was slower walking and sitting than Twin B, but speaks well; while Twin B can hardly speak intelligently so far, making only attempts at words and acting out everything. Do you think they will stay as they are?

No two siblings could be more different than these two and, as we could tell the mother, there is every chance that such a pair will always be very unalike, and may even become more unalike in various important ways as time goes on. By contrast now, consider the next pair of fraternals:

We simply don't understand about our twin girls, now two and one-half. They had one afterbirth, and, besides, they look and act so much the same we'd swear they were identicals. But when blood tests were made – not once, but twice – the doctors said there was positive proof they were fraternals. How can this be? The little girls are so alike in so many ways, in the colour of their eyes and hair, in their faces and their size, that most people can't tell them apart; and they're equally bright and healthy, and have the same sweet dispositions. If the blood tests were right, isn't there a possibility that they are part identical and part fraternal – that is, *mostly* identical?

Oddly enough, this mother's theory, while stated incorrectly, is not so far-fetched. For if we think of fraternal in terms of hereditary differences, then, unquestionably, some fraternal twins come much closer to being identical in makeup than others. To understand this better, let us expand on some of the facts about the workings of heredity which were given in Chapter 4. As we noted there, every parent carries an assortment of chromosomes containing the genes – the hereditary factors. At conception a child is dealt only half of each parent's chromosomes; and, *on the average*, about half of the chromosomes received by any two fraternal twins, or any two singletons in a family, are the same. But, as with cards, sometimes the deal to one pair of fraternals (or to two singletons) may include many more matching chromosomes than the deal to another pair. Thus, conceivably, one pair of fraternals could be alike in almost all of their chromosomes – and the hereditary traits produced by them – and another pair alike in only a few, and unalike in all the rest.

The foregoing is most strikingly shown in families where there are two sets of fraternals, as in the following instance reported by a puzzled parent: 'How can it be that our older fraternal twins, Eddie and Artie, have the same eyes and hair and look almost like identicals, but our younger set, Jim and John, are so different in almost everything you'd think they came from entirely different families?' The answer may be simply that the first pair received mostly matching chromosomes and genes, while the second pair received mostly those that were unalike.

The extent of the similarities or differences which can occur between fraternal twins (or any two singletons in a family) is also governed by how assorted are the parents' own hereditary factors, and how different or similar in hereditary makeup the two parents may be. To again enlarge on what was said in Chapter 4, suppose that the father and mother are first cousins of Scandinavian stock, and are both blond, blue-eyed, fair-skinned, and with regular features. Since these parents must carry a great many matching genes, *all* of their children would tend to have the same colouring, and their features would not be too different. But suppose – as with a pair of fraternal twins in Hawaii – one parent is of mixed American-Scotch, Spanish, and Japanese stock, and the other of mixed German, French, and Hawaiian ancestry. Each parent would be carrying an assortment of dissimilar genes, and the combination of hereditary traits of one fraternal could be much different from that of the other.

Added to the hereditary differences, the environmental influences from prenatal life onwards always have much to do with how fraternal twins compare in any respect. Any inequalities in nutrition or in opportunities for development – starting in the womb – will increase the initial differences between them. Further, since fraternals may be quite unlike in their inborn makeup and tendencies, any differences present between them at the outset – in size, build, looks, health, behaviour, and so on – are less apt to be overcome or to disappear in time than is the case with identicals, whose inner push is always towards similarity. Also, where the developmental patterns of identicals usually are closely parallel, in fraternals there may often be marked differences, so that one of a fraternal pair may begin shooting up first, and for a while may be considerably bigger, only to be outdistanced presently in height and physique by the other.

Most of the facts about the possible differences between fraternals in physical makeup, diseases and defects, and in mental traits, have been presented in the preceding chapters when we compared them with identical twins. Now we may ask, how can this knowledge be helpful to parents of fraternals and the twins themselves? For one thing, just being prepared for the differences can serve to ease many worries. One is not surprised or too much upset if the singletons in a family differ considerably in height and weight at the same age, or in physical attractiveness, health, mental capacities and talents, athletic prowess, personality, behaviour, and so on. There should be no more surprise if fraternal twins differ in any or all of these respects. Sometimes the differences are open to correction. Sometimes they must be adjusted to and accepted as natural without trying to exert frenzied efforts to make fraternal twins become more alike. *Fraternals aren't born to be alike.* And knowing this will increase the chances that each twin will be handled individually and with more understanding of the problems involved.

Another common error is to assume that the degree to which fraternals do or don't resemble each other physically is an indication of how much they should or shouldn't be alike in their abilities, personalities, and other traits. Actually, there need be no connection between the 'look' genes of persons and their 'mental' genes.

One pair of fraternals can resemble each other a great deal in appearance and yet be very different in their minds and personalities; another pair may be wholly unlike in looks, but quite similar in intelligence and capacities. As a Westchester mother reported about her thirteen-year-old fraternal boys: 'They are very unalike in looks, and one is much bigger than the other, but they are extremely alike in ability. Both are brilliant students, and each plays two instruments, the piano and also either the trumpet or oboe.'

In many other cases the contrast in abilities, personalities and temperaments between fraternals may be readily apparent. Here are a few examples:

– (*Fraternal boys, age 4½*). Arthur is more temperamental, extremely sensitive, with an avid curiosity about adults, a keen eye for beauty – such as for an adult's dress or the furnishings of a room – and an unusual memory for details. Larry, very bright, is much more outgoing, makes friends more easily, is a leader in his group, beautifully co-ordinated, and adjusts to new situations more readily than Arthur, who is emotionally immature by comparison.

– (*Fraternal girls, age 14*). We were troubled for quite a while because Virginia has always been the beauty of the twins, and has a more appealing disposition. But Linda has more zip, and when we found she had musical talent and a voice (her twin, by the way, is almost tone deaf), we got her to take lessons in singing and the guitar, and now she's a hit at parties. Both girls are equally popular with boys, though – luckily – not the same type of boys!

– (*Fraternal boys, age 15*). Freddie is more outgoing, more aggressive, with a quicker mind and a good memory, and is more popular because of his athletic prowess. But Billy, the weaker one, has outdone him in the arts, crafts and sciences. Although Billy sometimes feels inferior, and leans on Freddie in some ways, Freddie thinks his twin – who is the tall, slim type – is handsomer and more sensitive. What is important is that the boys don't clash, and are very fond of each other.

The cases cited here are especially significant because they bring out this point: In perhaps most instances where fraternals differ in capacities or qualities, the advantages of one in certain areas are balanced by advantages which his twin may have in other respects. Sometimes the compensating assets of a lagging twin may not show up readily, and it may then devolve upon the parents to search out his hidden potentials and help to develop them. If the differences between fraternals cannot be balanced (and the worst thing is to try to force a balance when natural factors in the twins prevent it), one may draw comfort from the fact that the backward twin will probably not be hurt as much as if he were an identical. The reason is simply that fraternals are not usually under as great pressure to equal each other as are identicals; nor are they as close, and as much affected by differences between themselves.

One situation occurring much more often with fraternals than with identicals involves discrimination between them on the part of their parents. When fraternal twins are dissimilar in traits, there may be a tendency on the part of each parent to identify with a different twin. '*A* is more *my* twin,' a mother may say or think. '*B* is her father's twin.' Often this distinction is made from the beginning solely on the basis of each twin's looks; although, as we noted earlier, the twin who looks most like one parent, or that parent's side of the family, may easily tend more towards the other parent in mind and behaviour. If the differences in twins' looks are not great, parental identification may be with other traits. For example, a father who is set on a 'masculine-type' boy may identify with the twin who is more aggressive; while the mother may favour the more timid and sensitive twin. Differences in intelligence, talents, or personality, as well as in prettiness or handsomeness, may all play a part in causing a parent (or members of his or her side of the family) to discriminate for or against either of a fraternal pair. Sometimes the reasons aren't apparent on the surface, and one may have to search deep into the parent's background and early life to find them. (Several examples of such psychoanalytical cases will be given in Chapter 21.)

One of the most detailed accounts of 'split parental-identification' between fraternals is the following, as reported to me by a New York mother of a five-year-old girl pair whom we'll call Lora and Letty:

One thing about the twins that at first worried me and now I think is very good for them is this: Lora has always been a 'Daddy's girl', and is very much like her dad, even physically, while Letty has always been a 'Mommie's girl', and physically resembles me. The degree to which this has gone is uncanny. For example, Bill, my husband, is a mechanic and has developed the habit of pointing with his middle finger on his right hand, instead of his forefinger, because he often uses his forefinger and thumb in holding or tightening something, and if he has to point must use the middle finger. Well, at a surprisingly early age Lora picked this up. There are other ways, too, in which she's like her dad, although despite this she's remained quite feminine.

I realized that people are always typing children to their parents, but the way it had gone with our twins troubled me so much that I consulted a psychiatrist. I was told it was probably healthier for the twins because the parents wouldn't have to be constantly worried about dividing attention – both twins would be getting the normal physical attention from Mommy during the day, and later the very special attention they both needed by being divided between their parents. For the children I believe it is better because, rather than having to share their parents, they have voluntarily chosen each her own 'whole' parent.

Whether the advice given and followed above was sound is a question. One may doubt that it ever is good for one child in a family – twin or singleton – to be too strongly identified with one parent, and another child with the other parent, especially if the children are of the same sex. A certain degree of parental 'slanting' is unavoidable where one fraternal clearly shows more tendency or capacity to go along with a parent's interests – as in music, science, sports, dress, or other activities. Nor can it be overlooked that differences in temperament between fraternals may provide a real basis for a closer association between a given parent and one of the twins. But such an association must never exclude a strong affectional bond with the other twin as well. Nor can one ignore the possibility of parental divorce or death during the twins' childhood, which may take away the parent with whom one of the twins was linked and thus leave him or her emotionally adrift. On the whole, too much discrimination or individual identification by parents among children in a family is never good, and is worse when it involves twins.

Attempts to treat and train fraternals as if they were identicals may be equally inadvisable. Fraternal twins so raised, and who have come to rely on the importance of their twinship, are headed for a letdown when people begin to say, '*Twins?* Hmpf. You don't look it.' So, too, parents who have overplayed the twinship of their fraternals may experience a letdown when the two no longer attract special attention. On the other hand, many parents feel relieved when this happens. The varying reactions when the twinship of fraternals decreases are shown in many statements which have come to me. On the negative side are these:

– 'Our twins now are no more alike than any two separate persons. They have their individual tastes and abilities, neither depends on the other, and they have become less like twins in many ways. We find it hard sometimes to keep thinking of them as twins.'
– 'We now are sorry we gave the twins similar names. They look different, have different personalities, and it seems funny for them to have names so much alike.'
– 'It's hard to see the twins almost stop being twins. It's as if something rare and beautiful had suddenly been lost.'

Brighter views appear in the following statements:

– 'All I can say is, thank goodness my twins have settled down to being just two normal *individuals*.'
– 'When I look back, I feel that watching two children whom I carried and bore at the same time, and tried to train in the same way, yet who have grown up to be so different, has been a fascinating and wonderful education. It has helped me a lot with the three singletons who have followed them, for it has taught me that parents can do just so much with a child – the rest is up to what's in the child himself.'
– 'I think the best thing about a fraternal pair is that at the start you have all the fun of having twins, but later you don't have all of the headaches that go with identicals.'

The foregoing statements suggest two questions: 'How important, after all, is fraternal twinship?' And next, 'What happens between fraternals as they grow older?' On the first question, let us affirm what was said near the beginning of this chapter, that none of the acts or views we have presented should be considered as minimizing the importance of the fraternal-twin relationship. While fraternals are very different from identicals in many ways, as we have seen, they nonetheless are not the same in their relationship as singleton siblings. The fact that each of the fraternal twins started off closely paired with another child can continue to be meaningful throughout their lives. What and how great the effects will be – whether the fraternals will feel mutually enriched and strengthened by their twinship and seek to maintain it or will become indifferent or even antagonistic to each other – depends always on both their conditioning and their individual characteristics.

What actually does happen with fraternal twins as they grow older will be discussed in two chapters to come (20 and 21). For the moment, on the questions that were posed, we would venture this opinion: The future relationship of any given pair of fraternals will probably be determined not so much by how they were raised specifically as twins, but by how much they were raised to be devoted brothers or sisters, and good human beings.

CHAPTER 18

Fraternal Twins
II. The Boy–Girl Pairs

ONE of the world's most famous remarks is that of the French legislator who, during a debate in which a colleague was stressing that human males and females are not the same, shouted exuberantly, '*Vive la différence!*'

This cry might well be echoed by everyone who is anxious to see individuality developed in twins. For, with the typical boy–girl pair, there is apt to be nothing but individuality. They are by all odds the least 'twinny' of twins. But they also are the most interesting in many ways. Summed up in them one can see unfolding all the differences between the sexes – those arising from inborn factors, and those developed by outside conditioning, although it is not always easy to tell the part played by the respective influences.

From the moment the boy and girl twin start off together in the womb, they begin going their separate ways. A biological 'maleness-magnet' pulls the boy's development in one direction, a biological 'femaleness-magnet' pulls the girl in another direction. When they are born the results of this may not be readily apparent. Except for their sex organs, there is little to distinguish them outwardly from fraternal newborns of the same sex. But inwardly they already are very different in innumerable respects.

In Chapter 1 we told how a boy and girl twin pair are conceived, and how the initial difference between them is in the sex chromosomes: the boy developing from a fertilized egg containing *one* X chromosome, plus a small Y; the girl from a fertilized egg containing *two* X chromosomes. As the original egg cell of each twin multiplies into trillions of cells, the cells of the boy receive the XY combination, and the cells of the girl the XX combination. This difference extends all the way, inside and out, from the tops of their heads to the tips of their fingers and toes. And it is this which

190

guides their development in separate directions, and leads to every subsequent manifestation of their biological maleness or femaleness. In addition it should be kept in mind that boy–girl twins, even more than same-sex fraternals, may be different in a great many of their hereditary factors.

Keeping possible exceptions in mind, the first important difference between the girl and boy of a twin pair is that their body mechanisms and structures are geared to develop at different rates, *with the girl almost always well in the lead.* That is, from conception onwards the little girl is growing at a faster rate than the boy. If at birth the boy still is somewhat larger, it is only because, as a male, he is headed towards a bigger size; and even though the girl is moving faster towards her growth goal, she usually will not quite overtake him, except for a short stretch during the puberty years. Inwardly, however, there are many indications that the girl is ahead of the boy in development at every week and month. One way in which the scientist can tell this is by examining the extent to which the bones have hardened (gauged by the amount of cartilage at specific skeletal points which has turned into bone). By this and other calculations, the girl twin at birth is usually about one and one-half months ahead of the boy in biological maturity, and with each month and year all the way through puberty her biological lead increases. In this sense, then, the little girl twin is always really older than her brother, even though chronologically they are of exactly the same age.

As the development of the boy and girl continues, the outer sex differences become more apparent. The boy tends to be larger in almost all the bodily measurements – chest, thickness of bones, girth of the fore-arm, and so on. It also can soon be seen that he is more muscular. The girl, in turn, is somewhat 'softer', there being a bit more fatty tissue under her skin. Yet a big mistake can be made in assuming that because the boy is sturdier in build and muscularly stronger, he also is healthier or less prone to sickness than the girl. The facts are almost completely the reverse: *If either twin is afflicted by a serious defect or illness, it is much more likely to be the boy.* This has become increasingly clearer as medical scientists have shown that the higher casualty rate among males at all ages, as compared with females, is by no means due simply to their

From the Sunday comic page series, 'Miss Peach', by Mell. Copyright 1958 by the New York Herald Tribune, Inc., and reproduced by permission.

leading harder or more reckless lives. While the environmental factors undoubtedly worsen the situation for males, there also is a basic sex difference. Nature has discriminated by making the female body and system more resistant than is the male's to the great majority of diseases and defects. Where there is an affliction or stress, the female is better able to take it. This is conclusively shown by the higher male casualty rate even in prenatal life, as well as at birth and during infancy – long before environmental differences between the sexes enter the picture (as we noted briefly in Chapter 3 and Chapter 12).

Space limits prevent our going into detail about the relative chances of diseases and defects in the boy and girl of a twin pair; nor do we wish to make too much of this, because the situation in their case is not very different from that of any singleton brother and sister pair in the same family. With this in mind we may summarize the health situation of boy–girl twins as follows:

– At birth, if there is any defect in a twin pair, it is more likely to be in the boy than in the girl; and if both are afflicted, the condition in the boy may be more serious.

– Many hereditary conditions, known to be sex linked, appear largely in males, and if these run in a given family, the boy of an opposite-sex twin pair may often be afflicted, whereas the girl twin usually will not be. Among these sex-linked conditions are colour blindness and certain other eye defects, haemophilia, several of the muscular disorders, and a number of rare skeletal and skin afflictions.

– If both the boy and girl acquire the same infectious disease, or are injured in the same accident, the risk of serious consequences is usually greater for the boy.

– If the twins are nervous or emotionally disturbed, the girl may show it more often by mannerisms such as nail biting, loss of appetite, or contrariness; the boy in a more active way by aggressive and unruly behaviour, and sometimes through speech disorders, such as stuttering.

None of the foregoing facts should be considered as suggesting that the boy twin is to be treated as a weakling or handled as if he were a fragile doll. But it is wise not to go to the opposite extreme, and think that just because he is a male, he need not be watched over as carefully as the girl, or that during childhood he should be conditioned towards rougher and less careful living. Also, one should always remember that the average facts may not necessarily apply to a particular boy–girl twin pair. Not infrequently, it may be the girl who, because of more defective hereditary factors or some accident or upset affecting her and not the boy, will be the least resistant to disease and defect thereafter. The safest policy, then, is to treat the boy and girl of a twin pair as individuals, while trying to ensure for each the utmost in sensible care, diet and proper medical attention.

Some of the most fascinating sex differences are revealed in the first performances of boy–girl twins. Since little girls are ahead of little boys in their rate of growth and bodily development, it might be expected that they would also be the first to start creeping, standing, walking. But, countering this, is the fact that boys are a bit more muscular and energetic. So it often is a toss up as to whether the boy or girl will stand or walk first, but with the odds a little in the girl's favour.

In one performance, however, there is little doubt of the girl's priority: *talking*. With few exceptions she's the one who starts to talk first. This was affirmed by almost every mother who reported to me on this point. It was not surprising, inasmuch as years ago noted child psychologist Florence Goodenough had observed: 'The talkativeness of the female sex – one of the standbys of the comics for generations . . . has some foundation in fact. Nearly all investigators have found that, on the average, girl babies begin to talk a little earlier than do boys, that their vocabularies at any age are a little larger, and that they use longer sentences.'

Another first for the girl almost always is her ability to dress herself before her twin brother can. This goes with the female superiority – as a rule from childhood on – in tasks requiring finer hand movements, which enables the girl to begin buttoning her clothes and tying her shoes in advance of the little boy. To compensate, the boy twin may soon show he is better in activities involving larger movements and more muscular force. A good example is in ball-throwing. Eager dads who try to turn both the girl and boy into baseball pitchers will find that as early as age $3\frac{1}{2}$ boys show themselves superior to girls in ease of delivery and accuracy of throw. As time goes on, there are more and more ways in which sex differences in body build and muscular development and co-ordination incline the boy towards superiority in physical and athletic pursuits, although training and interest in these activities add importantly to the results. If the girl twin should be athletically better than the boy, the very fact that *he* is expected to be superior can be a disturbing influence.

On the girl's side, while her twin brother is inclining towards greater physical activity, she usually is tending towards 'sitting' activities. In the twins' earlier years observant mothers have reported these comparisons: (*1¼-year-old boy–girl twins*): 'The girl seems to prefer cuddly objects or colourful small things, with which she plays happily and quietly. The boy likes things he can push around and make noise with' ... (*Two-year-old pair*): 'The girl likes to scribble or "draw" while the boy would rather play with cars, blocks, and so on' ... (*2¼-year-olds*): 'The boy enjoys placing small objects into large ones, or reaching hard to put toys on shelves (even when he can't make it). The girl loves to play with Teddy bears, dance and clap hands' ... (*Three-year-olds*): 'The girl treats every toy as gently as if it were a doll. The boy plays rough and soon breaks any toy given to him' ... (*3¼-year-olds*): 'The boy enjoys mechanical toys. He wants to fix things and use his father's tools. The girl enjoys playing with "femininities" – hair-dress or makeup – and applying this to her dolls.'

One cannot ignore the fact that whatever their inborn tendencies may be, the boy and girl of a twin pair also are *conditioned* to play in different ways. Parents with twins of the same sex may seek to give both the same gifts, to avoid implications of favouritism; whereas, with boy–girl twins, there may be a strong impulse to begin making distinctions early, and to give each the types of toys considered suitable for his or her sex. (One mother told me, 'Last Christmas my husband came home with gifts for our eighteen-month-old twins – a miniature kitchen set for the girl and, of all things, a pair of little *boxing gloves* for the boy. John had been to an office party just before, so maybe that explains it.') As childhood advances, then, one can't always tell how many of the differences in play interests and habits which develop between the boy and girl are due to the way Nature intended them to be, and how many are due to the way their parents and others want them to perform.

The foregoing also applies to differences in temperament, behaviour and personality which appear in the boy and girl of a twin pair. Many parents recognize such differences when their twins are the merest infants. The boy is usually reported as more restless and aggressive (which is consistent with the difference found in lower animals – the little rooster as compared with the little hen; the male puppy or kitten compared with the female). From age 2 the boy also is apt to be less timid and more quarrelsome than the girl, to have more frequent outbursts of anger, and to be generally less inhibited in behaviour. The girl twin, on the other hand, may start off by being shyer in the presence of strangers or acting in a contrary way. If the boy is displeased, he may kick out or fight. The girl may show anger in other ways. For example, a mother reports, 'Little Mary has a bad habit of sticking her tongue out at people she dislikes, but her twin, Tommy, never does. He prefers to commit mayhem – or may try to.'

A special factor in the behaviour development of the boy and girl twin is *sex consciousness*, which, in all probability, will come to them much earlier than to singletons or to twins of the same sex. Being in such close proximity, the boy and girl twin become aware very soon of the difference in their sex organs. When toilet training begins, the girl immediately sees that she must perform the urinary function differently from the boy – and perhaps not so efficiently. (Many mothers tell how their little girl twin tried to imitate her boy twin in what he was doing, and was chagrined to find she couldn't.) Psychoanalysts have made a great deal – perhaps too much – of 'penis envy' on the part of little girls and their feeling that they lack something important which the boy has; not only the organ itself, but all that goes with maleness in our world. When some girls grow older, this may show up in a determined desire to emulate or outdo men in achievement. But psychoanalysts also stress that the little boy who is strongly attached to his mother may feel envious because his twin sister is like her and he is not.

One special worry regarding boy–girl twins is that the closeness of two children of opposite sex may cause them to neutralize each other – that is, 'feminize' the boy and 'masculinize' the girl. This concern has two aspects, biological and psychological. The biological one relates to a very old belief that the female of an opposite-sex twin pair may be sterile – incapable of having children. This fear is often found in farm communities, because it stems from the long-known fact that when cattle give birth to male–female twins, the female calf almost never develops full femaleness, and in nine out of ten cases becomes a freemartin – a cow who does not give milk and cannot reproduce. The male calf, however, appears to be unaffected by the prenatal relationship. The reasons for this became clear a few decades ago with the finding that twins in cattle are carried in the same sac, and that male hormones from the male twin, which begin to be produced first, get into the system of the female twin and block her normal hormonal development. But, except for cattle and occasionally sheep, freemartins seem to be extremely rare in lower animals. And the situation definitely *does not occur in human opposite-sex twins*, because boy–girl twins – as with other fraternals – develop apart from each other in the womb, in separate bags and sacs.

The second cause for concern about boy–girl twins is that their closeness after birth may adversely affect them psychologically and socially. As a rule little boys and girls soon begin identifying themselves and associating with members of their own sex. For boy–girl twins this may be postponed as they continue to play together or with the opposite-sex friends of one or the other. But the girl twin may be more affected by this than the boy. The reason, as psychologist Helen L. Koch has suggested, may be that the male's activities are rated higher in our culture and may thus be considered more interesting and exciting; therefore, the little girl twin, if she has the chance, will more readily be drawn in to the boy's group than he to hers. Further, Dr Koch points out, 'In our culture it is more serious for a boy to deviate from the male type than for a girl to deviate from the female type.' So, if the boy–girl twinship affects their behaviour, it is more likely that the girl will become a tomboy than that the boy will become a sissy.

At any rate, parents of a boy–girl twin pair may have to face up to the early sex education of these children, and begin conditioning them towards an adequate adjustment to their respective sexes and sex roles at a considerably younger age than might be necessary with other twins or singletons. Among the first of the practical problems is how long to keep boy–girl twins in the same bedroom. As was briefly noted in Chapter 10, a frequent practice is to put them in separate rooms before their school years begin. But some parents believe in doing this almost as soon as the twins are weaned, and especially if there is for each a singleton of the same sex and not too disparate age with whom the twin can be placed.

Dressing the boy and girl twins (also touched on in Chapter 10) may be no problem if the parents do just what comes naturally. For a short time when the twins are babies they may look cute dressed alike – perhaps with a concession to 'blue for boys, pink for girls'. Thereafter, some parents who are set on prolonging the tenuous twinship connection of a boy–girl pair may seek to dress them in matching brother–sister outfits.* But this is quite a chore (not to mention an extra expense), and in most cases is thwarted before long by the physical differences developing between the twins, or by their personal inclinations to the contrary. Only occasionally, when the boy and girl have an unusual attachment, or have found some advantage in making their twinship known to others, do they show a desire to continue wearing similar clothing. This seldom persists too far into childhood – and really should not.

When the boy and girl twins enter school, there comes another question: Separate classrooms or together? In Chapter 11 we touched on this, and here we may add that while the decision, as with other twins, is best governed by individual circumstances, the boy and girl twins in most cases will present less of a school problem than do twins of the same sex. They will not be confused, one with the other; they will have their own friends and their own separate outside interests; and being so different in many ways –

* An extreme example of dressing a boy and girl as twins *even though they were not twins* occurred in the case of the late famed novelist, Ernest Hemingway, and his sister, Marcelline. In her memoir, *At the Hemingways* (1961), the sister wrote that when she and her brother were very young, and despite her being the elder by one and one-half years, their eccentric mother insisted on rearing them as twins – same infant apparel, same toys and dolls, and entering them in the same grade in school. (Psychologists may wonder whether this played a part in Ernest Hemingway's subsequent determination to play the he-man role and to stress it in his writings. There may also be speculation as to whether, in the case of a true boy–girl twin pair, trying to force them into the same patterns of initial training may not have unusual effects on their later thinking and behaviour.)

and expected to be different – each will be less concerned with what the other does or achieves. Is the girl better in her studies? 'Shucks,' says her boy twin, 'that's all she's good for. She can't fight or play football.' If the boy excels the girl, she may 'play feminine' and admire him for it, or she may fall back on the thought that being a 'brain' will not add to her success as a female.

But suppose the boy-girl twins *are* sensitive about comparisons: What can parents look for in their relative mental capacities and achievements so far as these are influenced solely by their difference in sex – that is, other than such mental differences as may be expected of any average fraternal twins carrying different hereditary factors? Here, then, on the basis of extensive studies of how the sexes generally compare in mental performance, is what parents usually can expect of their boy–girl twins (always allowing for exceptions in individual cases):

In the first evidences of mental workings during babyhood, the little girl, in addition to beginning to talk earlier, is likely to show more *social maturity*. She will evince more interest in and perception of people, and more awareness of details about her – in clothes, colours, and furnishings. The boy, in turn, may show more interest and curiosity in things that move, toys that work, or objects he can manipulate, and may begin experimenting on his own.

As the twins progress through school, some of these early mental trends often unfold into different types of achievement. In line with her lead in talking, the girl as a rule will do better in all subjects involving language (reading, writing, spelling). She also may excel in most studies where rote memory (learning things by heart) is essential, and in any area where an insight into and understanding of people plays a part. The boy, in turn, will tend to do better in subjects requiring practical thinking, mechanical ability, mathematical reasoning and inventiveness. This may not show up so readily at first in school subjects as in the boy's other activities. But in time the boy, in most instances, will go beyond the girl in mathematics, in the sciences, and in subjects involving more knowledge of the outside world.

In school grades, as a whole, girls usually have higher averages all the way through elementary school and well into high school, although by their junior year the boys may begin forging ahead.

On IQ tests, also, girls tend to score higher than boys up to the mid-teens, although the scores of the two sexes are reached in different ways, each doing better in the areas previously mentioned in which their sex excels. But in the senior year of high school, and most definitely in college, boys as a rule catch up to and then go beyond girls, both in average IQ and in most types of academic achievement. One theory offered by psychologists is that in their younger years girls apply themselves more to schoolwork, because of having fewer outside distractions than boys have, but that as they grow older, their intellectual drive is lessened as thoughts of romance, marriage, and motherhood loom large, whereas boys, heading for college and careers, become more study-minded.

Another theory is that inborn, biological factors largely account for the mental sex differences; that the girl's head start in mental (or school) performance goes with the biologically determined lead she takes in developing physically and reaching maturity earlier, while the boy is geared by nature to catch up thereafter and surpass the girl in height and size, as well as in mental achievement. Both of the theories mentioned have their advocates. But the question of how much of the mental differences between an average boy and girl – or a boy–girl twin pair – can be traced to inborn factors is hardly likely to be answered with any certainty so long as the lives, interests and aspirations of the two sexes are directed in different ways.

All this becomes most apparent with the onset of puberty. In girls the big changes take place normally between the ages of 12 and 14 (but sometimes earlier or later), whereas in boys puberty usually comes a year or more after that. The psychological impact on a boy and girl twin pair of all the puberty differences – not only in the time of onset but also in the accompanying biological and sexual changes – cannot be overestimated. Here all the meanings of sex, and all of the differences between males and females as they exist and are viewed in our modern world, hit the twins full force when they are still not mature enough to adjust to them. Adolescence is a period of stress during which any boy or girl requires the utmost in parental guidance and understanding; the need for this is especially great in the case of boy and girl twins.

Consider the boy, for example: He has been led to believe that the male is the bigger, stronger, more important, and his sense of masculinity requires a constant building up and maintenance of his ego. But suddenly his sister, who is matched with him exactly in age, begins sweeping ahead on all counts. Already she may have been ahead of him in schoolwork. Now even his physical superiority is challenged if (at least temporarily) she gets to be several inches taller than he, and, in some instances, stronger or more adept in athletics.

Apropos of the foregoing, one mother wrote: 'When our boy–girl twins were about five, the little girl was bigger and stronger than the boy. But he'd somehow heard from his friends that boys were always stronger than girls. So one day he picked a fight with his twin sister, and when she knocked him down and really began beating him up, he was so flabbergasted he yelled in tears, "You stop! You can't beat me – you're a *girl!*"'

Also, there are highly important social differences. The girl twin, with her lead in adolescence, has become far more mature socially than the boy, and more at ease with people than ever before. Hitting her twin worst of all is the girl situation. She is beginning to be courted by and having romantic interests in boys older than herself, while he hardly knows yet 'what it's all about'. If he does want the companionship of girls, he may have to content himself with ones younger than he. And this means that between his girl-twin's boy friends and his own girl friends there may be a gap of three or four years of age.

Viewing this social chasm that opens up between the girl and boy who have been reared as twins, it is no wonder that many parents of boy–girl twins are disturbed and perplexed. To quote one mother: 'It is distressing to see what's happened with the twins, who were so close until they started high school this year. Dora, who is a lovely fourteen and looks sixteen, is already going steady with a Junior boy who is the high-school football hero. Little Donald, who is three inches shorter than Dora, can't find any girl in high school to date, and won't go with grade-school "kids". So he's being very antisocial at the moment, and will hardly even talk to Dora.' Another mother, speaking of a similar situation with her twins, commented wryly, 'Nature made a boo-boo with boy–girl twins. If she'd had foresight, she'd have fixed it so that the boy twin would reach puberty first. That way, when they got to be teenagers, the boy's friends would be right for the girl twin, and the girl's friends right for the boy twin. As it is, the friends of neither are of any earthly use to the other.'

The girl twin may have plenty of peeves of her own. Human society is so constituted that the girl is (and perhaps for her own protection must be) more closely scrutinized, and the standards set for her – in speech, manners, dress, social relationships, and activities of all kinds – are much more rigid. She can't be allowed to go out as freely as the boy twin or stay out as late. 'Timmy has a latch key, why can't I have one, too?' she wails. 'We're *twins*, aren't we?' In the matter of dating, she resents having to wait for bids from boys, while her twin can imperiously do the asking. In many other respects she begins to feel that this is a man's world.

So, in seeking to maintain a balance between the boy and girl twin pair, parents must explain that if the boy is given greater freedom in some ways, he also has more curbs in other ways. When the girl feels unhappy or is hurt, she can cry; when she fails at something, other people won't criticize her as much; when she commits a wrong, punishment will be tempered by consideration for her sex. The boy is expected to be stoical, brave, strong-minded, successful; he is held more to account for his failures and misdeeds and, indeed, the strain of always trying to be masculine may impose on him as much of a burden as are the restraints and discriminations with which his twin sister may be saddled.

Taking everything together, most twins' parents have reason to be pleased with a boy–girl twin pair. Whatever advantages may be missed by their not being as 'twinny' as other twins, many of the major headaches also are absent. Think back to the twinship problems we've dealt with: Those related to dress, schooling, friendships, social activities, achievement; to conflict, competition, comparisons, and the fear that one twin will overshadow the other; to jealousy on the part of singleton siblings of the twins, or the twins' tendency to gang up against the singletons. All these problems are minimal and frequently non-existent with the boy–girl pair. In fact, many parents wonder if, after a while, they should continue to be thought of as twins. To quote the mother of a teen-age boy–girl pair: 'We sometimes must think twice to remember that Julia and John were twins to start with. We long ago stopped referring to them as such, and now they're two completely individual members of a happy family, the girl one of three daughters, and the boy one of two sons.'

Yet, as we concluded with regard to fraternal twins of the same sex, the twinship of a boy–girl pair should not be minimized. For they are not just a brother and sister. The close relationship with which they begin life is a unique one. Out of it, if properly cultivated, can grow a better understanding of the opposite sex, and a respect and sympathy for the opposite sex, which can help each of them towards more humanness and happier social adjustment throughout their lives. Something of this thought glows through the following two observations, one by the mother of an eight-year-old boy–girl pair:

'The boy squires his sister like a best beau. He carries her books, and holds her arm while crossing the street. But when he was ill and lost lots of school time, she helped him to make up all his work.'

And this is from another parent:

'It's strange and touching to see how Dena, at age ten, has become like a little mother to her twin Billy. She sees that he takes care of himself, she admires what he does, she soothes his feelings when they're hurt. And she's smart enough to never let him think she's being superior. She just loves him, that's all.'

CHAPTER 19

Supertwins: Triplets, Quads and Quints

IF two babies at a time is unusual, three at a time is remarkable, four at a time is astounding, and five at a time – well! – 'phenomenal' can hardly describe the event adequately.

Whatever has been said about twins applies in extended ways to triplets, quadruplets and quintuplets. Indeed, in almost all respects, these 'twin-plus' sets (or what we will call 'supertwins') are twins – *only more so*, or *much more so*, or *much, much more so*.

Starting with their conception, the processes by which supertwins are produced are basically the same as for twins. There may be fraternal sets, with each individual derived from a different egg, or there may be identical sets, with all members derived from the same egg. But there also is a third possibility in supertwin sets: namely, a combination of fraternal and identical members. How the various types and combinations of triplets and quadruplets may be produced is shown in the chart opposite. (We are not making sub-classifications according to sex, which would greatly increase the number of possible combinations. Nor do we attempt in this chart to go into the numerous possible types of quintuplets, and their production.)

Whether the members of any supertwin set are all identical, all fraternal, or a combination of the two, will usually become apparent, as with ordinary twins, during infancy or in early childhood. Any marked differences in hereditary characteristics, such as eye or hair colour, basic features, and so on, will point to a fraternal relationship, although similarities (unless they are so great that the children cannot be told apart), need not necessarily prove an identical relationship. Whenever there are doubts about the types, the rules given for twins in Chapter 4 can be applied.

Once supertwins are conceived, what are the chances of their

HOW SUPERTWINS MAY BE PRODUCED

1. TRIPLETS

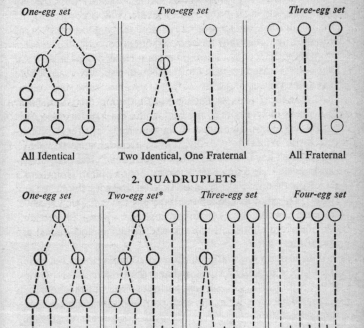

One-egg set   *Two-egg set*   *Three-egg set*

All Identical   Two Identical, One Fraternal   All Fraternal

2. QUADRUPLETS

One-egg set   *Two-egg set**   *Three-egg set*   *Four-egg set*

All Identical   Three   One   Two   Two   All Four Fraternal
                  Identical   Fraternal   Identical   Fraternal

*A two-egg quadruplet set consisting of two identical pairs is also theoretically possible, but no such set has yet been found (see Text).

3. QUINTUPLETS

Many possible types may be produced, ranging from all five identical (a one-egg set, such as the Dionnes) to – theoretically – all fraternal (five eggs), with various combinations of identical and fraternals in two-egg, three-egg and four-egg sets, derived through steps much as in triplet and quadruplet formation.

achieving birth and surviving? Obviously, the more babies there are in one womb, the greater the hazards; so, just as the relative prenatal loss among twins exceeds that among singletons, the loss among supertwins is progressively greater still, according to the number in a set. In fact, one can assume that a good many twins who are alive today may have started out at conception as triplets or quadruplets, but lost one or more of their set along the way. All in all, the relative pre-birth death toll among supertwins is double that among twins, and over six times that among the singly born.

Among the triplets who achieve birth, the mortality in the first four weeks thereafter is 30 per cent, and among quadruplets, it is 50 per cent. The major factor in these losses is, of course, premature birth. While individually at each prenatal stage triplets or quads weigh less than twins (who, in turn, weigh less than singletons), collectively a set of triplets outweighs a pair of twins, and a set of quads outweighs a set of triplets. So, with the increasing strain on the mother and among themselves as gestation proceeds, the push towards birth for supertwins becomes steadily stronger, and therefore almost all triplets, and all quads and quints, are prematurely born.

With so many unusual circumstances attending their conception and birth, it is hardly surprising that in the United States there are no more than 250 to 300 surviving triplet sets among the more than 4,000,000 babies entering life each year, and that in the country's total population, intact triplet sets of all ages number roughly only about 10,000.* As for quadruplets, although five or six sets approach birth in the United States yearly, it is only once in several years that a complete set manages to survive, so that the total number of such intact sets living in the country now may be barely a dozen.

---

* A term sometimes used for an individual member of a triplet set is 'trin' (either an abbreviation for 'trinity', or, as some dictionaries state, a combination of 'tri' and 'twin'). But there are as yet no officially approved terms for single members of higher multiple sets, although 'quad' and 'quint' are in common usage.

TRIPLETS

Since only triplets are in sufficient numbers among supertwins to have a personal meaning for any considerable group of readers, we will devote our discussion mainly to them and to the problems going with their rearing and adjustment. And what problems these can be! To those who've had experience with twins only, the parents of triplets can say (using an old slang phrase), 'Folks, you ain't seen nothin' yet!' Every practical and psychological problem dealt with previously in discussing twins becomes intensified in the case of triplets – expense, care and feeding, dressing, schooling, health and development, sibling rivalry, personal adjustment, and so on. Ample evidence of this has come to me first-hand from many mothers of triplets, and some triplets themselves, with whom I have talked. These contacts were facilitated by the Mothers of Triplets Association (a truly exclusive organization, considering the requirements for membership!), whose dynamic leader has been Mrs William Moloney, and whose New York Chapter I had the pleasure of addressing.*

While triplets may later turn out to be a joy, it isn't hard to see why many parents at first may view them as a catastrophe. (One father, I was told, staggered by the news that triplets had just been delivered, to add to his six other children, grabbed the obstetrician by the coat lapels and yelled, 'Doctor, you can't do this to me!') The initial expenses can be staggering, usually far beyond the total cost for three single babies because of the extended special care which most triplets require – incubators, sometimes blood trans-

---

*The Mothers of Triplets Association developed from a group which was brought together in 1946 by a Chicago woman, a Mrs Oswana, who had lost her own triplets when they were infants, and who wanted to help other mothers of such sets. Under the subsequent direction of Mrs Moloney, one of the original members, the Association has built an active membership of more than 200 mothers of triplets, almost all residing in the North eastern states. One of the country's unique gatherings is the Association's annual convention in New York City each spring, with an outing at Palisades Amusement Park across the Hudson River in New Jersey, to which many of the mothers come with their triplets. The author attended the 1960 gathering – and what a picnic he had!

fusions, extra nurses, mother's milk, and so on. Apart from the birth cost and the expenses for triplet layettes, formulas, laundering, and baby equipment, it is almost always imperative to engage outside domestic help, In short, for most parents of triplets there is a financial crisis added to and aggravating all the other problems.*

Some hint of what the *care and feeding* of triplets may mean is conveyed by this report kept by one mother: '*Bottles of formula* – 126 per week (18 bottles per day, or six for each baby), with constant bottle washing and sterilizing. *Diaper changes* – 30 to 40 each 24 hours (10 to 14 for each baby). Laundry (even with diaper and laundry service) – 'I stopped counting!' With the many other multiple duties required, the care of triplets in infancy and early childhood is an around-the-clock project, demanding the utmost in efficiency and resourcefulness, and making it virtually a necessity for the father and – if available – older children in the family, and relatives, to assist the harassed mother.

Even such a presumably simple matter as taking triplet babies for an airing becomes complicated. Years ago, Papa Moloney (whose wife we previously mentioned), in his role as a subway motorman and hence a 'transportation expert', designed a carriage with a triplet body on a twin-carriage chassis – which a baby-buggy company then produced. But mothers who bought such a carriage found that using it brought unforeseen difficulties, apart from the purely mechanical ones of manoeuvring it through doorways or up and down steps, and parking it. To quote one mother, 'When I took the triplets out in this buggy, it almost stopped the traffic.' Another mother thought that since her triplets were tiny,

---

* To ease the financial strain on parents of British supertwins, Queen Victoria in 1839 instituted the practice of bestowing a special crown bounty of one pound for each child of a triplet or quadruplet set. The bounty was abolished by Queen Elizabeth II in 1957, primarily because other forms of public aid had eased the problems of parents of supertwins, and the great decline in the value of the pound no longer made the bounty important. Instead, Queen Elizabeth began the practice of sending a congratulatory message to the parents of supertwins. Court records showed that in the twenty-one years since the Queen's father, George VI, had succeeded to the throne, royal bounties from the privy purse had been paid to the parents of 1,051 sets of triplets and 19 sets of quadruplets.

she could get by with putting all three of them in an ordinary twin carriage, 'But they used to kick themselves so much, being so crowded, I had to stop taking them out in this way.' Many other mothers also kept their triplets housebound throughout their infancy, but a few managed to give them outings by using a twin buggy or stroller plus a single one when someone else was along.

Health and physical development. The fact that virtually all triplets are premature babies and that many undergo unusual hazards before or during birth, should explain why more triplets than twins tend to be sickly, afflicted with defects, or initially backward in development. But, as with twins, once infancy and early childhood have been safely traversed, triplets begin to catch up with the average for singletons, and before long few differ in size or health from single siblings of their age and sex. Within the same set, however, triplets may vary considerably in health and growth, and in height, weight and proportions; although much less so, of course, if the three are all identical than if they are all fraternal. Almost any trait in which heredity plays an important part can be expected to appear at about the same time and in the same way in identical members of a triplet set, but not necessarily in fraternal members. Here the same rules and facts apply as were given for twins in previous chapters. To illustrate, we will cite cases of several triplet sets whose parents we interviewed.

The three blind Petraglia triplets of New York, two girls and a boy, were mentioned earlier in Chapter 12. Their condition – *retrolental fibroplasia* – was entirely environmental, being due to excessive oxygen in their incubators. The fact that they were triplets had nothing to do with the tragedy, for many singleton incubator babies had been similarly victimized at the same time. On the other hand, in the case of another triplet set of three identical boys, all with *haemophilia* (but fortunately in one of the milder forms), their affliction was due to the fact that the gene for the condition ran in the family. Among four older brothers, two also had haemophilia, which was not discovered until after the triplets arrived. (The plight of the five haemophiliac youngsters in one family led to a 'blood-raising' campaign in which more than a thousand pints of blood were contributed by sympathetic persons and deposited to the account of these boys in a Red Cross blood bank. Drawn on as emergencies arise, it is surely as remarkable a bank account as any boys in the world have ever had.) In still another triplet set – two identical boys and a fraternal girl – the boys suffer from colour blindness and the girl does not. Here, heredity accounts for the condition in the boys, whereas the girl, even if she had received the same 'colour-blindness' gene, would not have developed the defect (as explained in Chapter 18).

As for environmentally caused defects, these are understandably more frequent in triplets than in twins, because of the greater hazards three-at-a-time babies have to undergo before and after birth. But it should again be emphasized that *the large majority of triplets who survive their initial ordeals are fully normal and healthy;* as with twins, when once safely through the first few years they should then be no different from other children.

'Separateness' or 'togetherness' in triplets? In line with the popular saying, 'If you can't fight 'em, join 'em,' a great many parents of triplets presumably feel that since the uniqueness of such a set can't be ignored, one might as well emphasize it. Undoubtedly, there also is pride in the achievement of having had triplets, which may increase the desire to identify them as a threesome. Thus, giving *similar names* to triplets seems to be even more common than is the practice with respect to twins. Among the sets listed by members of the Mothers of Triplets Associations, fully half have triplet-type names. Examples: Lauverne, Lorraine and Louise; Angela, Amy and Allison; Jo Ann, Sue Ann and Carol Ann; and Donna, Dolly and Dean.

Sameness in dress for triplets also seems to be even more common than for twins. But in this, parental pride in displaying them may be only one factor. There are practical reasons as well. To quote one mother, 'Shopping around constantly for three different outfits, equally attractive but costing the same, is a lot more trouble – and usually more expensive – than walking into the store and saying, "Give me three of those."' In many cases the triplets themselves (not only girls but boys as well) have insisted on being dressed alike throughout much of their childhood. The exchange service of the Mothers of Triplets Association often eases the problem for members by making available threesome outfits for various ages. But hand-me-downs within a family can rarely be of much help when there are triplets.

School presents a bigger problem with triplets than with twins. Having triplets in one classroom – especially when they are look-alikes – can be very disturbing for other pupils, as well as for the teacher. But, if separation of the triplets is called for, how is this to be arranged? Few schools have as many as three classrooms for each grade; and if there are only two, separating the triplets means putting two in one room and one in the other. Sometimes this is done. In most cases, however, triplets are kept together. Mrs Moloney said that her threesome of two identical girls and a boy were in the same classrooms all the way through grade school, and that it worked out fine. 'There was always an advantage in that the three could get at difficult school problems together.' Another mother, with identical boy triplets, said that at age 8 they were doing well in the same classroom, all being equally bright and well-adjusted. Still another mother of triplet boys – two identicals and one fraternal – who would have preferred that they be separated at the parochial school they attended, found to her surprise that the principal and teachers felt they should be kept together.

In the *relationships among triplets* one can find every type of interaction, although there generally seems to be even more tendency for them than for twins to form a unit. One young woman member of an identical girl-triplet set told me, 'We all enjoyed being triplets and kept closely together until we were thirteen or fourteen. When we started going out, we usually triple-dated. But we did have our individual likings, and it showed up in the fellows we were going steady with.' Sometimes, however, triplets aren't satisfied with one another. A Milwaukee mother of a three-girl set, aged five, commented amusingly, 'When they go outdoors and can't find their friends, the three run back and say, "We haven't got anyone to play with!"'

We have touched on only a few of the problems which the arrival and presence of triplets may create in families. Obviously, the psychological and social effects on parents and singleton siblings are much greater than are occasioned by twins. And it can only be imagined how vastly greater the problems must be in the rare instances where quadruplets burst in on the family scene. We'll deal with the lives of these super supertwins next.

QUADRUPLETS

The relationship among quadruplets within a set has attracted considerable scientific attention because of the light this may throw on various psychological problems. Some of the best studies were made by the late expert on twins, Professor Horatio H. Newman, collaborating with Dr Iva C. Gardner. One particularly interesting foursome they reported on were the Keys girls of Oklahoma – the first quadruplets to go through college (graduating from Baylor University, Waco, Texas, in 1937). A three-egg set, consisting of two identicals (from one egg) and two fraternals (from the other two eggs), they were studied at age 22. Despite their having been reared so closely together there still were great mental and personality differences between the identical two (who were much alike), and the two fraternals (these, in turn, differing from each other).

Another foursome studied were the Morlok girls of Lansing, Michigan, born in 1930. They were the first *all-identical* quadruplet set known to have survived. Surprisingly, not too much fuss was made over them, nor were they raised in any special environment. Thus, when studied at age 10, they were found to be four quite normal girls, somewhat above average in intelligence, and emotionally well adjusted. Some slight differences in mental ability, personality and temperament were observed among them, but to what extent these persisted into later life is not known.

Other quadruplet sets studied were the Schenses (South Dakota, 1931), an all-fraternal foursome of two boys and two girls; the Perricones (Texas, 1929), an all-boy, all-fraternal set; the Kaspars (New Jersey, 1936), three identical boys and a fraternal girl; and the Badgetts (Texas, 1939), all girls, three identical and one fraternal.* The findings regarding these quads, as with the Keys

*The Perricones won added fame in 1951 when, at the age of twenty-one they became the first set of quadruplets ever to be inducted *en masse* into an army, after enrolling in the United States forces at Houston, Texas, for service in Korea. They insisted on being sent overseas together, and had to appeal over Army heads to achieve this. (The usual policy of the United

and Morlok sets, added further to the conclusion that when members of quadruplet sets are identical, they all tend to be much alike in mental ability and personality, whereas when they are fraternals (or, in a mixed set, fraternals compared with the identicals) they tend to differ much more. Perhaps it is because these facts have been so well established that little effort has been made by social scientists to study the other quadruplets – ten or so sets – that have followed the earlier ones in the United States.

QUINTUPLETS

Overshadowing all other supertwins in history have been the Dionne quintuplets. No human birth ever aroused such worldwide excitement as did that of the Dionne quintet on 28 May 1934, and the survival of all five. What is more, they were an *all-identical* set – from the same fertilized egg – a distinction not shared by any other set of quintuplets which has followed them to date.*

Born to a poor French-Canadian couple (Oliva and Elzire Dionne) on a backwoods farm near Callandar, Ontario, all of the quints together weighed 11 pounds 1½ ounces at birth, with a range from 31 ounces for the smallest to 46 ounces for the largest. No one – including the attending doctor, Allan Dafoe – expected them to survive. When they did, a full day passed before the outside world learned of their birth after an uncle naïvely inquired of the nearest country newspaper editor, 'How much would it cost to insert a birth notice for five babies born at one time?' Within hours millions everywhere began following the day-to-day progress of these famous babies. Soon tourists were flocking to see them at their specially built nursery, over roads newly constructed by the Canadian Government, which had taken them under its official wing; and a fortune poured into their trust fund from sales of rights to photos, movies, testimonials.

States armed forces has been to separate twins in service, particularly during wartime, one reason being to minimize the chances of both of a twin pair – or all of a supertwin set – becoming casualties at the same time.)

*Another all-girl quintuplet set (type unknown at this writing) was born in Pittsburgh, Pa., on 27 November 1966, but none survived more than two or three days. The mother, Mrs Michael Aranson, 22 years old, had not received any hormone treatments.

Scientists, of course, also were profoundly interested in the Dionne quintuplets. Doctors, geneticists and psychologists studied them in their first years as no babies had ever been studied before. Important from the genetic standpoint were the findings that the five had indeed all come from the same fertilized egg. Tests showed they were exactly alike in blood groups and in colour of eyes, hair and skin; also, they were strikingly similar in many other physical details (including a mild webbed-toe condition on each foot). In their behaviour minor differences soon began to appear, and before long those close to them could detect distinctive personality traits in each one. As the quints grew older their family took over control and permitted no further scientific study of them. A small private school adjoining their home was established for the quints, and after going through the grades, and then high-school courses, they enrolled in a convent college in 1952. Three of them – Marie, Emilie and Yvonne – sought to become nuns, but only Yvonne attained this goal. Emilie came to a tragic end with her death from suffocation during an epileptic seizure in 1954. (She was the only one of the five afflicted with epilepsy.) On their twenty-first birthday the four survivors came into their trust money, dividing almost a million dollars. Yvonne remained a nun; and the other three – Annette, Cecile and Marie – were married in 1957 and 1958, and now have children (among these are fraternal twins born to Cecile).

Looking back over their lives in a book published in 1965 (*We Were Five*), the surviving four of the Dionne quintuplets bared details of a cloistered childhood far different from what the public had imagined. They told of being reared in a harsh, restrictive and hostile home atmosphere, with only themselves to cling to for affection and understanding. Not until they were on their own, they said, were they able to begin living as normal and fairly happy persons, with an opportunity to develop their own interests and individualities.

What conclusions can we draw from the history of the Dionne quintuplets? Apart from their having been the first and to date the only set of identical quintuplets to survive to maturity, not much of scientific value was actually contributed by them. In part this is because scientists were unable to study them after the first few years. But also, it would have been impossible to make a study in the one way in which the findings could have thrown full light on the relative influence of heredity and environment: By separating the quints at birth, and having them brought up in five very different homes and under radically different conditions. Nevertheless, the Dionne quints have helped to reinforce some of the points previously made with respect to identical twins: That even when individuals have exactly the same hereditary factors, they may begin life with important differences already laid out by environmental discrepancies; and that even if they are reared together in the same way (and with as much calculated uniformity as the Dionnes experienced) their paths are nevertheless destined to diverge to some extent. Further evidence of this came with the death of Marie in 1969, aged thirty-five

Thirty years after the birth of the Dionnes two more *authenticated* all-surviving sets of quintuplets appeared in 1964: the Fischers, of Aberdeen, South Dakota, and the Prietos, of Venezuela. (Regarding the Diligentis of Argentina, see footnote.)* It was not to be expected that these others would cause as much excitement as did the Dionnes; but an added reason was that, unlike the all-identical Dionnes, the Fischers and Prietos were both mixed sets, combining identicals and fraternals. A year later, in 1965, the whole supertwin (and twin) picture was radically changed by science. For (as brought out in Chapter 5), where the appearance of supertwins had depended previously on a whim of nature expressed at rare intervals, it now became possible through the new pituitary-hormone treatments to produce such births almost at will. The living evidence came with the birth in 1965 through this method of two quintuplet sets, one in New Zealand (all five surviving) and one in Sweden (with only a single member surviving), plus three sets of surviving quadruplets, several sets of triplets, and a great many sets of twins. Most astounding was the

* Although the five Diligentis, born in 1943, have been widely reported as a quintuplet set, the facts about their birth have remained mysterious. No account of the simultaneous birth of these five – three girls and two boys – was given out or published until several months after their arrival. Nor, to the writer's knowledge, has any scientific study been made of them, nor have they been certified as a quintuplet set in scientific annals. It has therefore not been possible to list them with the other sets mentioned as authenticated quintuplets.

The Dafoe Nursery

THE DIONNE QUINTUPLET GUARDIANSHIP

OFFICIAL GUARDIAN FOR THE PROVINCE OF ONTARIO • P D WILSON K C ACTIVE GUARDIANS   HIS HONOUR JUDGE J A VALIN   ALLAN ROY DAFOE O B E M D, OLIVA DIONNE
F R MUNRO BUSINESS MANAGER   W H FLANNERY, SECRETARY TREASURER

CAllander, Ontario,
November 25, 1938.

Mr. Amram Scheinfeld,
New York City,
New York.

Dear Mr. Scheinfeld:

In looking through your interesting book,
YOU AND HEREDITY, I notice a rather
important inaccuracy with regard to the
Dionne Quintuplets.   You state on page
107 that I: "came to the conclusion
that they were fraternals."

Actually I was convinced from the first
that the were identicals. You will find
this accurately reported in the newspapers
in the weeks following their birth.

*Also am
enclosing copy of
my first monograph*

Very truly yours,

Allan Roy Dafoe

This partial copy of a letter received from Dr Dafoe, to attest his having
correctly diagnosed the Dionne quintuplets as an identical set, shows the
unique official letterhead (engraved) of the million-dollar enterprise which
was built around the five girls. (The author's original statement that the
Dionne quints were a fraternal set had come from a preliminary report in a
scientific journal, subsequently proved incorrect.)

delivery in 1966 by a hormone-treated Boston mother of *septuplets* – seven babies, four girls and three boys, weighing between 9 and 15 ounces each. None survived.

But, as we emphasized in Chapter 5, the quintuplet and other supertwin births induced through pituitary-hormone treatments have been and will have to be of the *fraternal* types – caused by stimulating a woman's ovary to release several eggs at one time. Whether science also can make possible the artificial induction of *identical* supertwin sets, by some treatment which can induce a single egg to undergo the required successive divisions, is still to be demonstrated.

SUPERTWIN INCIDENCES

The means already at hand for artificially inducing multiple conceptions may upset a long-standing statistical formula for predicting the relative frequencies of twin and supertwin births. Back in 1895, a German scientist, Dr D. Hellin, studying the ratios of these births, offered evidence (known thereafter as Hellin's law) that the incidence of triplets would be the square of the ratio of twins to single births; of quadruplets, the cube of this ratio; of quintuplets, the figure for twins carried to the fourth power. Thus, if twins occurred in a population once in 100 births, triplets should occur once in 100×100, or 10,000 births; quads once in $100 \times 100 \times 100$, or 1,000,000 births; and quintuplets, once in the latter figure multiplied by 100 again, or once in 100,000,000 births.

Records for many years have shown that the actual ratios of supertwins do conform roughly to Hellin's law. For example, in the United States for the decade from 1948 to 1958, with 38,239,794 births, there were 402,403 twin births, a rate of one twin pair in 95 births; there were 3,610 triplet sets, a rate of one set in 10,593 births and somewhat under Hellin's expectancy of one triplet set in 9,025 births (95×95); and there were 42 quadruplet sets, or one in 910,471 births, again somewhat less than Hellin's expectancy of one in 857,375 births ($95 \times 95 \times 95$). The figures given for actual twin and supertwin births refer to sets in which at least one child was born alive, and not just to surviving intact sets, which are

217

relatively fewer for triplets than for twins, and very much fewer for quadruplets.

Whatever the general chances for the birth of a supertwin set may be (under natural conditions) the possibilities that any individual mother will bear such a set are even more radically affected by her age and race than is the case with bearing twins. First, while the chance of having twins is three or four times as great for mothers aged thirty-five to thirty-nine as for those in their teens, the chance of having triplets is about six times as great, and of having quadruplets, about twenty times as great. Second, there is the enormous difference on a racial basis. Whereas Negro mothers in the United States produce about 35 per cent more twins than White mothers per 100,000 births, they produce about 90 per cent more triplets, and up to four times the proportion of quadruplets. The fact that there are relatively more childbearing Negro mothers in the older, 'supertwin-prone' ages contributes to this difference. But, as with twins, there also is a marked basic race difference in the supertwinning tendency. Among Japanese, Chinese, and other Mongoloid-race mothers, supertwins are far less frequent than even among Whites.

Apart from race and age, there is a strong indication that certain mothers start off with a greater than average tendency to bear supertwins, either because of heredity or of other factors, or a combination of these. What role heredity plays in supertwinning among human beings is uncertain, but we do know that a special tendency towards such twinning occurs among certain breeds of lower animals. For example, the nine-banded armadillo female (as mentioned in Chapter 5) regularly produces identical quadruplets with each pregnancy; and among goats, normally delivering a single offspring at a time, nannies of some breeds bear triplets quite often, and occasionally even quadruplets.

Finally, there is the question of whether we will be seeing more or fewer supertwins in the future. Here again, as with the changing twinning incidences, conflicting factors are at work. On the one hand, medical advances are enabling a greater proportion of super-twins to be born and to stay alive. On the other hand, the decrease in childbearing by mothers in the supertwinning brackets (older mothers, with many previous pregnancies) should be causing a drop in supertwin conceptions. Upsetting this balance, however, may be the increased production in supertwinning as a result of the new hormone treatments. Whether, and to what extent, the latter factor will result in a bumper crop of supertwins in the years ahead may depend largely on how many women are eager to give birth to a whole family at one time.

CHAPTER 20

The Crossroads

WHEN my twin was married and had to move to the other coast, my heart was broken. I cried for days. But, thank God, she and her husband moved back soon because she couldn't stand being apart any more than I could, and ever since, for thirty years now, we and our families have lived next door to one another.

Right after high school, the first chance we got my twin and I went our separate ways. We always fought and it was a relief not to have him on my neck any more. We seldom see each other, which is certainly O.K. with me.

These contrasting statements represent the extremes of feeling between twins in their adult years, although the first one is far more typical than the second. During childhood, as we noted in earlier chapters, the degree of closeness between twins is a matter of great concern. Sometimes there is worry that twins are not close enough; sometimes that they are too close. Parents who are in doubt about how far twinship should or should not be encouraged, tend to say, 'When they get older, they can decide for themselves.' What, then, *are* twins likely to do on their own about staying together or moving apart? And, seeing them as children, what can one predict about their future relationships?

Much will depend on what type the twins are: identical males or females, fraternal males or females, or a male–female pair. Identical twins, being most similar in makeup, capacities and interests, will be more likely than fraternal twins to keep together. Again, among twins of both types, sisters will tend to remain closer over the years than will brothers. Male–female twins, being the most different, will of course be least likely to maintain their twinship. Among twins of each type, however, there may be great variations in the degree of closeness as time goes on, depending upon how contented or discontented they are with each other's company, and what their need for each other may be.

The various factors that may decide twins' adult relationships come into sharp focus during adolescence. Since this period is one of social and psychological stress for all young people, twinship also will be under the greatest strain at this time. Rivalries and jealousies may become most acute. Grievances, real or fancied, may be nurtured. And the fight for individuality may reach a high point; for, in addition to the usual desire of adolescents to break away from parental control, there may also be, on the part of the twins, a strong desire to become independent of each other. The pressure to move apart will be greatly increased if the twins think or feel that their teenage group – whose judgements can be all-powerful – does not value or approve of their twinship. In the great majority of cases, however, twins come through the adolescent storms very well, and often are drawn even closer together by their joint tribulations. For it is during this period that young people feel the greatest craving for a pal and a soul mate of their own age – and this need can be beautifully filled by a twin.*

Another disrupting force may be any important physical difference which develops between the twins just prior to or during puberty. In dealing with boy–girl pairs in Chapter 18, we told of the psychological and social consequences when the girl jumps ahead of the boy in physical and sexual development. With twins of the same sex, who are not prepared so readily for a big difference between themselves, the effects can be much more acute. For example, psychologist Marjorie Leonard tells about identical girl twins, one of whom, at age 11, began to mature before the other. The one in the lead began to act as if she were a woman and her twin just a bothersome kid sister. She complained to her mother, 'Patsy follows me around all the time. She's such a baby, I'm ashamed of the way she acts.' (Remember, these were *identical* twins, so the situation may well have straightened itself out when the lagging twin caught up in growth.)

* Strikingly pertinent to the above observation is a statement (made after this section was in type) by Psychiatrist Ralph R. Greenson, of Beverly Hills, Cal. Addressing an American Medical Association meeting on current sex behaviour, and the tendency of young males and females to wear their hair and dress alike, Dr Greenson said that boys and girls now 'seek a twin, not a sweetheart or lover. They are only secure with someone who resembles themselves.'

Looks, also, have much to do with how girl twins adjust to each other. A close similarity in appearance may serve to keep them together; for, whether both are equally good-looking or equally plain, they may find an advantage in emphasizing their twinship. Matched cuties will attract more attention than two unmatched ones; they will get more dates, and may be much better bets for selection as twin cheerleaders, drum majorettes or performers in school plays. Should the girl twins not be favoured with good looks, the fact that they are constantly identified as the 'So-and-So twins' will still do much to enhance their charm and distinction. I was reminded of this one day when my wife and I were in a department store. We saw two young teen-aged girls who were dressed identically, although apart from their both being pudgy and rather homely, they looked too dissimilar even to be regarded as sisters. When I ventured to inquire why they were dressed alike, they drew themselves up haughtily and chorused. 'We're twins, and we've got a right to!' There is little doubt that these two will go on maintaining their twinship as long as they can.

When one twin of a fraternal girl pair is a glamour girl, and the other an ugly duckling, the situation isn't easy. The two aren't likely to keep together unless there is an unusually strong sisterly bond between them or the not-so-attractive twin has other, compensating, assets – more talent, wit, or social know-how. (We noted in Chapter 17 that wise parents can counter differences in twins by helping to develop additional accomplishments in the less favoured one.)

For male twins, neither the wish to stay together nor the pressure to do so is apt to be so great as with girl twins. Individuality and independence are encouraged more in boys as a matter of course; continuing to dress alike or staying too close to each other may be regarded as odd for boy twins when it would not be for girls; and, since male twins have a wider range of activities than girls and more chances for diversified careers, they are more likely to be drawn apart. Differences in looks have less effect on male than female twins, but a difference in strength and athletic ability may have much more importance in male pairs if it enables one twin to become an athletic hero during the teen ages, while the other is relegated to the background.

No less important in setting male twins apart more than female twins, and increasingly so in later years, are any marked differences in mental capacity and achievement. A good example appears in a questionnaire filled out by a disgruntled eighteen-year-old youth who took pains to express his hostility towards his fraternal twin. After telling how his twin and he were always fighting at home, and how his twin was 'conceited', 'egotistical', and 'goes out with girls I wouldn't be seen with', he added revealingly, 'In school he got better grades, and that was always thrown up to me.'

But, as was said earlier, the chance of continuing closeness between twins is much influenced by whether they are identicals or fraternals, males or females, or an opposite–sex pair. Good evidence for this comes through information which Professor Ernest R. Mowrer of Northwestern University obtained from more than 600 twins soon after they had been graduated from Midwestern high schools. Here are some of the questions that were asked and answered:

'*Who in your family understands you best?*' Of the identicals, 61 per cent answered, 'My twin', as compared with 39 per cent of the fraternals of the same sex, and 24 per cent of male–female pair members.

'*Which member of the family would you miss most if he or she died?*' Half of the identicals put their twin first, half their mother first. But only 25 per cent of the same–sex fraternals put their twin first, and only 13 per cent of those with an opposite-sex twin did.

'*Do you feel you should be closer to your twin than to any other brother or sister?*' Of the identicals, 70 per cent said Yes; of the same–sex fraternals, 56 per cent, and of the male–female twins, 44 per cent.

'*If you made a date, would you consider the approval of your twin very important?*' Of the girl twins of both types, approximately 30 per cent said Yes; of the boy twins, 18 per cent. Double-dating was most common among the girl identicals, not quite as common among male identicals or among fraternals of either sex, and least common among the male–female pairs.

'*After you marry, would you want to live next door to your twin?*' Of the female twins of both types, 30 per cent said they would like to; of the males, only 20 per cent.

Comparisons between young men twins, made by Professor Husén in his study of Swedish twin draftees, showed further how much closer identicals continue to be as they grow older than are fraternals. Twice as many of the identicals as of the fraternals said that they were in the habit of sharing everything together; and half of the identicals, but only a quarter of the fraternals, were keen on always being together and doing the same things.

As we follow twins into their adult years, we see a continuance of the patterns set in their relationships during childhood and adolescence. The great majority of the mature twins whom we queried told of having found much satisfaction in their twinship, and of feeling a special closeness to their twin not shared with other siblings. 'Twins were meant to be together,' or 'God intended twins to always remain close to each other,' were frequently expressed comments. Almost all the adult twins said they had been dressed alike as children, that they had enjoyed this, and that they would recommend the same thing for young twins being reared today. A large majority also said they had been in the same classrooms throughout elementary school, and often through high school; and about half felt that this policy, too, would still be a good one for most twins. For example, we have the account of Mrs Mitchell ('Sue') Glick, who is not only one of an identical-twin pair but also is the mother of identical-twin girls, and organizer of the Westchester Mothers of Twins Club. She and her twin sister have been very happy in their twinship (not surprisingly, because, as their mother told me, they both were – and still are – very good-looking, bright and popular).

'We were an inseparable unit,' Mrs Glick said. 'We always loved having each other as sister and best friend. In high school we got equally good marks, took dancing and music lessons together, played instrumental duets, and were twin cheerleaders. At college, too, we were close together, keeping pace in our studies and both majoring in journalism. Until the age of nineteen we always double-dated; until the age of twenty-one we dressed alike, and until we were married (to men similar in education and career interests, but otherwise different) we pooled our allowances and earnings, and had a joint bank account.' Mrs Glick and her twin continue to be close, living within easy visiting distance, and each still regards the other as 'my best friend'. But she also said, 'While we've been one hundred per cent happy in our twinship, and turned out to be well-adjusted, I think now I might disapprove of such closeness between twins and will try to make my own more independent of each other.'

Among the most unusual reports about grown-up twins were those that came through questionnaires filled out by the celebrated twin family of Emeritus Professor John E. Anderson, University of Minnesota, long one of the nation's leaders in the field of child psychology and development. Of his five adult children four are twins (one identical male pair, one male–female pair), while the fifth, a singleton daughter, is the mother of twins. They are an exceptionally brilliant group, with very high IQs, the three male twins being scientists – the identical sons, Dr Richard D., a mathematician, and Dr John L., a nuclear-research chemist, and the fraternal third son (of the male–female twin pair), Dr Theodore, a sociologist.

Most significant, all the adult Anderson twins and their parents agreed on this point: *Twinship was greatly enjoyed in the Anderson family, and was not played down.* The identical-twin sons always dressed alike through preference until they completed high school, and were always in the same classrooms – reporting that it 'worked out fine' for them – until they went to different colleges. The male–female twins, Theodore and Dorothea, were for a time in different classrooms, but when this created difficulties they were put back together and remained so for most of their school years. They told of always having felt, and continuing to feel, an unusual degree of

STAYING TOGETHER

How degrees of continuing closeness between twins in adult life tend to vary with twin types

FEMALE IDENTICALS

Most apt to remain very close through the years.

MALE IDENTICALS

Likely to remain much closer than singleton brothers, especially if in the same work and/or locality.

FEMALE FRATERNALS

Less close than most identicals, but closer than most singleton sisters, often depending on how near to each other they live.

MALE FRATERNALS

Not nearly so close as identicals, but usually closer than singleton brothers – how much so depending on similarity of interests and where they live.

MALE–FEMALE TWINS

Least close of twin pairs, though closer than ordinary brother and sister. But continuing closeness may depend mainly on the female partner's efforts.

closeness to each other. (Learned readers may have noted that
'Theodore' and 'Dorothea' are prime twin-type names, being
derived from inversions of the same Greek words: *Theos* for 'God'
or *Thea* for 'Goddess', and *doron* for 'gift'.)

The continuing closeness of many of the adult twins with whom
I was in touch is evidenced by their joint participation in various
enterprises or professions.* Among the women were twin beauty-
shop proprietors, twin real-estate agents, art dealers, telephone
operators, and a number who were or had been twin show girls or
singers. Among the men were twin policemen, twin partners in
various business concerns, and many pairs of twin doctors,
lawyers, dentists, and other professional men. Oldest of the twin
professionals with whom I was in contact were the identical dentist
pair, Drs Henry G. and Thomas D. Williams of Shelbyville,
Kentucky, who had practised together until they entered their
eighties. 'Our twinship has brought us much happiness and a
wonderful companionship,' they told me.

Two other identical men twins known to me were for years, until
parted by death, partners in business in a Southern town. They occupied adjoining houses with their families and dressed exactly
alike – one calling up the other early each morning to decide on
their outfits for the day, from hats down through suits, shirts, ties,
shoes and socks.

Among adult male–female twins, who usually are least close,
many nonetheless told of a bond which went beyond that between
any singleton brother and sister. Here is how a New York nurse,
about fifty years old, spoke tenderly about her twin brother:
'When we were children Jimmy always protected me. When I
began going out, Jimmy always called at my date's home to see
what kind of Mom and Dad he had, and he'd watch my date's

---

*The desire of many adult twins to hold together and to emphasize their
twinship is shown by the existence of flourishing twin clubs in many cities.
The central organization, International Twins Association, was organized in
1935, and has held annual conventions ever since. Anywhere from 500 to
1,000 twins may attend, ranging in age from youngsters to very old pairs.
The annual gathering and the local meetings are largely social. Not unexpectedly, by bringing together unattached twins of both sexes, the clubs
have been responsible for many twin marriages, some of these being
double-double events, with twin brothers marrying twin sisters.

manners, and then report to my parents whether he was O.K. or not.' Later, when illness kept her brother from being as educated or advanced as she was, she became the protective one. In another situation, the male twin's dependence on his sister largely explained their later closeness. He wrote, 'Socially I've always leaned on Mary. When we were young she was always ahead of me in social ease. In high school I wanted her to be around always, as in double-dating, because I needed her to get me started in conversation. Today I feel we're closer than ever.'

Sometimes one could suspect that the continued closeness between adult twins has resulted mainly from lack of proper adjustment to other people on the part of one or both. An example was offered by two identical twin sisters, in their late forties, who were partners in a decorating firm and lived in the same apartment, together with the husband of one and the son of the other. The childhood of these twins, although in an upper-level environment, had been marred by an abnormal home life – a philandering father, a neurotic, neglectful mother, a homosexual older sister, and an alcoholic older brother. Although there was considerable conflict between the twins – one being prettier, the other more aggressive and dominant – the unhappy experiences they had shared kept them together.

This brings us to a question frequently asked: ' *Doesn't twinship affect the chances of getting married, or being happily married, or having children?*' The answer seems to be No – or at least not to any significant extent. Among the studies on this point are those made by the late Dr Franz J. Kallmann and his associates, who investigated the life histories of a large number of adult twins. They found that these twins had differed very little from their singleton siblings or other persons with respect to the proportion who had remained bachelors or spinsters, and that the married twins had about as many children proportionately as the rest. While one can indeed find many elderly twins who have stayed together and never married (as also is true of many singleton bachelor brothers or spinster sisters), it may well be that the twinship was not the cause of the failure to marry, but that the failure to marry was the cause of the continued closeness.

Not only, then, do twins marry in the same proportion as

singletons, but in many cases the chances of both twins marrying are heightened by the fact that if one twin finds a prospective mate and is planning a marriage, the other twin is spurred on to follow suit so there can be a double wedding. This happens most often with identical twins; and of special interest are the *double-double* weddings in which identical-twin brothers marry identical-twin sisters. Among examples coming to our attention in recent years have been the St Martin twins, Wilfred and Edwin, who married the Christodoro twins, Marjorie and Marie, in Boston; the Rataczaks, Arnold and Donald, married to Lucille and Louise Baker, in Joplin, Missouri; the Rubins, Hyman and Benjamin, married to Sylvia and Ruth Reisman, in Long Island, New York; the Krafts, Raleigh and Roman, married to Ruby and Ruth Martens, in Kansas City; the Chases, Herbert and Delbert, of Thornton, Colorado, married to Jane and Jean Sweet; the Pearsons, Andrall and Richard, married to Joanne and Janice Pope, in Beverly Hills, California; and the Benevides, Antone and Robert, married to Joan and Jane Silvia, in Fall River, Mass.

In some of the double-twin marriages the relationship was intensified by the fact that the twin husbands and their twin wives made their homes together, either in the same house (as with the Chases and the Rubins) or in adjoining houses (as with the Rataczaks of Joplin, whose homes, side by side, are exact duplicates inside and out, and furnished identically). A further intriguing fact about the double identical-twin marriages is that in several instances the children of the two sets of identical-twin parents were brought up as if they were brothers and sisters – *which, in terms of heredity, they actually were*. That is to say, while legally the offspring of these identical twin couples are double first cousins, the fact is that the two fathers have identical hereditary factors, and the two mothers identical hereditary factors, which make the genetic results as much the same for all the children as if they all had the same father and the same mother.

The most unusual and historic of all twin weddings was that of the original Siamese twins, Chang and Eng. Born in 1811 in Siam, the twins were joined at the breastbone by a thick, flexible band. They grew to be an extremely agile and resourceful pair, and, as their fame spread, they became world-wide exhibition celebrities.

At age 30, having amassed a small fortune, they settled down in the farming community of Mt Airy, North Carolina. Two years later they married two farm-girl sisters in surely the oddest wedding ceremony ever performed. There was immediate speculation as to whether – and how – these marriages would work out. But work out they certainly did, and fruitfully so. (One couple had twelve children, the other ten.) The two families lived in separate houses, and the Siamese twins alternated between spending several days in one house and several days in the other with their respective wife and family. Death came to Chang and Eng in 1874 – first to one, after he'd suffered a stroke; then a few hours later to the other. (An autopsy indicated that the second twin may have died of shock or fright, although it was also shown that the livers of the twins were connected, which might have made separation hazardous.)*

From these Siamese twins have come more than a thousand descendants to date. The assumed family name of the twins, 'Bunker' (which can be seen on their tombstone at White Plains, North Carolina) is borne by a great number of their descendants. These have included several distinguished persons, among them a former president of the Union Pacific Railway and a major general of the United States Air Force.

Coming back to psychological problems of twins, another common question is whether the closeness of twins may not lead to *sexual maladjustment*, including the risk of developing homosexual tendencies. Again, there is no evidence to back up this fear. However, one of Dr Kallmann's studies dealt with instances where homosexuality had occurred among twins, and showed that if one of a pair manifested this behaviour, it was much more likely to have appeared or to appear in the other twin if they were identicals than if they were fraternals. Dr Kallmann believed this suggested that some hereditary influences contribute towards homosexual

* After the death of the original Siamese twins, other conjoined pairs appeared from time to time as public attractions, but none had the appeal of the original two; and also, fortunately, with the decreasing public interest in seeing such twins exhibited, more and more effort has been made to separate any who now are born, as soon as possible. In many cases both twins have survived, but in a few instances only one of the pair could be saved. The large majority of Siamese twins, however, fail to live very long after birth.

tendencies. But most psychiatrists view any abnormal sexual behaviour as chiefly environmental in causation, and argue that similar conditioning would largely account for the dual cases of homosexuality in identical twins.

Criminality, or *delinquency*, when occurring in both members of an identical twin pair – which it also does much more often than in both of a fraternal pair – is likewise attributed more to similar conditioning than to any matching hereditary tendencies. While it is possible that similar hereditary quirks may sometimes incline identical twins to similar antisocial behaviour, the more likely explanation may be sought in their equally adverse conditioning, as well as in the fact that identicals interact with and influence each other more than do two fraternals or two singleton siblings.

A special factor in twin criminality, one may guess, would be the temptation of criminally motivated identicals to make use of their likeness for baffling and eluding authorities. (The pattern for this sometimes begins in school, when identicals find they can delude teachers or get away with tricks and misbehaviour.) To cite one of several cases in the news, Chicago, in 1960, was menaced for a while by two identical-twin hoodlums, twenty-two years old, who allegedly committed a series of simultaneous holdups miles apart, and relied on their remarkable physical resemblance – compounded by wearing the same false moustaches – to thwart positive identification. When victims were later confronted with both of the twins together, it was impossible to swear that this or that one had committed the specific crime. However, convincing evidence was finally produced which convicted them both.

Perhaps most strongly rooted of the beliefs about twins is that there is a *mystic bond* between them throughout life which permits one to sense the other's feelings or to read the other's thoughts – even when they are far apart. Stories about this phenomenon came to me from many twins. They told of how they had known when their twin was ailing, or in danger or trouble, and of many coincidences in their thoughts and actions. Often twins in school turn in examination papers so similar that they are suspected of having cheated. In repeated instances, however, identical twins have been proved not to be in collusion, and to have produced closely matching papers only because of their parallel thinking. This happened with the Anderson identicals, Drs Richard and John, mentioned earlier in this chapter. Also, there was the case of the twin French generals, the Bretts, mentioned in Chapter 13.

What has science to say about this supposed psychic closeness between twins? If the phenomenon does exist, there may be some basis for it theoretically in the fact, noted previously (Chapter 16), that the brain waves of identical twins have been found to be remarkably alike throughout their lives. If brains send out waves, then wouldn't it follow that two brains with the same 'wave lengths', attuned in the same way, could broadcast to each other and receive the other's messages? A good theory, but without any proof to support it. Further, how account for the telepathic communication also claimed between fraternal twins, who do not have matching brains and brain waves? Or the stories of thought transmission between a mother and child, or even between unrelated persons?

Above all, if there is any scientific evidence for 'telepathy' between twins, the one most likely to know it would be Dr Joseph B. Rhine, who devised the extrasensory perception (ESP) tests specifically for measuring possible thought transmission. In these tests, one person looks at successive cards imprinted with various symbols, and another person, some distance (or even a great distance) away, tries to name the symbol as each card is turned up. Many more right guesses than chance allows would indicate extrasensory perception. Have twins been subjected to these tests? Yes, numerous times. And here is what Dr Rhine told me:

Although popular belief would have led us to expect that there was exceptional telepathic communication between identical twins, nothing outstanding has occurred in any single case of identical twins tested so far. The averages on the extrasensory tests were approximately the same whether the sender and receiver were identical twins, fraternal twins, or simply friends or both members of the same family. While cases have been reported to us from time to time of what would appear to be exceptional telepathic rapport between identical twins, my impression is that they are not more outstanding than similar cases involving a mother and daughter, a young couple in love, or other close relationships of affection and friendship.

We must assume, then, that if and when unusual coincidences of

232

thought or action do occur between twins, they are merely what might be expected when two persons have shared many of the same experiences, have come to think much alike, and are much concerned about each other.

A remaining possibility – for believers in astrology – is that a special bond is created between twins by their being born under the same heavenly configurations. As it happens, however, twins have been a source of embarrassment to astrologers, because, if the stars greatly influenced people's characters and destinies, there should be little difference in the life courses of twins; and, particularly, fraternal twins would be as similar in talents, capacities, temperaments, and other traits (as well as in 'fated' experiences) as are identicals, since all twins are alike in that both of a pair are born under exactly the same sign, constellations, zodiacs, or what have you. But, as we've seen, twins of any type can differ considerably in their traits and life histories, and fraternal twins can be as different as are singleton siblings with birthdays far apart. Not least, if there were anything to astrological principles (which modern scientists deny), twins would tend to die at almost the same time. But do they?

The instances in which adult twins have died on the same day (when not through accident) are extraordinarily rare. Most amazing were the simultaneous deaths of two 32-year-old identical-twin sisters in a North Carolina mental hospital in 1962. They had been admitted with precisely the same schizophrenic symptoms, and after several years had deteriorated in the same way. Then, one night, despite their having been separated and occupying rooms far apart, the two were found to have died within moments of each other. The causes (or cause) of their death remain mysterious, but, as reported by Drs Ian C. Wilson and John C. Reece, were quite likely a combination of physical and pathological factors which attuned them to react to stress in almost identical ways.

Less striking are a few other cases of dual twin deaths in recent decades. One, in 1942, was of twin brothers in Cambridge, Minnesota, who dropped dead within five minutes of each other (presumably both had heart disease, and the shock of one's death proved fatal to the other twin, who was visiting him). In another case, in 1952, two 90-year-old twin sisters were found dying of

INTERVALS BETWEEN TWINS' DEATHS
(At ages 60–69)

If one twin dies in his sixties, the other twin's death comes on an average *this much later:*

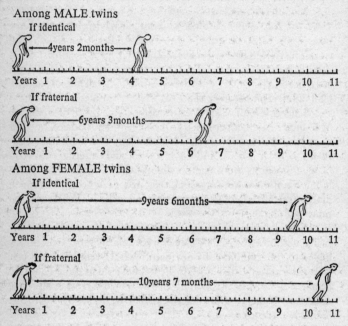

Among MALE twins
  If identical
←4years 2months→
Years 1 2 3 4 5 6 7 8 9 10 11

  If fraternal
←6years 3months→
Years 1 2 3 4 5 6 7 8 9 10 11

Among FEMALE twins
  If identical
←9years 6months→
Years 1 2 3 4 5 6 7 8 9 10 11

  If fraternal
←10years 7 months→
Years 1 2 3 4 5 6 7 8 9 10 11

Data from study by Drs Lissy F. Jarvik, Arther Falek, Franz J. Kallmann and Irving Lorge. *Am. J. Hum. Genet.*, 12:2, June, 1960.

malnutrition in a Greenwich Village apartment, and later expired within a few hours of each other. But it is well to keep in mind there have been innumerable similar coincidental deaths of two singleton brothers or sisters.

It may also be noted that a great many twins have survived as pairs into extreme old age. The oldest pair of whom we have record were the Morterud twin identicals, Bernt G., of Chicago, and

Gulbrand, of Odalen, Norway, who had reached the age of almost 102 in 1960 when Bernt died. Several other pairs in recent years lived to the age of 100 before being separated by death.

The clearest picture of twin longevity is provided by the study of the life histories of about 1,400 elderly twins (all aged sixty or over when the study began) made by Dr Kallmann and his associates. Among the conclusions were these: (1) Twins reaching middle and old age have just about the same life expectancy as others in their families at the same age. (2) If the deaths of adult twins usually come more closely together than those of two singleton siblings, it is only because the twins are of the same age. (3) Identical twins tend to be considerably closer in their life spans than do fraternal twins of their sex because identicals have the same hereditary makeup and also are usually more alike in their conditioning and habits. But, unless the death of the first identical twin is specifically due to some serious condition also present in the other (which is seldom the case), the second twin can count on approximately the same further life expectancy as any singleton person of the same age and sex. (4) Since females considerably outlive males, as a rule, women twins usually go on living as a pair longer than do male twins. (5) The chance of any two twins, of any type, going on into very old age together is greatest if both their parents were long-lived (to seventy-five and over) and least if both parents were relatively short-lived (under fifty-five). In all cases, however, allowances should be made for the deaths of parents having been due to accidents or to other causes unrelated to inherent longevity tendencies.

Finally, *suicide* among twins was a special point explored by Dr Kallmann and his colleagues. Not only were twins found to be no more prone to suicide than singletons but – further refuting notions about morbid closeness between twins – the records showed only a single case in which both twins of a pair had taken their lives at about the same time.

In sum, if twins as a rule are indeed much closer than singleton siblings in their thoughts and relationships, and in what happens to them, it is definitely not because of any mystic bond or anything else supernatural. Any unusual psychological or social closeness between twins, persisting through the years, could easily be ascribed to the way they were trained and have come to feel about each other. In the case of identical twins, moreover, a special closeness, and perhaps intuitive understanding of each other, could be traceable to their matching hereditary makeup, and the many similarities in traits and experiences arising from it.

Yet the fact cannot be ignored that some twins strongly reject closeness or are seriously disturbed by their twinship – as will be brought out in the next chapter.

CHAPTER 21

The Analyst's Double Couch

ALMOST any day, in the secluded office of a psychoanalyst some-
where, one could find on the couch a man or a woman who is a
twin. Unseen in the room, but whose presence is felt just the same,
is someone else – the other twin. And, as the patient under analysis
talks out his or her disturbed thoughts, this other twin often keeps
edging into the picture.

The problems of twins under analysis, as with singly born
patients, can be of many kinds – sexual difficulties, marital conflicts, fears of facing life or responsibilities, failure to adjust to other
people or to hold a job, alcoholism, and so on. But the difference in
the case of twins who seek psychoanalytical help is that their
problems are frequently (if not in most cases) assumed to be
largely the outgrowth of their twinship. In previous chapters we
have told about special situations going with twinship which cause
concern, such as jealousy, competition, hostility or overattach-
ment, the fight for individuality, sexual involvement, and other
difficulties arising from the fact of two persons being born together
and reared closely as a unit. Examples were given of the less
serious effects of these situations. Now let us consider the most
extreme results, as seen among twins who are so maladjusted in
their adult years that they require psychoanalytical treatment.

For readers not familiar with psychoanalysis and when it is
called for, this may be said: Primarily the psychoanalyst treats
persons who are not mentally diseased – that is, *not insane* – but
who are seriously disturbed by emotional and psychological difficulties with which they can no longer cope by themselves. The
analytical treatment consists in bringing to the surface and making
clear to the patient the true causes of his difficulties, and helping
him to adjust to his life in a more mature way. The situation is
different for persons who have 'sick brains' – who are suffering
from schizophrenia, manic-depressive insanity or other mental

diseases, and who may require medical treatment from psychiatrists and possibly hospitalization in mental institutions. But, as pointed out in Chapter 13, twins are relatively no more prone to or afflicted by these mental diseases than are the singly born.

The stories which follow are actual cases of twins who underwent psychoanalysis. The accounts are drawn from reports published in psychoanalytical journals or given at analytical meetings; from personal reports made to me by analysts; or, in a few cases, obtained directly from the twins themselves. In reading these accounts, however, it is important to keep constantly in mind that the twins who were analysed, and their experiences, are the big exceptions. They are no more representative of twins as a whole than seriously disturbed singly born individuals are typical of all other persons. Further, in almost every instance, as will be seen, the analysed twins had had an abnormal home environment, making it difficult to tell the extent to which their twinship itself was responsible for their maladjustment. Even when the twins saw each other as the chief cause of their difficulties, we must still remember that most persons under analysis are beset by hostilities or unnatural attachments (or both) to persons close to them; so it should not be surprising when a disturbed twin's feelings strongly centre on the other twin.

Thus, the cases cited must not be given an exaggerated importance with respect to twins who are reared under average and normal circumstances; nor should one consider the 'horrible examples' as justifying extreme policies with respect to separating all twins or suppressing their twinship. (*Unfortunately, some of the very cases we will discuss have been used as major arguments for advocating such policies.*) Despite these reservations, however, an insight into the lives of badly disturbed twins can have much value to other twins and to parents of twins; for it may indicate how the milder forms of the situations revealed in analysis could have arisen or can arise, and how the more serious effects may be prevented in twins now being reared. As stressed before, the type of twinship is an important factor, and so we will present the case histories in five groups: identical males, identical females, fraternal males, fraternal females, and opposite-sex twins. All of these – to repeat – are accounts of *actual cases*; although, to preserve the

238

anonymity of the twins and to permit freer discussion, we will use coined names and not link any case with a specific analyst.*

David, a man in his mid-thirties, had for years been unable to shake himself loose from the thought of his identical twin, Daniel, who had died at the age of eighteen. Their impoverished parents could not attend to them properly, so the twins had learned to become a self-reliant unit. But David had felt inferior to his twin. Being the second-born, he thought he'd been an 'intruder' in the womb, and he believed that his twin was handsomer and brighter. During adolescence David began trying to become an individual by keeping secrets from his twin and striving to surpass him in school. Then, in their freshman year at college, tragedy struck. While the twins were taking an examination, Daniel left halfway through the period. David thought that, as usual, his twin had raced through the test easily, so he stayed on to complete his own paper more carefully and perhaps get a better mark. As it turned out, Daniel collapsed in a subway with an appendicitis attack. Several days later, after peritonitis developed, he unexpectedly died.

David could not face the reality of his twin's death. He would tell people that Daniel was merely away on a trip. Each night before retiring he'd say 'Good night' to his brother's empty bed, and on walks by himself or visits to Daniel's grave he'd 'talk' with his twin. Eventually David had a serious breakdown, developing symptoms of hysteria, claustrophobia, and various psychosomatic ailments. *Why had his twin's death so affected him?* The analysis brought to light that David had a morbid sense of guilt because, having been resentful of his twin and perhaps having wished some-

---

* The psychoanalysts whose case histories and interpretations of twins are given or referred to in this chapter include: Drs Hilda C. Abraham, Jacob A. Arlow, Hubert J. Cronin, Henry M. Fox, George E. Gardner, Peter Glauber, Jules Glenn, Heinz Hartmann, Edith Jacobson, Edward D. Joseph, Benjamin Karpman, Robert P. Knight, Lawrence C. Kolb, Theodore Lidz, Joseph A. Lubart, Douglass W. Orr, Eveoleen N. Rexford, Brandt F. Steele, Julius Steinfeld, Jack H. Tabor, and Jesse Zizmor. Also consulted were group reports on disturbed twin cases by Drs E. Gardner Jacobs and Alvin M. Mesnikoff, and Drs Paul Lowinger, Calvin Shorer and Richard S. Knox.

times to be free of him, he felt he had somehow 'killed' him. Thus, he tried to reject the thought that his twin was really dead, and, when he could no longer delude himself, he went to pieces. (His claustrophobia came from thinking of any enclosed place as the 'womb' in which his vengeful twin might be lurking.) Only when David was brought to fully realize that his early resentment of his twin was natural, and that he had in no way been guilty of his death, could he become properly adjusted.

Henry, another adult identical twin, was pretty much of a mess. He was untrustworthy in business and personal dealings, a pathological liar, and sexually mixed-up. Looking back into his twinship, he had been the older of the pair (by three minutes), and when he grew up to be a runt in size (as was his twin), he concluded this was his twin's fault for having crowded him in the womb. Subsequently when he got an apartment of his own, he would lock himself up in it, refusing to have callers or to answer the phone – in fantasy he was back in a womb to which his unwanted twin would not be admitted. Again, when in restaurants he persistently complained and quarrelled about food; this, too, was traceable to his resentment at having had to share food with his twin before birth. In turn his hostility to his twin carried over in his feelings towards other persons, interfering with success at any job, or with normal responses to women. His twin, as it came out, was also emotionally warped and disagreeable. But could all this be blamed on their twinship?

The twins' father had been a hard, arrogant, egotistical businessman, who, though well off, was extremely stingy and obsessed with the fear of going bankrupt and starving. Their mother, about half her husband's age, was also self-centred, cold and stingy. When the twins were young, she had left them with servants and resumed work in her husband's business. Little wonder that in this selfish and loveless home atmosphere the twins had become withdrawn and hostile, and could not make mature adjustments to other people.

In the case of two other identical males, Morton and Joe, it was a morbid homosexual closeness which caused them to seek analysis at the age of thirty-three. (Each was treated by a different analyst, the two doctors then submitting their reports to a third analyst for comparison, providing a clearer, 'stereoscopic' picture of the disturbed twinship.) For a number of years the twins had been living together as a homosexual 'couple'. Morton kept house, cooked and cleaned; Joe gave the orders and acted like the husband. The pattern for this was set when they were children, and their mother had played a major role in setting it. An ex-school-teacher, brilliant but severe and domineering, she had bossed her meek, hardworking, adoring husband. Having wanted a girl baby, she was cool to the twins; and, sensing this as children, they tried hard to please her. Morton sought to be like the girl she'd hoped for, feeling also, when he saw how his mother dominated the home, that it was best to be a female. Joe sought to please his mother in a different way – by emulating the masculine side of her nature. Contributing no little to the twins' abnormal development was the fact that their mother acted seductively with them and often paraded around the house in a transparent negligee. Thus stimulated, the twins began playing sex games with each other, leading in time to overt homosexual activity.

The twins had remained close together in school and in the Army (driving sergeants frantic with their twin tricks and misbehaviour). All this time their warped twinship had acted as a unifying force: Morton liked being the clinging vine to his twin, and Joe enjoyed playing the male of the pair and being catered to. As the more aggressive one, Joe became a crack salesman by driving himself neurotically. But his shell of outer strength was shattered when his twin suddenly became involved with a girl and married – or was married by her. So Joe, the presumably strong one, was the first to seek analysis; and when he did, Morton, feeling that if his strong twin needed treatment, he certainly must too, followed suit. As the analyses proceeded, Morton was able to make a passable adjustment to his marriage (though as a 'feminine-type' husband and father). But Joe's case proved more difficult, for he could be neither feminine nor masculine. In the case of these twins, then, the analyst who reviewed the reports saw one of many instances where the supposedly strong and dominant member of a pair may be actually the one with the greatest inner instability. Similarly, the presumably weaker twin may, by playing mother to the more dominant and more erratic one, prove to have the most inner strength and resiliency. (Another example will be given later, in the cases of Janet and Julia.)

One of the weirdest of the identical twin cases, in which both of a male pair were homosexual for a time (although not with each other), could be traced to the fact that their highly neurotic mother was also one of a twin pair. Marge, the mother, had both hated and envied her fraternal twin, Mildred, for being more attractive and capable than herself. Both sisters had seemed on the way to remaining spinsters when, at age 40, Mildred became engaged to a wealthy widower. Marge hurried to corral for herself a wishy-washy little man, five years her junior, so there could be a double wedding. Each sister (with little childbearing time left) then set her heart on having twin children. Mildred could produce only three singletons, but Marge, after having one single boy, triumphed with an identical-twin boy pair. At last she'd got even with and surpassed her sister.

The little twin boys promptly became the apples of their mother's eye. Nothing and no one else mattered. The weakling husband was banished from her bedroom to the one occupied by the singleton son, while she took the twins in with her. She felt they were so much part of herself that when she was ill and took medicine, she always gave some to the twins as well. She dressed them alike until they were ten, punished them as a team, and washed and bathed them together until they were fifteen, sometimes displaying her own nude body to them. Throughout this she encouraged them to ignore their father. (Once, in their late teens, when one of the twins took her over his knees and spanked her, and the father tried to interfere, the mother exclaimed, 'Mind your own business!' and told the boy to resume his spanking.)

Little wonder that the two turned into brats known in their community as the 'Twin Terrors'; that in secondary school they homo-sexually seduced other boys, on occasion stealing each other's male 'sweetheart'; and that, going on to separate colleges, each one independently developed the practice of dressing up as a girl and sallying forth furtively on evenings to be picked up by men. Eventually one twin landed in a mental institution for a while, and both later underwent analysis. Whether they will ever become well adjusted remains to be seen.

Another strange sexual complication was a triangle involving two identical-twin men and the wife of one of them. All their lives the twins had been extremely close. When one got married, the other was woebegone. But then the wife in the case (pretty much mixed-up herself) seduced the bachelor twin, and, intrigued by the situation, insisted on setting up a triangular household in which she decided each night which twin would be her partner. When she finally left them, the twins cracked up and sought psychoanalytical help. In this case the analysts did feel that twinship had interfered badly with the emotional development of both men; for one thing imbuing them with suppressed homosexual impulses towards each other which they could express vicariously for a while by sharing the same woman. The family background of the twins is not reported. But one may suspect that there was something askew in their previous conditioning to have made possible the marital morass into which they got themselves.

Among the analysed women identical twins, disordered family settings clearly played a major role. The facts about one pair – the identical twin-sister interior decorators – were given in Chapter 20. In their case, as described, an alcoholic father, a neurotic, indifferent mother, and a homosexual older sister could easily explain their later maladjustment. Indeed, as was also pointed out, there might have been more serious effects if they had not had their twinship to give them mutual comfort and security. The same kind of stabilizing influence of twinship, rather than its disruptive effects, was seen by an analyst friend of mine in the case of a young society woman who was one of his patients. She and her identical-twin sister had been born into an upper-class, but unenviable, family, with a harsh, vain, neglectful mother and an irresponsible, alcoholic father. Often the twins, from the time they were eight or nine, had to go to some bar to get their drunken father and bring him home. Said the analyst, 'Such a setting would have menaced any children, and it is not unlikely that had the twins been singletons, they might have been less able to cope with their problems than they could together as a unit.'

In the analytical case histories of *fraternal twins*, the dominant themes are usually rivalry and jealousy, as well as the fight for individuality (or what analysts call 'ego identification'). But, as with identicals, there is always the total family picture to be considered. A good example is that of a forty-year-old male fraternal, John, who was deeply enmeshed in marital and business difficulties, alcoholism and drug addiction. His past revealed a tough, overbearing father and a bird-brained, incompetent mother, who, already having a son, had been hoping for a girl when the twins were born. The mother then proceeded to treat the twins as if they *were* girls, and dressed them alike as such until they were four. Thereafter, John, who was the more delicate of the twins, continued to act girlish to win his mother's favour, while his twin brother sought to be rough and tough, like the father. But John was also beset by the urge both to win his twin's love and to equal him in all ways – which was not possible because of their inherited fraternal differences. The inner conflicts grew and worsened until, when drink and drugs offered no relief, he sought analysis. (In this instance the analyst felt that apart from other aspects of John's abnormal upbringing, much harm had been done by the failure to recognize that he and his twin were not identicals and should not have been reared as if they were, or made so conscious of their twinship.)

The constant gnawing desire of a fraternal twin to rival and equal his partner, despite their inborn differences, was also evident in another case, that of Fred, a professional man. His sense of inferiority was traceable to several facts: He was the second-born of the twins; the other one, Frank, was named after their father and preferred by that parent because he was somewhat bigger and stronger, and also handsomer. During their high-school days Fred managed to achieve some sense of balance with Frank by leading in their studies and becoming president of the senior class, while Frank starred as an athlete and as a ladies' man. But, when the twins separated to go to different colleges, Fred suddenly realized how much he'd depended on having his twin around. 'You're the dearest person in the world to me,' he wrote. 'My life is shattered without you.' Trying to find a love substitute, he began a succession of unsatisfying affairs with girls. Then came a mental breakdown, a period of recovery – during which he completed his training – and another crisis when his twin, by now started successfully in business, got married. After analytical treatment, Fred straightened himself out, married, and became independent of his twin. 'We see each other and write to each other only occasionally,' he reported. 'I no longer stand in awe of him, but we entertain for each other a genuine affection, built on mutual respect and appreciation rather than the shifting sands of neurosis.'

Yet why, as Fred admits, was this neurosis not shared by his twin, whom he described as 'a well-adjusted extrovert', only mildly interested in the twinship and little influenced by his twin? The analyst felt it was primarily because these men, being fraternals and thus differing in inherent makeup, also differed in their reactions to outside influences. While Fred's neurosis might not have arisen if there had been no twin to be linked and compete with, it likewise might never have developed – even with the twin present – if he had not had some inner instability which made him unusually susceptible to stresses.

Turning to *women fraternal twins*, among those analysed was a twenty-six-year-old alcoholic who had been sexually promiscuous from the age of fifteen. But what a sick childhood she'd had! She and her twin were the only children of a heavy-drinking, vicious father, who fought constantly with their ineffectual mother, frequently beat the twins, and ran around the house naked. As 'Cora', the patient, grew up, she reflected her feelings about her father by hating males, though envying them. But she was plagued as well by conflicting sex urges. During childhood she and her twin had indulged in mutual sex play, and soon her greatest fear was that she might become a lesbian. To guard against this, she began a succession of affairs with boys and men, although to overcome her dislike of them she always had to precede her acts by becoming drunk. Subsequently she had an affair with the husband of her own twin sister, who had married early; and, as a disastrous sequel, the husband then decamped, leaving both twins. Cora attempted suicide and spent a period in a mental hospital. But through all this her fraternal twin was never too disturbed, nor given to Cora's vices or homosexual fears – despite their having had almost the same childhood experiences. So, again, there is the question from Cora's analyst: 'Was it because of the twinship situation, which made one suffer at the expense of the other, or was it because they were different in their inborn traits and predispositions?'

In a second case of women fraternals, definitely unlike physically and in character, both were badly maladjusted, but in different ways. One, an unhappily married professional woman, sought analysis at the age of thirty-seven, after a suicide attempt; the other, an artist, had never married, and had had a disordered life punctuated by a period in a mental hospital. Although their twin-ship may have coloured and heightened their problems, analysis revealed abnormal sexual elements in their childhood, including the exposure to violent sex scenes between the parents when the mother would take one of the twins to bed with her as a buffer against her husband's sexual demands. In another case, in which both women of a fraternal pair were seriously disturbed, also in different ways, mental illness had been so prevalent in their family – with four out of six older singleton siblings having required psy-chiatric or psychoanalytical treatment – as to raise doubts about how much the twinship itself had to do with their own neuroses.

It is almost a relief to proceed from the warped adult twins with unwholesome family backgrounds to the story of two refined, now quite well-adjusted, youngish twin grandmothers. In the case of these fraternal-twin women, the psychological problems which disturbed them – problems turned inward and never leading to any unseemly outward behaviour – did apparently stem in large part from their twinship. Highly intelligent and perceptive, they gave their accounts to me separately, each from her own point of view. As children, although they differed greatly in looks, capacities and interests, they nonetheless were dressed alike and treated by their parents as if they were identical twins. But, as they grew, their characters became more and more distinct, one from the other. Janet, presumably the dominant, strong twin, turned out to be the most disturbed of the two (as in the case of the strong twin, Joe, mentioned earlier in this chapter). This is what Janet told me (and her twin later confirmed):

During our childhood Julia was the smaller and sicklier one, and required and received more attention. She became mother's pet, so in addition to my feeling that I wasn't a whole person – only part of a twin unit – I had to contend with the feeling of being rejected to boot. This led to my acting up, yelling and screaming. Julia was the good one, the dependable, capable one, and I soon felt I could never do *anything* better than she, and shouldn't even try; since, as my twin and part of me, her achievements were in a sense also mine. 'Let Julia do it,' I'd think – and she always did. She was generally first in her class, and it was only because we were separated in grade school and in high school that I managed to get through my studies.

All this time, notwithstanding, we were made to feel that we were part of each other, and that there was something very special in our being the Twins. Through our first year in college we continued to dress alike, were given everything in pairs, and slept in one bed. We felt a desire to pull apart, to be individuals; while, at the same time, there was a tremendous tie and very great dependence on each other. Despite my own desire to break away from Julia, wherever I turned I was always searching for someone else to replace her as a twin. We both married at twenty-six, and yet we still couldn't feel we were each a complete person. After years of trying to get clear about myself, I sought analysis at the age of forty-five. It's truly been much better since.

Both Janet and Julia, at this writing, have brilliant grown children. They live in different communities, but phone each other often, visit frequently, and, while sharing many friends, live fully independent lives. Tracing their own difficulties largely to having been forced to be like identical twins when they were not, they offer this advice to parents of fraternals:

Always treat fraternal twins as separate personalites and allow them to develop according to their inherent natures. Forcing them to try to become alike may have the reverse effect: Each may attempt to be the opposite of what the other is, even if it means going counter to her true nature and impulses.

In members of *male–female* twin pairs who have been analysed, the special source of maladjustment has usually been the failure of one or the other to develop the feelings and attitudes considered proper for his or her sex: either the male twin had been feminized or the female twin masculinized by the twinship; or one – or both – had otherwise become seriously disturbed by two close contact with the other. We should stress again that the cases to be cited are exceptions. The great majority of male–female twin pairs seem to be little affected by each other, and even if they are during childhood, the effects seldom seem to be serious or long-lasting. Nor, as with other disturbed twins we've told about, need it follow that emotional breakdowns of twins of opposite-sex pairs are due primarily to the twinship.

One example is that of a maladjusted man who felt that his attachment to and identification with his twin sister had kept him from properly adjusting to marriage and a normal sex life. But his mother also can be seen as having played a major role in the picture. During the early childhood of the boy and girl twin pair, she had dressed them alike – *both as girls* – and she so dominated the home and the father (as in several cases previously mentioned) that the boy grew up in a 'female' atmosphere in which he could not develop normally as a male. This also could explain his extreme jealousy of his twin sister, for being of what he regarded as the preferred sex, and the fact that his resentment was coupled with a deep attachment to, and dependence on, her. Pointing out that other men with twin sisters did not turn out to be as disturbed as this man was, his analyst asked, 'Could it not be that the underlying emotional involvement was really not with his twin but with his overly-possessive, dominant mother? And, while the presence of a twin sister as a rival may have increased his conflicts, might he not have become a maladjusted mama's boy even if he had been a singleton?'

The impact on a male twin when his twin sister takes the lead in any way, which we touched on in Chapter 18, was the basis of another analytical case. In this situation the patient was a young man of a middle-class family whose attractive twin sister had always been ahead of him in maturity, poise and popularity. His only consolation had been the thought that, being a male, he would eventually outdistance her in achievement. But suddenly, when she was eighteen, she married a well-to-do thirty-year-old society man. At one swoop she attained wealth and social position; whereas he, barely started in college, had a long hard row to hoe. Married at twenty-two and struggling to make ends meet, he began taking out his frustrations on his wife. Analysis helped him to see himself as an individual, without the need to constantly link himself and compete with his twin sister.

The reverse situation, in which the female twin is the disturbed member of an opposite-sex pair, showed up in the case of a professional woman who outwardly was successful, but inwardly was an emotional mess. She and her twin brother had been born to poor, immigrant, working parents. The boy twin, who was frailer, had been nursed by the mother, while the girl had been placed with a wet nurse outside the home until she was two years old. The feeling that she, a female, had been rejected in favour of her brother, a male, stayed with her. Seeking to be masculine, in her teens she was a tomboy member of boy gangs and began an early sex life. Driven by ambition, she worked her way through college and got a Ph.D., while her brother, less bright, was left far behind. When she married, her masculine streak kept her from accepting the role of wife; so divorce and a severe depression followed. After several years of analysis she became better adjusted to her sex and to herself, married a doctor, and at last reports, was happy with him and their two bright children. But even in this case the analyst questioned whether the male–female twinship had been the primary cause of the woman's conflicts; for, as it came out, the other women in her family – the mother and two singleton older sisters – were all of the dominant, aggressive type, with the same neurotic 'masculine protest' urge to be like men.

In still another male–female twin case, the maladjustment of the woman seemed much less related to her having a twin brother than to the fact that she had abnormal parents. A bright, petite blonde, she had reached an emotional breaking point at the age of thirty-one when she found she couldn't work or mix with other people and really feared she was going insane. These symptoms worsened after her twin brother married, and it was through his efforts that she underwent analysis. The facts that came out were these: The childhood of the twins had been a miserable one, but much more so for her than for her twin brother. She had had to take care of their bedridden, invalid mother, a cranky, untidy shrew who constantly berated her. The father, an eccentric writer, treated the girl as a lover, kissing her passionately. When she was thirteen she was operated on for an ovarian cyst, and the rumour spread that she'd had a baby by her twin brother (causing her to dread that this might happen). These were only some of her harrowing experiences. When, under analysis, she lamented bitterly that she'd never been a 'complete person' and should have been 'either a Siamese twin with her brother, or else born alone as a boy' – were these fancies really induced by her twinship? Or were they mainly the products of a mind warped by gruelling early tribulations and focusing on the twinship only because it was the situation closest at hand?

We may conclude, then, that – whatever the twin type, or whatever the disturbance portrayed in the case histories presented here – *there is little real evidence that twinship of itself is the predominant factor in serious emotional maladjustment unless the individual is initially unstable and/or unless the environment in or outside the home is sufficiently adverse so that even a singleton might become neurotic.* Stated another way, all the abnormalities described, such as homosexuality, phobias of various kinds, extreme dependency, failure to adjust to other people, masculinization of a girl or feminization of a boy, delinquency, and so on – all of these defects in development, if and when they occur in twins, do so, as in singletons, from a combination of specific inner weaknesses and outer stresses, in which the role of the parents is almost always crucial. Without this combination of adverse factors there need be little fear that any twin will become a candidate for the psychiatrist or for the analyst's couch. *And the fact is that only a tiny minority do.*

Nevertheless, it cannot be denied that being one of a twin pair does have a significant bearing on a person's emotional and psychological development, and that each type of twinship has its special effects. But – and this is always important – the effects need by no means be harmful. Rivalry between twins, as between singleton siblings, can be a useful incentive; and if equality is not achieved, this, too, can be a realistic preparation for an adult world in which not everybody can be best. So, also, if closeness between twins may have its dangers, the sense of continual closeness to another human being can also be a source of comfort, and indeed may provide stability as well.

Another point stressed in the psychoanalytical case histories is the conflict between the desire of twins to achieve independence from each other and a corresponding need to hold on to each other. But this conflict, too, is not unique with twins. All human beings have the desire to be independent and also the desire to belong. Married couples are repeatedly beset by the urge – real or fancied – to break apart but are held back by their mutual need for each other. Children want to be free of their parents, yet are forever attached to them. The mature person can adjust to both pulls, towards independence and towards attachment, in any situation. And the twin who has been helped to achieve maturity will be happily and wholesomely adjusted not only to his or her twin, but to all other people as well.

CHAPTER 22

Twins in Myth, Folklore, and Literature

To obtain a well-rounded view of the world of twins, it is necessary to go beyond the facts and into the realms of myth and folklore, fantasy and fiction. For it is in these outer realms – whether in the past or the present, or among primitive or advanced peoples – that one may often find the origin and explanation of many of the existing attitudes towards twins, and the beliefs about them, with which we have been concerned.

Not surprisingly, the interest in twins as special human beings can be traced as far back as records exist. It may even have begun with Adam and Eve. At least, in religious lore we find the theory that Cain and Abel each had a twin sister, and that their quarrel began over one of these girls. However that may be, the Bible has several significant stories about twins. The first deals with Jacob and Esau, the twin sons of Isaac and Rebekah (Genesis 25:21–34). According to prophecy they were destined to be different ('. . . two manner of people . . . the one . . . shall be stronger than the other'); and we also know they were different in physical traits (Esau being hairy, Jacob smooth), so in all probability they were fraternal twins. Further, we are told, the twins struggled together within the womb (perhaps the earliest recorded onset of twin rivalry or sibling rivalry). Legend also has it that they fought before birth over who would be the first to emerge into the world, and that Jacob yielded precedence only because Esau threatened he would be the first out even if it killed their mother. Jacob, of course, squared matters later by getting Esau to forfeit his birthright, and then, with his mother's connivance, tricked Esau out of the paternal blessing and endowment by covering his hands and neck with goat-skin to make his dying blind father think he was his hairy twin.*

*Twins are again linked with Jacob in ancient Hebrew lore, which held

TWINS IN MYTH, FOLKLORE, AND LITERATURE

The second notable Bible twins (told about also in Genesis, Chapter 38), were grandsons of Jacob – Pharez and Zarah – born to a widow, Tamar, after she had inveigled her father-in-law, Judah, into siring them. In this story, too, there was apparently a conflict between the twins before birth over who should emerge first; for, after the one twin, Zarah, had begun to appear, and was tagged by the midwife for identification, the other twin pushed him aside and came out first. Pharez and Zarah are named again in the New Testament, at its very beginning – Matthew 1:3 – where it is stated that Pharez was in the direct line of ancestors from whom Jesus descended. The only other twin mentioned in the New Testament is the Apostle Thomas, whose name is derived from the Hebrew word for twin, *te-om* (literally, 'a match'), and which some scholars say gave rise to the Greek word for twin, *didymus* (referred to in St John 20:24).

It will be seen that both the Bible stories – of Jacob and Esau, and of Pharez and Zarah – associate twins with something unnatural (if not supernatural), a theme which not only runs through most of the twin lore among the civilized ancients and among primitive peoples but occurs repeatedly in modern beliefs as well. Many of the mythological gods were twins. Rome had her legendary twin builders, Romulus and Remus. The Greeks had their twin deities, Castor and Polydeuces (the latter called Pollux by the Romans), who were the hero sons of Zeus and Leda and eventually took their place in the heavens to form the twin constellation Gemini – see Illustration, p. 256. (The old American slang expression 'by Jiminy' comes from 'by Gemini'.) Also in Greek mythology we have the brother–sister twins, Apollo and Artemis, or Diana, as she was known among the Romans.

In the mythology of India there are the twin gods, the Acvin (dual Acvinan), who looked after the weak and oppressed. In Scandinavian myths there are the gods Balder and his blind twin

---

that ten of his eleven sons were each accompanied at birth by a twin sister, and that subsequently the male and female of each pair married. These ten sons, beginning with Reuben, founded the Ten Tribes of Israel. The eleventh of Jacob's sons – Joseph – was the only one not reputed to have had a twin. (From Louis Ginzberg, *Legends of the Bible*, Simon & Schuster, 1956, p. 173.)

brother Hoder, by whom he was slain after they had quarrelled over a goddess. The ancient Aztecs of Mexico paid tribute to their chief goddess of fertility, Xochiquetzal, as having been the first mother of twins. And in many Asiatic religions we have the twin motif among the gods, sometimes in the form of 'Siamese-like' twins – gods with two heads and one body, or one body and several sets of limbs.

The Egyptian female deities, Isis and Nephthys, have been referred to as twins in some modern accounts; while in others Isis and her brother Osiris, to whom she was married, are also listed as having been twins. But Egyptologist Bernard V. Bothmer of the Brooklyn Museum emphatically questions these assumptions. He told me that not only is there no reference to twins in any Egyptian writings up to the Christian era but there is no evidence that the ancient Egyptians were much concerned with twins or had any specific word for them. Nor have any twin mummies ever been found. However, the ancient Babylonians and Assyrians were sufficiently conscious of twins to introduce them into astrology, identifying and naming seven twin constellations.

Among primitive peoples, past and present, there certainly was no dearth of interest in twins. Wherever primitive tribes have been studied in recent centuries, innumerable myths, superstitions and practices relating to twins have been found. American Indians were extremely twin-minded. The Crow, Kiowa and Shoshonean tribes all had stories of individual boys who became divine twins by being cut in half through magical power. (This, as we have seen, is not far from the way identical twins are produced in the embryonic stage.) The Pueblo Indian mythological counterparts of Adam and Eve were credited with having had five pairs of twins. Among the Navaho gods are twin brothers, sons of the Sun-Carrier, and the Zunis have twin gods who guided the emergence and early journeyings of the first human beings. The Mohave and Yuma tribes also tell of twin male gods who aided in the creation of the world.

One common feature of many American Indian myths about twins is the distinction made between the first-born twin, who is generally the hero and doer of good (or the 'good guy' in modern Western-story terminology), and the younger twin, who is frequently a magic maker or sorcerer, and the 'bad guy'. When it comes to mortal twins, however, American Indians lean to the belief that both twins are born to be 'bad guys', or, at least, bad portents. (As one Indian chief allegedly observed, 'Papoose double make heap trouble.') A former practice of some California Indians was to smother either both twins at birth or the second-born of the pair (or the girl in an opposite-sex pair). Zuñi pueblo Indians and some Navahos – despite their having deities who were twins – scornfully likened twins to litters of lower animals. The Mohave Indians, however, believed that twins were the reincarnation of an old person returned to earth in double form; so twins were treated with the same respect shown to the old.

Most African primitives, like most Indians, generally take a cold or suspicious view of twins. In many tribes twins are regarded as products of evil spirits, and the mother bearing them as accursed. In some parts of West Africa almost the worst thing you can tell a woman is 'May you become the mother of twins!' Often a woman who does bear twins is required to go through purification rites, and in extreme cases mothers of twins have been put to death. The Kaffirs were said to have treated a mother of twins as a disgraced female, in accord with the belief of many primitives that twins are sired by two fathers and that the woman bearing them must therefore have committed adultery. Thus, in some Zulu tribes only one of a pair was legitimized, the other being left nameless.

The practice of killing one or both twins was widespread among primitive peoples as diverse as the Eskimos, the Ainus of Japan, Australian aborigines, numerous Africans, and various North and South American Indians. Usually this practice stemmed from the excessive difficulty of sustaining and rearing two infants at the same time, a particular burden for people engaged in a constant struggle for existence. Among the Eskimos, where tribes were continually on the move in search of food, it was also extremely difficult, if not impossible, for a mother to carry two infants on her back simultaneously. Other factors also entered into the practice of killing twins. Among the Ashanti of West Africa twins were not killed except when born in a royal family, in this case very possibly because of the problem of succession to the throne. (How European royalty has dealt with this aspect of twinship was discussed in

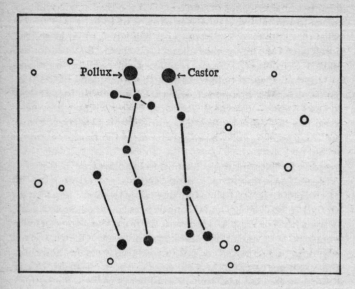

GEMINI: 'THE TWINS' CONSTELLATION

Tender Gemini in strict embrace
Stand clos'd and smiling at each other's face.

from 'Astronomica' by MARCUS MANILIUS (A.D. 20)

The 'Gemini' constellation is located immediately above and to the east of Orion. At the heads of the constellation are the bright stars named Pollux and Castor, after the twin warrior sons of Zeus in Greek mythology (or of Jupiter in Roman mythology). Lesser stars in the constellation, if connected by imaginary lines as shown above, will give the appearance of twin 'stick' figures.

Chapter 8.) The Incas of Peru regarded twins as an ideal sacrifice to propitiate the gods of pestilence and famine.

Boy–girl twin pairs have been singled out among most primitives for special treatment – usually worse than for same-sex twins, but occasionally more favourable. Many primitive peoples of the Pacific islands of Oceania, Micronesia, and of other regions, shared the belief that twins of opposite sex had had an unwholesome relationship in the womb, and thus looked at these twins askance or even killed them at birth. In Bali this practice was (and may still be) followed among the common people, but not by the upper castes, according to Professor Edwin M. Loeb of the University of California. In contrast, Dr Loeb also reported that some Bantu tribes in Africa hail twins of opposite sex with joy as infant 'newlyweds' who had been 'married in the womb'. In the Philippines, certain tribes actually required members of the male–female twin pairs to marry each other when they matured, as did some of the ancient Japanese.

Happily, one can also tell of many primitive groups which accord a bright reception to twins of all kinds. The Dahomeans of West Africa have a joyous ceremonial when twins are born. Among the Ewe of Africa the mother of twins proudly wears special adornments; and the Berber Moors address the mother of twins as 'my Lady'. In the Nigerian Benin district the birth of twins is publicly celebrated, and the king provides a wet nurse for them.* Among some African peoples, parents of twins are associated with fertility, and are called on to perform rites over seeded land, plants, and domestic animals to stimulate reproduction. Parents who have had more than one set of twins are in special demand to preside at these rituals.

An interesting custom in several African tribes is that of fashioning little carved figures to represent twins. This practice has been carried out most elaborately by the Yoruba Negro tribes, living chiefly in the western part of what is now Nigeria, and in the region once known as the African Slave Coast. (Many American Negroes are of Yoruba descent.) There is good reason why the Yorubas should be twin-minded, for they are the most prolific producers of twins in the world, as noted in Chapter 5, with a reported incidence of up to one twin birth in every twenty-five pregnancies. Proud of twins, the Yorubas believe them to be good-luck omens, the embodiment of spirits who entered the womb desiring to be born as humans. After twins arrive, their parents have two carved figures

---

* Customs and practices regarding twins in African tribes, as reported here, prevailed until quite recently, but in rapidly changing Africa they may not now be the same.

made to symbolize them. (These figurines, about seven inches high and known as 'Ibeji', are in no sense likenesses, inasmuch as they usually have a mature form, with oversized heads.) Professor Paul Wingert of Columbia University, an expert on primitive art, told me that if one of a Yoruba twin pair dies, his or her figurine is lovingly looked after – often carried about by the survivor – and 'fed', washed and dressed like the living twin. If both twins die, the two figures are cared for by the parents. The family keeps them in a little shrine for generations, and, as successive twins are born, sometimes a score or more of the 'Ibeji' will accumulate in a household.

Other African tribes known to have twin figures include the Chokve of Angola, among whom the survivor of a twin pair always carries a symbolic little figure representing his lost twin, and the Agotime of Togoland, where the mother of dead twins carries a pair of wooden dolls to replace them. (See illustration opposite.)

One may gather from the great variety of myths and conflicting practices regarding twins that there is no instinctive, or natural, reaction to them among human beings. We have seen that while many people welcome twins, many others do not; some regard them as portents of good, some as evil omens. Often we find a certain logic in the attitudes. To people who have no clear idea of how even a singleton baby is conceived and produced, any birth out of the ordinary may seem awesomely divine or fearfully diabolic, depending on how the results are interpreted. The bad reaction to twins could easily have arisen from the various disadvantages and problems they present, especially under severe hardship conditions where even an excessive number of singleton children may be regarded as an affliction. On the other hand, in the more favoured groups where children are ardently desired, the advantages and joys of having twins (or of being one of twins) would be most strongly stressed, and twins would most likely be received with open arms. All of these situations and attitudes are reflected in the various ways in which twins are received by individual parents and families in our own world.

Again, if some of the primitive beliefs about twins seem wholly preposterous, it might be well to remind ourselves that no less preposterous notions have been held and circulated among peoples of

PRIMITIVE TWIN SYMBOLS
Used in West African tribes

'Substitute' twin dolls carried by mother of twins one of whom has been lost.

Doll, representing the lost twin, is carried by the survivor throughout his childhood.

Twin

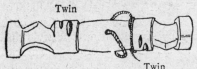

Twin

'Fertility' figure, representing twins, is used to make magic in inducing fertility.

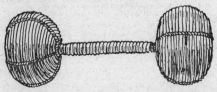

Twin 'warning rattle' is carried by mothers of twins in some tribes and shaken to warn off other people.

'Consoling' twin dolls are carried by mother who has lost both twins.

what is called the civilized world. In old European histories there are many exaggerated accounts of enormous litters of twins born to this or that woman. Most fantastic is the solemnly presented story that in the year 1276 a Dutch countess, Margaret of Henneberg, was punished by Providence for mocking a poor mother '*by being delivered of three hundred and sixty-five children, in bigness all like newbred mice*'. Of this total (one for each day of the year), 182 were allegedly sons, and 182 daughters. The odd one, ingeniously, is reported as a 'hermaphrodite'. It is further stated that the Bishop of Utrecht baptized the supercolossal supertwin litter *en masse* and, to simplify matters, named all the males 'John' and all the females 'Elizabeth'. (What he named the hermaphrodite is not recorded.) Immediately after the baptism, the accounts conclude, all the infants and their wicked mother died.

This story, and similar accounts of fantastic supertwin births, continued to be published in books and believed in by Europeans for centuries. Nor were the Puritan Fathers of America beyond such beliefs. The spirited nonconformist, Anne Hutchinson, who was banished from the Massachusetts Bay Colony in 1638, was solemnly reported in the writings of the Reverend Samuel Clarke as having brought forth 'thirty monstrous births at once, in punishment of her monstrous heresies'. (The same Anne later helped to found Portsmouth, Rhode Island.)

In the fields of drama and fiction, we find, happily, that twins have usually been dealt with in a lighter vein. The pattern for this was set by the ancient Greek dramatists, one of their favourite themes being mistaken identity involving twins or one twin changing places with the other to mislead people. This theme was used by the Roman dramatist, Titus Plautus, in his comedy *The Menaechmi* produced two thousand years ago. The plot deals with the identical-twin sons of a merchant of Syracuse, one of whom wandered off and was lost as a child, and of the adventures and mix-ups that befell them before the twins were re-united. Versions of this comedy appeared thereafter in many countries and in many languages. In some variations the twins became an 'identical-looking' male–female pair, for it was a common notion of dramatists and storytellers (and occasionally is even today) that twinship could make a brother and sister almost identical in appearance, quite contrary to what we now know to be the fact.

Shakespeare is among those who borrowed heavily from these early plots. In *The Comedy of Errors* we have mix-ups involving two sets of identical-twin males – one pair of noble birth, one pair their servants – born, significantly, in that same city of Syracuse in which the ancient Plautus comedy was set. In a second play of Shakespeare's, *Twelfth-Night, or, What You Will*, we have variations on the other early theme of mix-ups between a brother–sister pair of twins – in this case, Sebastian and Viola, who, when clothed, are presumably exact look-alikes. Shakespeare may have had a personal interest in this latter plot, for he himself was reputedly the father of a boy–girl twin pair, Hamnet and Judith. This may also explain his preoccupation with twins in *The Comedy of Errors*, and his references to twins elsewhere.*

The twin-comedy bridge from Plautus to Shakespeare was further extended into our own times with the Broadway production, in 1938, of the musical comedy hit, *The Boys from Syracuse*, which composer Richard Rodgers and lyricist Lorenz Hart adapted (more or less) from *The Comedy of Errors*. An earlier Broadway musical hit was *Two Little Girls in Blue*, in which the talented Fairbanks identical twins, Madeline and Mariane, starred in the roles of twin sisters involved in some ship-board mix-ups. (During the play's long run a special performance was given for an audience made up entirely of adult twins. Recalling this, one of the women who attended wrote to me, 'I remember feeling distressed at seeing so many elderly women twins still dressed alike.')

Triplets were the central characters in still another great Broad-

---

* Other plays in which Shakespeare deals with or refers to twins or twinship include: *Henry V*, Act IV, Scene 1, line 253 (*K. Hen.* 'O hard conditions, twin-born with greatness'); *Henry VIII*, Act IV, Scene 2 (*Grif.* 'Those twins of learning that he rais'd in you, Ipswich and Oxford!'); *Merry Wives of Windsor*, Act II, Scene 1 (*Mrs Page.* '. . . To thy great comfort . . . here's the twin-brother of thy letter'); *Coriolanus*, Act IV, Scene 4 (*Cor.* '. . . Whose house, whose bed . . . Are still together, who twin, as 'twere'); *Othello*, Act II, Scene 3 (*Oth.* 'Now, by heaven . . . Though he had twinn'd with me, both at birth'); *The Winter's Tale*, Act I, Scene 2 (*Pol.* 'We were as twinn'd lambs that did frisk i' the sun'); *Antony and Cleopatra*, Act III, Scene 10 (*Scar.* 'When vantage like a pair of twins appear'd').

way musical comedy, *The Band Wagon*, which opened in 1937 with
Fred and Adele Astaire as stars. The show had as funny a song as
ever written on the supertwin theme, with words by Howard Dietz
and music by Arthur Schwartz. Entitled 'Triplets',* its chorus
went as follows:

> We do everything alike;
> We look alike, we dress alike, we walk alike,
>   we talk alike, and what is more we
>   hate each other very much.
> We hate our folks, we're sick of jokes on
>   what an art it is to tell us apart.
> . If one of us gets the measles, another one gets
>   the measles, then all of us get the
>   measles and mumps and croup.
> How I wish I had a gun, a little gun, it
>   would be fun to shoot the other two
>   and be only one.

In novels and short stories, which came on the creative scene
only in recent centuries, there have been countless twins among the
characters. The fictional plots, like those in plays, most often have
been involved with mistaken identities or with identical twins
changing places. A number of notable works, however, have dwelt
on such aspects of twinship as bitter rivalry between twins, or their
strong and sometimes psychic attachment. The Dumas novel, *The
Vicomte de Bragelonne*, made use of the legend that France's 'Man
in the Iron Mask' was actually the twin brother of Louis XIV,
whom the King sought to keep out of the way. Dumas dealt again
with twins in *The Corsican Brothers*, one of whom avenges the
death of the other. Rivalry between identical twins is, again, the
dominant theme in the novel *Esau and Jacob* (recently translated
into English) by the late famed Brazilian writer, Machado de Assiz.

Opposite-sex twins have been dramatically depicted in many
works – usually in tragic emotional or even sexual involvement.
Most notable are the male–female twins Siegmund and Sieglinde
in Wagner's opera *Die Walküre*. (Thomas Mann drew inspiration
from these ill-fated twins in his short story about another male–

TWEEDLEDUM AND TWEEDLEDEE

The most famous identical twins in literature are these two droll characters from Lewis Carroll's classic *Through the Looking Glass*, as depicted in the original drawing by the famed artist, Sir John Tenniel. The names were not original with Carroll, having long been applied in situations where two persons, things or alternatives were nominally different but yet so much the same there was little to choose between one and the other. (The earliest recorded use of 'tweedledum and tweedledee' was in 1720, in a satirical verse by John Byrom about the rival musicians, Handel and Bononcini.)

female pair, *The Blood of the Walsungs*.) And Edgar Allan Poe, in his *The Fall of the House of Usher*, portrayed a weird brother–sister twin pair. The presumed mystic bond between twins – a favourite theme – was dealt with by Thornton Wilder (himself a twin), in his novel *The Bridge of San Luis Rey*.

However, as in plays and musical comedies, most fictional twins have been happy characters, and this is particularly true of the twins who have appeared in scores of books for children. (Some of these books can be found in almost every bookshop or public library.) Mark Twain was much intrigued by the twin theme. In *The Prince and the Pauper* he deals with pseudo-twins – two lads who, though unrelated, are so alike in looks that they could pass for identical twins. Another pair of unrelated look-alikes, who were exchanged as infants, appear in Twain's satirical narrative, *Pudd'nhead Wilson*, and among the other characters is a pair of true identicals. Still another Twain satire, 'These Extraordinary Twins', deals with a Siamese pair.

America's greatest humorist, Twain also got fun out of pretending that he himself had been a twin. On one occasion (reported in the book, *Mark Twain Tonight*, by his impersonator, Hal Holbrook), Twain confused a pesky newspaper reporter by confiding, 'My twin and I got mixed up in the bathtub when we were only two weeks old, and one of us drowned but we didn't know which. Some think it was Bill, and some think it was me.' Asked what he himself thought, Twain sighed, 'I would give worlds to know.' And then he whispered, 'But I'll tell you a secret . . . One of us had a peculiar mark – a large mole on the back of his left hand; that was *me. That child was the one that was drowned.*'

Closely similar in theme to Mark Twain's story – and perhaps even having inspired it – is the humorous verse classic, 'The Twins', written by Henry Sambrooke Leigh (1837–83). Long popular as a piece to be recited by twins, it started off, as did the Twain story, with one of the identical pair telling how he and his twin had been mixed up in the bathtub soon after their birth, so that '. . . my brother John got christened me, and I got christened him.'* The narrator goes on to tell how he was flogged in school in place of his nitwit twin; how his 'intended bride became his brother's wife'; and how, year after year,

* A real-life situation, paralleling the fictitious twin mix-ups, occurred with the noted Guttmacher twins, Drs Alan (referred to earlier in this book) and Manfred (Baltimore psychiatrist). As told by Alan, when he and his twin were born, they were identified by different-coloured ribbons; but a nurse, after bathing them, tearfully told their parents she had mixed up the ribbons and didn't know which twin was Alan and which Manfred. The parents thought they could tell, but the present Alan was never sure he was the one originally so named. The question achieved practical importance when, some years later, a godfather willed $500 to 'Alan' as having been the first-born. The twins thereupon divided the money. (Today Dr Alan Guttmacher – a world-famed authority on twins – advocates that immediately after the birth of an identical-twin pair, the one born first be tattooed with a small, permanent identifying mark.)

The same absurd mistakes went on,
And when I died, the neighbors came,
And buried brother John. *

In the movies there have been innumerable films with mix-ups between identical twins as the central theme. One example was *The Parent Trap*, in which a pair of girl identicals connive to get their divorced parents to remarry. Of particular interest have been several film comedies about supertwins. In 1943 there was the uproarious *The Miracle of Morgan's Creek*, about the arrival of sextuplets in an American backwoods area. In another comedy, *The Sheep Has Five Legs*, the French star, Fernandel, had a field day enacting five identical quintuplet brothers, each in a different occupation.

The comic strips also have had their twins. Most famous – dating back to the very beginning of the Sunday comics, in the late nineties, and still running – are 'The Katzenjammer Kids' (or, in another version, 'The Captain and the Kids'), presenting twin brats, who, with different-coloured hair, are presumably fraternals. More recent arrivals in the comics have been 'The Jackson Twins'.

Perhaps it is significant that while twins have been given comedy roles in innumerable books, plays, movies and features, they have been principals in relatively few tragedies. Which is as it should be; for, by and large – despite what some pessimistic modern theorists might try to tell us – twinship is more often productive of mirthful situations than of sad ones.

*The entire poem will be found in many collections of humorous verse.

CHAPTER 23

The Studies of Twins

IN a lovely old section of Rome stands a beautiful modern building which is one of the unique scientific institutions in the world: It is devoted chiefly to the study of *twins*.

Officially named the 'Gregor Mendel Institute' (after the discoverer of the basic principles of heredity), there could be no more fitting site for this 'House of Twins' than the city which, legend had it, was founded by the twins Romulus and Remus. The institution grew from the dream of its guiding spirit, Dr Luigi Gedda – a medical scientist with a special interest in twins – who enlisted widespread support for the enterprise from leaders of government, science and industry in Italy. Opened in 1953, it has been the centre of the examination and study of thousands of pairs of twins. From the Institute, also, has come a stream of publications about twins, including a quarterly which gives much attention to twins, *Acta Genetica, Medica et Gemellologiae* (the last word being Italian for 'twin study').

In many other institutions throughout the world – at colleges, research institutes, and hospitals – twin studies also have been carried on for many years. In addition, thousands of medical men, geneticists, psychologists and other scientists working independently have been studying and reporting on twins. The results can be seen in the hundreds of new listings under 'Twins' which appear in scientific and medical journals each year.

What accounts for all of this scientific preoccupation with human beings who just happen to have been born two or more at a time? (Or, as a pair of Southern twin belles said to me, 'Why are yo' all so in'trested in li'l old us?') As you may already know from the facts that have been presented in this book, there are indeed many reasons why twins and parents of twins are called upon to supply information to scientists. Obviously, much of this information can be of direct benefit to twins themselves. But, in a larger sense, twins, through their own lives and experiences, are often in a position to render service to other members of their families and to human beings generally.

Let us first look briefly into the history of twin studies. Until the last quarter of the nineteenth century the area of knowledge about twins was almost a barren waste, marked only here and there by scrubby legends and folk tales, and with only a few sprouts of medical observations that had some scientific validity. Notice had been taken of the different types of twins, and of peculiarities or abnormalities that might occur in both of a pair, such as Siamese twins, and there was speculation as to how these might be produced. Also, in 1865, a Scots doctor, J. M. Duncan, reported that there seemed to be some connection between mothers' ages and their chances of having twins (a deduction which, as we've seen, has been amply confirmed).

But it remained for Francis Galton, an eminent British scientist and a cousin of Charles Darwin, to first recognize the broader possibilities in twin study. In 1875 he began publishing reports on his observations of twins. Among other things, he made the guess that look-alike twins were alike in their hereditary factors and might come from a single egg, whereas look-different twins were different in hereditary makeup and might be products of two different eggs. Though there was then no evidence to back up his guess, Dr Galton made the further deduction that a study of the two types of twins could throw light on the relative influences of 'nature' (heredity) and 'nurture' (environment). He sought facts from and about large numbers of twins; but, bearing in mind that it was not known at the time how to distinguish accurately between identical and fraternal twins, or how the process of heredity worked, his methods, findings, and deductions, while opening new avenues of research, had many flaws.

Only a few other twin studies of importance (listed in the Appendix, 'Trailblazers') followed after Galton's initial attempt. A more scientific background was needed. This began to be supplied at the dawn of the century when Mendel's theories about heredity, although formulated back in 1865 with respect to plants, were recognized as holding good for human beings as well as for all other living things. Before long, the new study of twins became directly interwoven with the study of heredity. Additional findings about human inheritance showed how identical twins differed from fraternals, and how the two types could be distinguished. In turn, studies of identical compared with fraternal twins threw increasing light on which traits were largely or almost wholly hereditary, and which were not, or were due largely or wholly to environment.

In general, the studies in which twins or their parents have been asked (or may be asked) to participate, involve the following methods, and the gathering of material along these lines:

– *Prenatal and birth experiences* of twins. The compiling of statistics and information about twin conceptions, prenatal development, and delivery conditions. This has been of much value in illuminating the road to twin births, suggesting how to prepare for more successful twin maternities, stimulating the development of safer methods for twin delivery, and insuring twins a better chance of survival.

– *Trait-similarity* studies. These seek to find the extent to which the same given traits (physical, biochemical, pathological) appear in both members of identical-twin pairs as compared with both members of fraternal pairs. Since identicals have matching hereditary factors, whereas those of fraternal twins may differ, such studies help to show how far any trait is or is not influenced by heredity. Findings from these investigations have thrown light on the nature and causes of innumerable diseases and defects, as well as on the derivation and development of normal traits.

– *Longitudinal* studies of twins. These refer to continuing studies for extended periods of sizable groups of twins, following up their development from birth through childhood and comparing their growth rates, health and progress with the standards for singletons.

– *Comparison* studies of twins and singletons. Identical or fraternal twins are compared with singleton siblings in given traits, to find out whether these traits do or do not occur more often in twins. By this means added knowledge may be gained as to how far the special environment of twins, before or after birth, may tend to make them different from other persons. While such studies have revealed some of the initial drawbacks of twinship, they have also helped to show that once twins pass safely through childhood they have much the same chance for health, longevity and social adjustment as do other members of their respective families.

– *Twins' psychological relationships.* Studies in this area seek to investigate the nature and effects of rivalry and jealousy between twins; dominance of one twin over the other; separating or keeping twins together in school; being the 'oldest' or 'youngest' of a pair; undue attachment of twins to each other, and so on. Many of the findings from these studies (including those made by the author) have been presented in preceding chapters of this book. But much more about these aspects of twinship remains to be explored.

– *Co-twin control* studies. These involve the deliberately different training or conditioning of two members of a highly similar identical-twin pair in specific ways and for a prescribed period, and then seeing what trait differences develop between them – and how long these last – as a result of the differences in training or other environmental influences. The co-twin control method was first experimented with in 1905 by K. Elsässer, who put two newborn identical twins in different sleeping positions to learn how far infants' head shapes could be modified by such means. Various other co-twin control experiments have been made since then, mainly with respect to behaviour conditioning or to evaluate the effects of given treatments, diets, and exercises. (Results of one of these experiments were reported in Chapter 16.)

– *Reared-apart identical twins.* Findings from studies of twins who were separated early in life and reared in different homes and environments have been dealt with at length in Chapters 14, 15, and 16. The general conclusions drawn from studies of such separated and reared-apart twins is that heredity exerts its strongest effects on looks and physical build, but has less pronounced effects (though still very important) in producing similarities in intelligence, behaviour and personality, and achievements. In weighing the findings with respect to any given separated pair of identical twins, it is important to consider the degree of difference in their environments. For, where the physical and cultural environments were much alike, it is far harder to ascribe the similarities between the twins to heredity than it is when their environments were very different.

That all these studies of twins have contributed greatly to the scientific knowledge about human beings is attested to by the detailed attention given to such studies in medical literature and in college textbooks of psychology, human genetics, and other subjects. Thus, parents of twins – and twins themselves – who are asked to aid in these studies can feel that they are in a unique and privileged position to be of service to other people as well as to themselves.

CHAPTER 24

You and Your Twin – or Twins

'I KNOW that the statistics about twins are important, but *my two identicals aren't statistics* – they're a couple of very much alive little boys! So just what will you tell me about *them* that will really be helpful?' A mother asked this question soon after I had begun work on this book. Similar questions popped up repeatedly thereafter whenever I talked to parents of twins, or to adult twins, and told them what I was working on. Now that the book has been written and we've come to our concluding chapter, I hope that the practical – and personal – value of the information presented has been made clear to readers.

First, if you are a *parent* of twins, how do you sum up the pros and cons of having twins? While the overwhelming majority of the parents we queried did indeed say they were delighted with their twins, it also was apparent that a great many were worried about them. This was hardly surprising, for, as we noted at the outset of our book, there has been a tendency in recent decades to play up the problems, difficulties and disadvantages which may come with twins, and which have frightened parents into thinking that everything must be done to eradicate or suppress twinship relations. We have made clear that many of the arguments for individualizing twins (by different dress, separate classrooms, conditioning them to be apart as much as possible, and so on) are only theories, without scientific evidence to back them up. To throw out twinship because of these cloudy theories is a little like throwing out the baby with the bathwater.

We have certainly not implied that all modern psychological teachings or suggestions about twin-rearing are questionable or of little value. Some of them, as we noted, have contributed greatly towards a better understanding of twins, as they have of all children. At the same time it must be recognized that many aspects of the twin-rearing theories are only extensions of general child-rearing theories. And there is much to indicate – as many psychologists now would be the first to admit – that a good deal of what has been said about child-rearing in the name of psychology is open to doubt, and has brought unjustified fears and grief to parents who have accepted untested theories as gospel.

Specifically, many psychologists have recognized that much confusion, and perhaps considerable damage, has been caused by the successive waves of child-rearing dogmas, ranging from extreme 'restrictiveness' (forcing the child into specified patterns of behaviour) to extreme 'permissiveness' (letting the child develop in any which way, according to his impulses). As the failings of various child-rearing formulas and generalizations have become apparent, there has been a counter-tendency to advise moderation and common sense. A growing trend is to recognize that just as there are many kinds of children in many circumstances and family settings, there are many possible variations in the ways that children can be helped to develop and fulfil themselves adequately. And this most certainly applies to twins.

Not only can there be no set formula for rearing twins but, as we also pointed out in previous chapters, serious mistakes can be made if one attempts to apply the same formula to all twins, regardless of whether they are identicals or fraternals of the same sex, or a male–female pair. For each type, and for each individual pair, the needs and problems may be different. In the case of identicals, the prevalent fear is that they may become too attached to, and dependent on, each other (not sufficiently individualized). It is indeed a grave error to try to bring up identical twins as if they were halves of the same person; to make them believe they *must* always be close to each other, and that they should feel guilty if they aren't close. Any attachment between identicals (or other twins) that is compulsive – forced, resented or maintained as if under a spell – may very well threaten their future adjustment, and should be discouraged or eased into a freer and more desirable relationship. On the other hand, an attachment between twins that is based on true liking, understanding, and mutual interests should be welcomed fully as much as one between two singleton siblings. When twins are getting along happily together, one should think twice before trying to break up what may well be one of the most rewarding kinds of human experience.

In the case of fraternal twins of the same sex, the sensible conclusion is not to try to rear them as if they were identical twins. This does not mean that the twinship of fraternals should be ignored, for the fact of their being born together and nurtured together in their early years does create a special bond between them. It may well form the basis of a lasting and cherished brotherly or sisterly attachment going beyond that of any two singletons. But how strong this fraternal twinship attachment can be, or should be encouraged to be, must depend largely on the traits and inclinations of the two individuals concerned. In most cases, however, the relationship between fraternals can be expected to diminish and, if there are worries about it, to present few difficulties as time goes on.

In male–female twin pairs, as we've also stressed, there is the least degree of natural twinship. Little good can therefore result from trying to force similarity or undue attachment upon a boy–girl pair; and particularly so in a world which expects each person to manifest traits and attributes considered proper for his or her sex. It might seem best, then, to rear each of the two members of a boy–girl twin pair in much the same way that parents would rear an individual girl and an individual boy, without thinking too much of their twin birth. If this policy is followed, the two will seldom have any problems of adjustment (other than the minor ones discussed in Chapter 18).

In short, once parents have an understanding of the nature of their twins, the wisest procedure may be to give the twinship only the importance that the facts justify, and at the same time to raise each of the twins according to his or her own traits and capacities. How alike or how differently twins should be treated can be governed by how similar or dissimilar they reveal themselves to be in makeup, abilities, and interests. With this in mind, parents can allow themselves considerable leeway in deciding *whether*, *when*, and for *how long* their twins should or should not be dressed alike, given the same playthings, put in the same classroom, sent to the same summer camp, or in other respects conditioned towards or away from togetherness.

Any policy embarked upon with respect to a given pair of twins should continually be evaluated as to how well it is working out. Usually the twins themselves provide the clue. In time, also, most parents may find that they can ease their fears about the psychological adjustment of the twins. The emotional difficulties of twins are seldom more serious than those of singletons in the same family, nor are their conflicts apt to be more acute. Badly maladjusted twins may stand out like two swollen red thumbs. But we will recall from Chapter 22 that when the emotional disorders of twins are truly serious, it is almost invariably because of abnormal or unfavourable home conditions and/or some inborn instability which would have led to about the same unfortunate results in singletons.

Worries about the normality of twins, in their health and mental capacities, also, as a rule, go much beyond what the facts justify. We are not forgetting about the 'preemies', and the anxiety which attends their initial period; nor can we be unmindful of the fact that 3 per cent of all surviving twins (as compared with 2 per cent of singletons) remain handicapped in body or mind. These are casualties along life's highway for which only rarely can anyone be blamed. The same accidents happen to singletons, and, in numbers, there are far more cases of two defective singletons in a family than there are of defective twins. This may be small comfort to the parents whose twins are among the unlucky ones. They need all the sympathy and help they can get. One can say only that growing hope for many handicapped children is being offered by new treatments, by advances in special educational methods and institutional care, and by increasing concern on the part of scientists, the public and the government. For future twins, improvements in prenatal conditions and in delivery techniques will undoubtedly reduce the number entering the world with defects.

But even now, as we've repeatedly emphasized, the great majority of twins come safely through their first years, and thereafter are in every way as sound, alert and capable as are the singleborn. Any fears that twins are perforce delicate individuals should have been eased by the list (presented in Chapter 23) of twins who have won top laurels in rigorous sports; while any doubts about twins' mental capacities should have been dispelled by the roster of twins with high IQs and those eminent in many fields of achievement

(Chapter 13). What one or both of *your* twins can or can't do in the world depends far more on factors other than their twinship.

In sum, parents of twins can accept the fact that any problems and worries that go with rearing twins are rarely more than extensions of similar problems that go with singletons. The same measures of common sense, love and understanding which resolve difficulties with other children can almost always resolve those with twins. Given a happy home atmosphere and twins who are physically and mentally normal, no special techniques or other self-conscious methods are needed to raise them to become well-adjusted individuals. One might especially bear in mind that if twins do present extra challenges, they also can bring excitement and pleasure much beyond that ordinarily coming with one-at-a-time children.

Now for *grown-up twins*: If you yourself are an adult twin, what conclusions might best be left with you?

Where this book may have been most helpful is in making clear your biological relationship to your twin, and what it has implied and still implies for both of you. If your twin is of the same sex, you should be reasonably sure by this time whether the two of you are an identical or a fraternal pair; if doubt remains, the tests referred to in Chapter 4 can clear them up.

Suppose you and your twin are an identical pair. You know, then, that all of your hereditary factors are the same, and that to whatever extent heredity has charted and can chart the courses of your lives, you will continue to be similar. But you also know that some of your similarities are due to environment – to your having been reared in the same home in the same way. Had you been raised apart – as the studies of separated identical twins have shown – you would not be nearly so alike, at least not in your thinking and personalities. As it is, you and your twin *were* reared apart in some degree, for your environments were never precisely the same, not even before birth; and your subsequent experiences, circumstances, illnesses, good and bad breaks all must have increased your differences. Further, any divergences in your education and careers, and not least – if you are married – in your family lives, must have compounded these differences. Thus, there should be no doubt that each of you is a complete and distinct individual.

Nor will your identical twinship prevent either of you from exercising your own will and being the 'master of your fate and the captain of your soul' to the same extent that any other human beings can be.

Moreover, no matter how close you and your identical twin may have been or choose to continue being, you might bear in mind (regrettably, if you would have preferred it otherwise) that science offers no support for the theory that there is any mystic bond between the two of you. If your thoughts seem to run along similar lines, if you often can sense what is in your twin's mind or what he or she is experiencing, you need not look for any supernatural explanation. What may seem like mental telepathy is often only the logical result of your long early association, the similarity in your mental workings, and your deep concern for each other. But, if for any reason you do not feel or desire closeness to your twin, it may be deplored, but it should not make you guilt-torn. The degree of your continued attachment must realistically be dictated by your mutual wishes and feelings of family responsibility. No law or moral code can say, 'Because you came from the same egg, you must forever thereafter be united.'

Yet it will not be surprising if you always feel yourself more closely linked with your identical twin than with any other living person, and have the knowledge that your twin feels the same way about you. You may look back to your childhood and recall the fun of confusing people or of attracting attention as one of a pair. You may think of the advantage of always having had with you a playmate, a fellow adventurer, a confidante. You may recognize that your twinship taught you very early about co-operation and learning to live with and adjust to another person. Or your memory may fix on some of the disadvantages of your twinship: Never being the sole object of attention as a child, never having anything all to yourself – not even a birthday; always having someone to be compared with, to try to equal, to have to think about and worry about. How you add up the score of your twinship will be a highly individual matter. In all likelihood, from what other identical twins have reported, your twinship score will be strongly on the plus side.

Suppose your twinship is of the *fraternal* type. Your relationship to your twin may then range from almost the same degree of closeness that exists between an identical pair to the extreme uninterest or even estrangement that sometimes is found between singleton siblings. When the latter situation exists, it can only be lamented. But it must be accepted as a possibility. Uninterest in your twinship may result if you and your fraternal twin have always been so dissimilar and your paths have gone so far apart that you now feel the two of you have little in common. Estrangement may develop if you got along badly as children because of clashes of temperament, conflicting interests, or marked differences in abilities and achievements. Often any marked degree of antagonism between twins may be less a result of their own inherent natures than a reflection of a generally discordant situation in the family. In any explosive home atmosphere, the children – twins or singletons – may well be propelled in different directions. But this would be the exception. In the case of most adult fraternal twins (and this is quite probably true for your twin and yourself) the evidence indicates that there was enough warmth and cohesiveness to keep them together in adult life, and closer than singleton siblings. The word *fraternal*, remember, means 'brotherly'. And if a warm brotherly or sisterly relationship is to be cherished, that which persists between fraternal twins throughout their lives should be especially valued.

Are you one of an *opposite-sex* twin pair? What you may have confirmed for yourself is that your natural twinship ties are quite probably weaker than those of twins of the same sex – particularly identical twins – but still stronger than those between most singleton brothers and sisters. Except for the first few years, when you were actively reared as twins, you normally would have been led to move apart. The growing awareness of your differences in sex – dictated both by nature and by your training – have always tended to pull the two of you more and more in divergent directions. The crucial period in your relations probably came during adolescence, for it is then (as noted in Chapter 18) that a boy–girl twinship is subjected to its greatest strain. Also governing the extent of your closeness in adult life will be the same factors (personality, interests, degree of family solidarity) which would have operated to keep the two of you together or move you apart had you been singleton siblings of opposite sex and close to the same age. Nevertheless, some degree of twinship feeling will have been preserved, for there is always – as with other fraternals – the remembrance of your starting out together in life, and having the same birthday.

One can argue about how much attachment there should be between adult brother–sister twins. It certainly is extremely bad if their attachment remains so close as to prevent either or both from achieving normal opposite-sex relationships and, sometimes, from marrying. It also is unfortunate if they break away from each other completely. What a brother–sister twin pair can contribute most to each other is a sympathetic understanding of the opposite sex which singletons and people generally do not acquire. Continuance of a warm, mutual brother-and-sister devotion can surely enrich both of their lives. As a rule, it is the sister of the pair who mainly determines whether the twinship feeling is maintained and sustained, in keeping with the fact that women tend to be more sentimental and family-minded than men.

And now, as we come to the end of our book, the author hopes that it has proved helpful to all of you who are twins, who have twins or are otherwise interested in twins. Twins always will have a special place among human beings because not only are they unusual but also, as has now been recognized, the facts about them can be helpful to other human beings. The more we learn about twins, their development and relationships, and the handling of their problems, the better insights we will acquire into all children and grownups, and the ways of making them happier.

If there is any final message that can be conveyed by the author after his own long and satisfying exploration into the world of twins, it would be this:

Those of you who are parents of twins have every reason, in the great majority of cases, to feel yourself fortunate.

Enjoy your twins.

And those of you who are twins yourselves should also, in the great majority of cases, have reason to consider yourself fortunate in sharing what can be among the most rewarding of human experiences.

Enjoy your twinship.

As for myself, I can endorse these sentiments in no stronger way than by saying, in all sincerity. 'I wish that *I* had a twin.'

Appendix

TRAILBLAZERS IN TWIN STUDY

HERE are listed, chronologically, the pioneer scientists, findings, and events which blazed trails for our present-day knowledge about twins. Entries are carried to the year 1940. Those of importance thereafter are almost all cited in the text or referred to in the Bibliography.

1865   J. M. Duncan (Scotland) notes relationship between mother's age and chances of having twins (more for older mothers).

1875   Francis Galton (England) notes distinction between two kinds of twins, guesses they may be the products respectively of one egg and of two eggs, and makes first study of 'look-alike' and 'look-different' twins to throw light on the relative importance of 'nature' (heredity) and 'nurture' (environment). Published 'The History of Twins, etc.' in *Fraser's Mag.*, 12:566ff. Also, 'Short notes on heredity, etc., in twins.' *J. Anthrop. Inst.*, Great Britain and Ireland, 5:324ff.

1883   Galton's book, *The History of Twins*, published.

1885   G. Veit reports on frequencies of twin, triplet and quadruplet births in Germany.

1895   D. Hellin formulates law by which ratios of triplets, quadruplets and quintuplets to twins are governed.

1898   J. Bertillon finds that twin incidence is highest in mothers aged thirty-six to forty.

1901   W. Weinberg works out principle for estimating the relative proportion of one-egg to two-egg twins at birth.

1905   E. L. Thorndike compares mental performances of identical and fraternal twin pairs to throw light on inheritance of intelligence.

1906   K. Elsässer makes first 'co-twin control' study of effect on head shapes of identical-twin infants by putting them in different sleeping positions.

1907–1909   Galton publishes *History of Twins* (2nd ed.) and *Memories of My Life*, summing up his observations on twins.

1909   H. H. Newman and J. T. Paterson, reporting on discovery of how identical quadruplets are produced in armadillos, establish fact that one-egg twinning takes place among mammals.

1917 H. H. Newman publishes *The Biology of Twins*, the first of a number of important books in the field.

1922 Paul Popenoe makes first report on identical twins separated in infancy and reared apart.

1922 L. B. Arey coins terms 'monozygotic' and 'dizygotic' for one-egg and two-egg twins.

1924 H. W. Siemens reports on skin defects in many pairs of twins and several sets of triplets, and proposes a 'concordance–discordance' testing method by which identical twins can be distinguished from fraternals.

1926 Gunnar Dahlberg publishes *Twin Births and Twins from a Hereditary Point of View*, the first detailed work on the inheritance of physical characteristics in twins and others.

1927 Discovery of new blood groups M-N, P and S by Karl Landsteiner and Philip Levine greatly increases the accuracy of 'twin-typing' tests.

1929 Arnold Gesell and Helen Thompson report on a co-twin control performance experiment with a pair of girl twins.

1931 M. T. Lassen shows that identical twins can have different placentas.

1931 First twin reunion, later to develop into International Twins Association, held in Warsaw, Indiana, arranged by Edward M. Clink and his twin sister.

1932–1936 Soviet studies and extensive experiments made on twins at the Maxim Gorky Institute in Moscow, to throw light on relative influences of heredity and environment, but project abruptly terminated when held in conflict with Communist ideology. (No further Soviet twin studies until political and ideological shifts in the 1960s.)

1934 Dionne quintuplets born, the first quintuplets to survive as an intact set (and the only all-identical set to date).

1936 Franz J. Kallmann begins studies of twins.

1936 Twin dairy calves are used in experiments at Animal Breeding Institute at Wiad, Sweden.

1937 W. E. Blatz and group of Canadian scientists publish report on detailed studies of the Dionne quintuplets.

1937 Lionel Penrose – reporting on identical twins, only one of whom had congenital syphilis – proves that prenatal influence can be different for two twins.

1939 O. von Vershuer shows further that the placental method of diagnosing one-egg and two-egg twins may often be wrong, and that about one pair in every four identical-twin pairs may have separate placentas and chorions.

1940   Halbert L. Dunn (Chief of U.S. Bureau of Vital Statistics) formulates detailed programme for gathering and compiling statistics on twins.

1940   A. S. Wiener and I. L. Leff show further how blood tests can be used in identifying identical twins.

Bibliography

THE literature on twins, dealing with the subjects discussed in this book, is so largely technical that most of the following references will be useful mainly to professional persons, teachers and college students. The references in popular, or non-technical, language are marked by a star (*). Books and periodicals listed will be found in most large university or medical libraries, and in many public libraries, although not every book or periodical will be found in every library. (When a particular item is urgently needed, the librarian usually can arrange to secure it.)

PRENATAL LIFE
(*Chapters 1, 2, 3*)

CONCEPTION AND PRENATAL DEVELOPMENT: Corner, George W. *Am. J. Obst. & Gynecol.* 70/5, November 1955. || Guttmacher, Alan F., and Kohl, Schuyler G. *Obst. & Gynecol.* 12/5, November 1958. || Gedda, Luigi. In, *Twins in History and Science* (Chas. C. Thomas, 1961), pp. 18–154.

DETECTING TWIN PREGNANCIES: Novotny, Charles A., *et al. J.A.M.A.*, October 1959. || Larks, S. D., and Golda, G. *Am. J. Obst. & Gynecol.* 90/8, 15 December 1964. || Hon, E. H., and Hess, O. W. *Am. J. Obst. & Gynecol.* 79:1012, May 1960. || *Ultrasonograms, *Sci. News Let.* 82:362, 8 December 1962. || *Telemetering, *Sci. News Let.* 84:338, 30 November 1963.

SEX DETERMINATION: Scheinfeld, Amram. In, *Your Heredity and Environment* (Lippincott, 1965), Chap. 7, pp. 42–5.

SIAMESE TWINS: Aird, L. *Brit. Med. J.* 1:1313, 1959. || Gedda, Luigi. In, *Twins in History and Science*, Chap. 7. || Walker, Norma Ford. *Acta Gen. Med. et Gemel.* 1/2, May 1952.

SURVIVAL AND BIRTH
(*Chapter 3*)

MORTALITY, PRENATAL, POSTNATAL: Seski, A. G., and Miller, L. A. *Obst. & Gynecol.* 21:227, 1963. || Barr, A., and Stevenson, A. C.

Annls. Hum. Genet. 25:131, 1961. || Butler, N. R., *et al. Lancet*, 7 December 1963. || *Vit. Stat. U.S.*, 1961, Vol. II, Sec. 4.

– SECOND TWIN, HIGHER MORTALITY: Wyshak, Grace, and White, Colin. *J.A.M.A.*, 30 November 1963.

PREMATURITY EFFECTS: Knobloch, Hilda, *et al. Am. J. Pub. Health* 49/9, September 1959. || Butler, N. R., *et al. Lancet*, 7 December 1963.

RETROLENTAL FIBROPLASIA EFFECTS: Lubchenco, Lula O. *Am. J. Dis. Child.* 106:101, 1963.

BIRTH WEIGHTS: Trimble, George X. *J.A.M.A.*, 5 October 1963. || U.S. Natl. Center for Health Statistics, Series 21, Nos. 3 and 6, 1965.

TWIN-TYPING TESTS

(*Chapter 4*)

TRAIT DIAGNOSIS OF TWIN TYPES: Sutton, H. Eldon, *et al. Am. J. Hum. Genet.* 14/1, March 1962. || Walker, Norma F. *Acta Genet. et Statist. Med.* 7/1, 1957. || Allen, Gordon. In, *Progress in Medical Genetics*, Vol. IV (Grune & Stratton, 1965), Chap. 8.

BLOOD-GROUP CRITERIA: Juel-Nielsen, N., *et al. Acta Genet.*, Basel 8:256, 1958.

EYES: Ziv, Benjamin. *A.M.A. Arch. Opthal.* 63:243, 1960.

FINGERPRINTS: Slater, Eliot. *Acta Psychiat.*, Scand. 39:1, 1963.

LEUCOCYTE TEST: Bain, B., and Lowenstein, L. *Science* 145:1315, 1964.

LOOKS: Cederlof, R., *et al. Acta Genet.*, Basel 11:338, 1961.

'MIXED-UP TWINS' CASE: Franceschetti, A., *et al.* (In French, English abstr.) *Bull. de l'Acad. Suisse des Sciences Med.*, Vol. 4, 5/6, 1948. || *George Kent. *Reader's Dig.* November 1951.

MIRROR-IMAGING, HANDEDNESS, SITUS INVERSUS: Torgersen, Johan. *Am. J. Hum. Genet.* 9:273, 1955. || Brandt, H., and Revaz, C. J. *Genet. Humaine, Geneva* 7:1, 1958. || Falek, Arthur. (Handedness.) *Am. J. Hum. Genet.* 11:1, March 1959.

PLACENTAS: Potter, E. L. *Am. J. Obst. & Gynecol.* 87:566, 1963. || Benirschke, K. *Obstet. Gynec.* 18:309, 19161.

CHANCES OF HAVING TWINS

(*Chapter 5*)

TWINNING INCIDENCES AND FACTORS INVOLVED: Scheinfeld, Amram, and Schachter, Joseph. (Bio-social effects.) *Proc. 2nd. Intl. Cong. Hum. Genet.* (Rome, 1961), Nos. 401, 403, || Bulmer, M. G. (Europe, Africa). *Annls. Hum. Genet.* 24/2, May 1960. || Eriksson,

Aldur (Finland). Acta Genet., Basel 12:242, 1962. ‖ Karn, Mary N. (England, Italy). *Acta Genet. Med. et Gemel.* 2/2, May 1953, and 3/1, January 1954. ‖ Inouye, Eiji (Japan). *Am. J. Hum. Genet.* 9/4, December 1957. ‖ McArthur, Norma (Australia). *Acta Genet. Med. et Gemel.* 3/1, 1958. ‖ Stocks, Percy (England and Wales). *Acta Genet. Med. et Gemel.* January 1962.

HEREDITARY AND FAMILIAL FACTORS: Bulmer, M. G. *Annls. Hum. Genet.* 23/1, 1958; 23/4, 1959; 24/1, 1960. ‖ Dahlberg, Gunnar (in German). *Acta Genet. Med. et Gemel.*, January 1952. ‖ Torgersen, J. *Am. J. Phys. Anthrop.* 9/4, December 1951. ‖ Waterhouse, J. A. H. *Brit. J. Soc. Med.* 4/4, 1950. ‖ White, Colin, and Wyshak, Grace. *Am. J. Pub. Health* 55/10, October 1965; *New Eng. J. Med.* 271/19, 5 November 1964.

LOWER ANIMAL TWINNING: (Cattle.) Mechling, Ed. A., II, and Carter, R. C. *J. of Hered.* 55/2, March–April 1964. ‖ Winchester, C. F. *Science*, 11 July 1952, p. 3. ‖ (Chimpanzees.) Peacock, L. J., and Rogers, C. M. *Science*, 10 April 1959, p. 959. ‖ (Marmosets.) Hampton, J. K. and Suzanne H. *Science*, Vol. 150, 12 November 1965. ‖ (Mice.) Wallace, M. E., and Williams, D. A. *J. of Med. Genet.* 2/1, March 1965.

HORMONAL INDUCTION OF HUMAN TWINNING: Milham, Samuel, Jr. *Lancet*, 12 September 1964, p. 566; comments on, Eriksson, Aldur W., *Lancet*, 12 December 1964:1299. ‖ *Fantastic drug that creates quintuplets. *Life Mag.* 59/7, 13 August 1965. ‖ *Advance in female fertility. *Look Mag.*, 19 May 1964.

REARING TWINS, PROBLEMS
(Chapters 6–11)

Books

*Graham, Phyllis. *The Care and Feeding of Twins*. Harper, 1955.
*Gehman, Betsy H. *Twins: Twice the Trouble, Twice the Fun*. Lippincott, 1965.

Booklets

*'. . . And Then There Were TWO.' Child Study Assn. of America, 1959.
*Twins in Infancy. Twin Mothers Club of Westchester (N.Y.), 1959.
*Twin Care. Ohio Federation of Mothers of Twins, 1956.
*For Two, Please. Main Line Mothers of Twins Club (Pennsylvania), 1959.

BIBLIOGRAPHY

Articles

Plank, Emma N. Reactions of mothers of twins. *Am. J. Orthopsychiat.* 28/1, January 1958. ‖ Leonard, Marjorie R. Twins: the myth and reality. *Child Study*, Spring, 1953.

PHYSICAL ASPECTS OF TWINS
(Chapter 12)

DEVELOPMENTAL, GENETIC, ANTHROPOMETRIC: Clark, Philip J. *Am. J. Hum. Genet.* 8/1, March 1956. ‖ Osato, S., and Awano, I. (in German). *Acta Genet. Med. Gemel.* 6/3, 1957. ‖ Sontag, L. W., and Garn, S. M. *Acta Genet. et Statist. Med.* 6/3, 1957. ‖ Vandenberg, S. G., and Strandskov, H. R. *Hum. Biol.* 36/1, 1964.

PREMATURITY EFFECTS: Dann, Margaret, *et al. Pediatrics* 22/6, December 1958. ‖ Drillien, Cecil M. *The Growth and Development of the Prematurely Born Infant.* Williams & Wilkins, 1964.

BIOCHEMICAL TRAITS: Sutton, H. Eldon, *et al.* (Hereditary abilities study.) *Am. J. Hum. Genet.*, March 1962.

ATHLETICS IN TWINS: Wright, Logan. *J. Genet. Psycho.* 99:245, 1961. ‖ Gedda, Luigi. *Acta Genet. Med. et Gemel.* 9/4, October 1960.

MENTAL AND BEHAVIOURAL TRAITS
(Chapter 13)

INTELLIGENCE (FRATERNAL AND IDENTICAL PAIRS): (Genetic aspects.) Erlenmeyer-Kimling, L., and Jarvik, Lissy F. *Science* 142, 12 December 1963. ‖ Burt, Cyril. *Amer. Psychologist* 13/1, January 1958; *Eug. Rev.* 49, September 1957. ‖ Conway, J. *Brit. J. Stat. Psychol.* 11, Part II, November 1958. ‖ Husen, Torsten. *Psychological Twin Research* (in English). Almqvist & Wiksell, Stockholm, 1959. ‖ (Physical and mental growth.) Besch, O. F., *et al. Brit. J. Educ. Psychol.* 31:265, 1961. ‖ Churchill, John A. *Neurology* 15/4:341, 1965. ‖ *Famous premature babies. Laughlin, Rose A. *Hygeia*, March 1939.

MENTAL DEFECTS AND DISEASES: (Mental retardation.) Allen, Gordon, and Kallmann, F. J. *Am. J. Hum. Genet.* 7/1, March 1955. ‖ (Mongolism.) McDonald, A. D. *J. of Med. Genet.* 1/1, September 1964. ‖ Slater, Eliot. *Psychotic and Neurotic Illnesses in Twins.* London, H.M.S.O., 1953. ‖ (Schizophrenia.) Rosenthal, David, ed. *The Gerain Quadruplets.* Basic Books, 1963.

PERSONALITY AND BEHAVIOUR: Gottesman, Irving I. *Psychol.*

Monogr. 77, 1961. ‖ Kallmann, F. J., and Baroff, G. S. *Acta Genet. et Statist. Med.* 7/2, 1957. ‖ Shields, J. *Eug. Rev.* 45:213, 1954.

EPILEPSY IN TWINS: Lennox, William G. and Margaret A. In, *Epilepsy and Related Disorders*, Vol. 1, Chap. 17. Little, Brown, 1960. Also, *J.A.M.A.*, Vol. 146, 9 June 1951.

IDENTICAL TWINS

(*Chapters 14, 15, 16*)

SIMILARITIES: For references on specific comparisons between identical and fraternal twins, see preceding sections. For extended references regarding all inherited traits, in which identical twins tend to be highly similar, see the author's book, *Your Heredity and Environment* (J. B. Lippincott, 1965).

IDENTICAL TWINS OF OPPOSITE SEX: Turpin, R., *et al. Acad. Sci., Paris.* 252:2945, 1962. ‖ Also, Lindsten, J. *Lancet*, 9 March 1963 (Letters), p. 558.

REARED-APART IDENTICAL TWINS: Juel-Nielsen, Niels. *Acta Psychiat. Scandinav. Suppl.*, 183:1–158, 1964. Also (with Mogensen, A., and Harvald, B.), *Acta Genet. et Statist. Med.* 7/2, 1957, and 8/1, 1958. ‖ *Gardner, Iva C., and Newman, H. H. (Twins 'Lois' and 'Louise'.) *J. of Hered.*, March 1940. ‖ *Newman, H. H., Freeman, F., and Holzinger, K. *Twins: A Study of Heredity and Environment.* U. of Chicago Press, 1937. ‖ Shields, James. *Monozygotic Twins.* Oxford U. Press, 1962. *Lindeman, Bard. The twins who found each other. *Sat. Eve. Post*, 21 March 1964; also, *Reader's Dig.*, August 1964. ‖ Stephens, F. E., and Nunemaker, J. C. Spondylitis in identical twins reared apart. *J. of Hered.* 41/11, November 1950. ‖ Burt, Cyril. (Differences in intelligence.) *Brit. J. Psychol.*, 57/1–2, 1966.

PSYCHOLOGICAL TRAITS: Cattell, R., *et al. Am. J. Hum. Genet.* 7:122, 1955. ‖ Clark, P. J., *et al. Hum. Biol.* 33:163, 1961. Magnussen, D. *Scand. J. Psychol.* 1/2, 1960. ‖ Otsuki, Takashi; Yasumasa, Miki; Amau, Yukiko. (Japanese studies on differences in MZ twins evoked by parental treatment.) *Bull. Fac. Educ.*, U. of Tokyo, 1956; English summaries, *Psycholog. Abst.*, February 1961, Nos. 684, 697, 698. ‖ Vandenberg, S. G., and Kelly, L. (Vocational preferences.) *Acta Genet. Med. et Gemel.* 13/3, July 1964. ‖ Gesell, A., and Thompson, H. (Twins 'T' and 'C'.) *Genet. Psychol. Monogr.* 23:3, 1941.

TRANSPLANTS OF ORGANS, TISSUES: Murray, Joseph E., *et al. New Engl. J. of Med.* 269:341, 1965. ‖ Rogers, Blair O. *Dis. Nerv. Syst. Monogr. Suppl.*, 24/4, April 1963. ‖ *Merrill, John P. *Sci. Amer.*, October 1959.

BIBLIOGRAPHY

FRATERNAL TWINS, SAME SEX
(*Chapter 17*)

PHYSICAL AND PSYCHOLOGICAL TRAITS (compared with identicals): See references given for Chapters 4, 12, 13, 14, 15, 16, 20, 21.

BOY–GIRL TWINS
(*Chapter 18*)

SEX DIFFERENCES IN BODY FORM, GROWTH, BEHAVIOUR, PERSONALITY, ETC.: *See* Scheinfeld, Amram. *Women and Men*. Harcourt, Brace, 1944. *Also*, author's *Your Heredity and Environment*. J. B. Lippincott, 1965. All discussions indexed under 'Sex differences', and references for Chapters 22, 39, and 40 in that book.

SEX DIFFERENCES IN DISEASE: Scheinfeld, Amram. *The mortality of men and women, Sci. Amer.*, February 1958. Also discussions (as listed in indexes) in author's books, *Women and Men*, and *Your Heredity and Environment*.

SUPERTWINS
(*Chapter 19*)

INCIDENCES: Allen, Gordon, and Firschein, Lester I. *Am. J. Hum. Genet.* 9/3, 1957; also, Allen, *Am. J. Hum. Genet.* 12/2, June 1960. || Bulmer, M. G. *Annls. Hum. Genet.* 22, Part 2, 1958. || Nichols, John B. Quintuplet and sextuplet births in the U.S. *Acta Genet. Med. et Gemel.*, May 1954.

TRIPLETS: (Study of five sets.) Gardner, Iva C., and Rife, D. C. *J. of Hered.*, January 1941.

QUADRUPLETS: Allen, Gordon. *Acta Genet. Med. et Gemel.*, April and October 1960. || Walker, Norma Ford. *Am. J. Hum. Genet.* 2/4, December 1960. || *See also* studies by various authors in *J. of Hered.*, 1940: April, July, October; 1942: September; 1943: September, October; 1944: March; 1948: March.

QUINTUPLETS: (Dionnes.) Blatz, W. E. *The Five Sisters*. Wm. Morrow (New York), 1938. || Brough, James, and the Dionnes. *We Were Five*. Simon & Schuster, 1965. || Dafoe, Allan Roy (Birth of Dionnes.) *J.A.M.A.*, 1 September 1934. || MacArthur, John W., and Dafoe, Allan R. (Genetics.) *J. of Hered.*, September 1939. || MacArthur, John W., and Ford, Norma. *Biological study of the Dionnes*. U. of Toronto Press, 1937. || (Fischer quintuplets.) *Articles in *Sat. Eve. Post*, 2 May and 26 September 1964. ‖ (Prieto quin-tuplets.) *Article in *Sat. Eve. Post*, 3 October 1964. ‖ (Lawson quintuplets of New Zealand.) *McCall's*, June 1966.

'CROSSROADS'

(Twins in maturity, Chapter 20)

RELATIONSHIPS: Mowrer, Ernest R. (Affectional adjustments.) *Am. Sociolog. Rev.* 19/4, August 1954. ‖ Kallmann, F. J., *et al.* (Senescent twins.) *Am. J. Hum. Genet.* 3/1, March 1951. ‖ Storms, Lowell H., *et al.* (Twins' self-evaluations, etc.) *J. Proj. Techn.* 24:182, 1960. ‖ Brooks, Marjory, and Hillman, Christine H. (Non-marriage in identicals.) *J. of Marrg. & Family* 27/3, 1965. ‖ Mittman, Howard (Adjustment of twins.) *Dissertation Abstracts* 25/5:3678, 1964. ‖ *Vanderbilt, Gloria, and Thelma Lady Furness. *Double Exposure.* (A twin autobiography.) David McKay, 1958. *Bolton, Isabel. *Under Gemini.* Harcourt, Brace & World, 1966.

SIAMESE TWINS (ORIGINAL): Daniels, W. B. *Med. Ann. District of Columbia* (Washington) 32/7, 1963. ‖ *Chang-Eng's American heritage. *Life Mag.*, 11 August 1952. *Lives and loves of the Siamese twins. McEvoy, J. P. *Kiwanis Mag.*, and *Reader's Dig.*, September 1943.

LONGEVITY, OLD AGE, MORTALITY: Jarvik, Lissy F., *et al. Am. J. Hum. Genet.* 12/2, June 1960; also (intellectual changes), *J. of Gerontology* 17/3, July 1962. ‖ Falek, Arthur, *et al.* (Longevity, intellectual variation.) *J. of Gerontology* 15/3, July 1960. ‖ Sandelius, G. 99-year-old identical twins. *J. of Gerontology* 11/2, 1956. ‖ Wilson, Ian C., and Reece, John C. Simultaneous deaths in schizophrenic twins. *Arch. Genl. Psychiat.*, Vol. II, October 1964.

DISEASES: Harvald, Bent, and Hauge, Mogens. Twin studies, in: Genetics and epidemiology of chronic diseases. U.S. Pub. Health Serv. Publ. No. 1163, February 1965. ‖ Jarvik, Lissy F., and Falek, Arthur. (Cancer.) *Am. J. Hum. Genet.* 13/4, December 1961. ‖ *See also* references under 'Longevity', above.

SUICIDE IN TWINS: Kallman, F. J. *Am. J. Hum. Genet.* 1/2, 1949.

HOMOSEXUALITY: Kallmann, F. J. *Am. J. Hum. Genet.* 4/2, 1952. ‖ Rainer, J. D., *et al. Psychosomat. Med.*, July–August 1960. ‖ *Mesnikoff*, A. M., *et al. Am. J. Psychiat.* 119:732, 1963.

EXTRASENSORY PERCEPTION: Duane, T. D., and Behrendt, Thomas. *Science*, 150, 3694, 15 October 1965, p. 367. Criticisms of, *Science*, 3 December 1965 (Letters), pp. 1240ff.

BIBLIOGRAPHY

PSYCHOANALYSES OF TWINS

(Chapter 21)

Note: The following are the sources of most of the case histories of psychoanalysed twins discussed in the text. However, other case histories cited were in unpublished reports given at psychoanalytical meetings, or communicated directly to the author by analysts.

Abraham, Hilda G. *Int. J. Psychoanal.* 34:219, 1953.

Arlow, J. A. *Psychoanal. Qu.* 29:175, 1960.

Brody, M. W. *Psychoanal. Qu.* 21:172, 1952.

Burlingham, Dorothy. *Twins.* Intl. Universities Press, 1952.

Demarest, Elinor W., and Winestine, Muriel C. *Psychoanal. Study of the Child* 10:336, 1955.

Gardner, George E., and Rexford, E. N. *Qu. J. of Child Behav.* 4:367, 1962.

Glenn, Jules. (On opposite-sex twins.) *J. Amer. Psychoanalyt. Assn.* late 1966 or early 1967.

Hartmann, Heinz. *Psychiatric Studies of Twins.* Intl. Universities Press (N.Y.), 1964.

Holden, H. M. (On homosexual MZ twins.) *Brit. J. Psychiat.* 111/478, 1965.

Joseph, Edward D., and Tabor, J. H. *Psychoanal. Study of the Child* 16:275, 1961. Also, Joseph: *Psychoanal. Qu.* 28:189, 1959; and *J. Am. Psychoanalyt. Assn.* 9:158, 1961.

Karpman, B. *Psychoanalyt. Rev.* 40:243, 1953.

Lidz, T., *et al. J. Am. Psychoanalyt. Assn.* 10:74, 1962.

Orr, Douglass W. *Psychoanalyt. Qu.* 10/2, April 1941.

Peto, Andrew. *Intl. J. Psychoanal.* 27, 1946.

TWINS IN MYTH, FOLKLORE, LITERATURE

(Chapter 22)

MYTHS AND PRACTICES REGARDING TWINS, GENERAL: *Frazer, J. G. *The Golden Bough*, 3rd ed. Macmillan, 1920. Suppl. Vol., 1937, pp. 154–8. ‖ *Hambly, Wilfrid D. *Sexology*, May 1956. ‖ *Loeb, Edwin M. The Twin Cult in the Old and New World. *Miscellanea Paul Rivet* (Mexico), 1958. ‖ *Lanval, M. *Sexology*, pp. 224–9, 1955. ‖ *Gedda, Luigi. *Twins in History and Science*, Chapter 1. Chas. C. Thomas, 1961. ‖ *Stevenson, Isobel. Twin myths. Ciba Sympos. 2/10, January 1941.

AFRICAN TWIN MYTHS: Schapera, I. *Royal Afr. Soc. Jour.* 26:117, 1927. Dorman, S. S. S. *Afr. J. of Sci.* 29, 1932. ‖ Lagercrantz, Stuve

BIBLIOGRAPHY

(in German). Ethnological studies, Goteberg, 1941. Nos. 12, 13; pp. 5–292.

AMERICAN INDIANS: Devereux, George. *Amer. Anthrop.* 43/4, 1941. || *The Mythology of All Races* (Vol. 10, North American mythology). Archaeological Inst. of Amer. Marshall Jones (Boston), 1932. *See also* references above for Loeb; Metraux; Hambly.

ESKIMOS: *Weyer, Edward M., Jr. *The Eskimo* (killing of twins, p. 132). Yale U. Press, 1932.

JAPANESE: Veith, Ilza. Twin birth: blessing or disaster? *Intl. J. Soc. Psychiat.* 6:230, 1960.

TWINS IN LITERATURE: *Walsh, Groesbeck, and Pool, Robert M. (Twinning in the Bible, Shakespeare.) *Southern Med. & Surgery*, Vol. 102:173, 1940; Vol. 103, No. 3, March 1941. || *Gedda, Luigi. *Twins in History and Science*, Chapter 1. Chas. C. Thomas, 1961.

STUDY OF TWINS

(*Chapter 23*)

METHODS: Allen, Gordon. *Progress in Medical Genetics*, Vol. IV, Chapter 8 (Steinberg, A. G., and Bearn, H. G., eds.). Grune & Straton, 1965. || Falkner, Frank. *Eug. Qu.*, June 1957. || Gittelsohn, A., and Milham, S. *Am. J. Pub. Health* 54/2, February 1964. || Price, Bronson. (Primary biases.) *Am. J. Hum. Genet.* 2/4, December 1950. || Vandenberg, Steven G. Contributions of twin research to child development: Report No. 5. U. of Louisville, January 1965. || Waardenburg, P. J. *Proc. First Intl. Congr. Hum. Genet.*, Part IV:10. S. Karger, 1957. || Sympos., World Health Organization. Use of twins in epidemiological studies. *Acta Genet. Med. et Gemel.*, 15/2, April 1966. || Vandenberg, Steven G. Contributions of twin research to psychology. *Psychol. Bull.*, 66/5, November 1966.

Index

———

Note: Inasmuch as this book deals entirely with twins, all general entries in this Index may be assumed to relate to them. The Bibliography has not been indexed but most of the persons active in twin research will be found either cited in the text, and thus indexed, or named in the sections of the Bibliography where their contributions are listed.

MORE ABOUT PENGUINS
AND PELICANS

Penguinews, which appears every month, contains details of all the new books issued by Penguins as they are published. From time to time it is supplemented by *Penguins in Print*, which is a complete list of all available books published by Penguins. (There are well over four thousand of these.)

A specimen copy of *Penguinews* will be sent to you free on request, and you can become a subscriber for the price of the postage. For a year's issues (including the complete lists) please send 30p if you live in the United Kingdom, or 60p if you live elsewhere. Just write to Dept EP, Penguin Books Ltd, Harmondsworth, Middlesex, enclosing a cheque or postal order, and your name will be added to the mailing list.

Note: *Penguinews* and *Penguins in Print* are not available in the U.S.A. or Canada

THE SAFETY OF THE UNBORN CHILD

Geoffrey Chamberlain

The unborn child is usually perfectly safe. However, various risks are occasionally given publicity, and these often build up to become major worries to the pregnant woman. Often she feels that it would be childish and time-wasting to air these problems to others but they remain in her mind.

This book gives a straight presentation of the hazards to the unborn child, assesses them, and displays them against the background of normality. It therefore deals with material not often discussed outside the confines of the consulting room, and sometimes not discussed frankly enough even there. It is offered as a practical contribution to the understanding of pregnancy, and also in the hope of allaying many unspoken worries of pregnant women.

CHILD CARE AND THE GROWTH OF LOVE

NEW ENLARGED EDITION

John Bowlby

In 1951, under the auspices of the World Health Organization, Dr John Bowlby wrote a report on *Maternal Care and Mental Health* which collated expert world opinion on the subject and the issues arising from it – the prevention of juvenile and adult delinquency, the problem of the 'unwanted child', the training of women for motherhood, and the best ways of supplying the needs of children deprived of their natural mothers. This book is a summary of Dr Bowlby's report, freed from many of its technicalities and prepared for the general reader.

This new edition contains chapters based on an article by Dr Mary Salter Ainsworth, written in 1962 also for the World Health Organization when it once again made an important study of child care.

'It is a convenient and scholarly summary of evidence of the effects upon children of lack of personal attention, and it presents to administrators, social workers, teachers and doctors a reminder of the significance of the family' – *The Times*